AGRICULTURAL PRICE ANALYSIS

Geoffrey S. Shepherd

Professor of Economics, Iowa State University

Agricultural Price Analysis *fifth edition*

Iowa State University Press, *Ames,* Iowa, U.S.A.

About the Author

GEOFFREY S. SHEPHERD is professor of economics in agricultural marketing and price policy in the Department of Economics and Sociology at Iowa State University.

His approach to problem solving — based on an appreciation of the layman's point of view — has broadened the scope of research in analyzing prices and policies in the fields of grain, livestock, and dairy marketing. He has undertaken to apply economic theory to current agricultural price problems; these applications enrich the theory at the same time that the theory helps to solve the problems.

Early years on a ranch in western Canada engendered in Geoff Shepherd a love of the outdoors and a deep desire to make use of the findings of science to improve economic opportunities for farmers.

In addition to his undergraduate work at the University of Saskatchewan he holds the master's degree from Iowa State University and a doctorate from Harvard University. He has been a vice president of the Farm Economics Association and has served in a number of advisory positions in Washington, D. C., West Germany, Japan, Burma, and Venezuela.

Dr. Shepherd is author of two other books, *Marketing Farm Products* and *Agricultural Price and Income Policy*, numerous bulletins and technical papers, and an article in the Encyclopedia Britannica. *Farm Policy Forum*, a specialized periodical, was developed under his chairmanship.

Composed and printed by
The Iowa State University Press,
Ames, Iowa, U.S.A.

First edition, 1941
Second edition, 1947
Third edition, 1950
Fourth edition, 1957

FIFTH EDITION, 1963

Library of Congress Catalog Card Number 62–16494

PREFACE

The fifth edition of this book includes a number of substantial changes and additions, to keep it abreast of the new concepts and techniques that are rapidly being developed in the field.

Most of the analysis of long-run and short-run price movements is new. So is the explanation of cyclic movements. The technique of distributed lags is treated at some length, in relation to the determination of the elasticity of long-run and short-run demand and supply curves. A clearer exposition and appraisal of simultaneous equations, worked out by my son William Geoffrey Shepherd at Yale, replaces my earlier version.

The significance of statistical tests of significance is explained more fully than before. A new chapter shows how to compute and compare the costs and effects on prices of supporting prices by different methods. An entirely new and more extensive analysis and appraisal of parity prices — the last word that I at least have to say on the subject — is given in the last three chapters.

The book now reminds me of the axe that has been in our family for three generations. The handle splintered and had to be replaced several times, and the axe-head wore down and had to be replaced twice, but it's still the same axe. Only in this case the book is a better one, for the replacements are made of more modern materials.

I feel a debt of gratitude to the research projects that I have been conducting, to the classes in price analysis that I have been teaching, and to the graduate students who keep coming to their major professor with their problems. They make me think concepts

[v]

and procedures through to the point of application, and the application provides the additional grasp that comes from experience. Many times we felt the thrill of explorers pushing into unknown territory, and students had the added zest of feeling that their professor was only half a jump ahead of them. There was always the chance they might catch him! But this was an expedition, not a chase.

GEOFFREY SHEPHERD

CONTENTS

Part V

ANALYSES WITH RESPECT TO PLACE AND FORM

Part VI

ANALYSIS OF PARITY PRICES

one

CHANGES IN PRICES OVER PERIODS OF TIME

1

Long-time Movements in Agricultural Prices

Price analysis is coming of age. It used to be an inconspicuous economic discipline, wherein empirical quantitative data fleshed out the bare bones of economic theory — a nice economic exercise, but not much more. Now it is becoming an indispensable basis for government and business operations running to billions of dollars. Policies of this order of magnitude now are adopted or rejected on the basis of technical coefficients of elasticity of demand, partial regression coefficients, derived by the use of distributed lags, inverted matrices, and simultaneous equations. Terms like these, so much Greek to many people a generation ago, are gradually intruding into their everyday language now.

The field of price analysis is of necessity breaking up into specialized parts. One of the most important and well developed of these parts is agricultural price analysis. Agricultural income remains low, and more government programs are being developed to supplement or replace the free market as the allocator of resources and incomes. These programs require more and more agricultural price and other analyses. The results of these analyses are no longer merely academic curiosities; they are immediately put to work as bases for huge programs, often with a blithe disregard of their limitations that causes palpitations of the heart among their originators.

Enormous quantities of data are becoming available for analysis. Esoteric analytical tools of a high degree of sophistication are being developed to deal with them, and the electronic computer has become not merely a luxury but a necessity. The brain reels in the attempt to keep ahead of the flood of new data, concepts, and equipment.

But, brain-reeling or not, progress rolls on. New concepts and symbols arise and rapidly become institutionalized, even in hierarchies. This is illustrated by the following tongue-in-cheek classification of academic jargon and research tools, based originally on an article which classified social status into two classes — upper class, denoted by U, and lower class, denoted by non-U:

> *Symbol* is U (i.e. correct, proper, legitimate, appropriate); *word* is non-U. *Variable, role,* and *interaction* are U. So are *model,* especially *equilibrium model, matrix,* and *cell* (*cells in a matrix* is exceedingly U). *Empirical* is U, as in *empirically oriented* . . . . *Process* is as U as it can be . . . . *Quantitative* is U, as against *qualitative* non-U . . . . U articles feature *correlations. Mathematics and statistics* are U . . . . *Game theory* is ultra-U in U circles.[1]

One recent technical bulletin in the field of price analysis,[2] half an inch thick and including several tables with more than 700 coefficients each, carried out to 5 decimal places, has become a best seller among price analysts and policy makers. One of the coefficients in one of these tables, showing that the demand for turkeys is elastic (-1.4) became the basis for recommending to the turkey producers that they do not seek to reduce turkey production, since with an elastic demand that would reduce their total income. Meanwhile, a program to reduce corn and other feed grains production goes into effect, where the demand is inelastic $(-0.5$ for corn$)$ so that reduction increases total income.

LONG-TIME PRICE MOVEMENTS

Agricultural price movements are caused by different forces according to the length of time involved. Long-time movements, for example, are cause by changes in population, in the technology of production, in real income per capita, etc. These forces are slow to move. Short-time movements are caused by different forces — annual variations in weather, wars, booms, and depressions. Still shorter movements are caused by still other forces.

The analysis of agricultural price movements over periods of time, therefore, can be broken down into several parts according to the length of time involved. Our analysis will begin with the broadest perspective — with price movements over long periods

---

[1] Arnold A. Rogow, "A Short Note on U and Non-U in Political Science," *Western Polit. Quart.* Vol. 13, No. 4, Dec., 1960.

[2] G. E. Brandow, "Interrelations Among Demands for Farm Products and Implications for Control of Market Supply," Pa. State Univ. Agr. Bul. 680, Aug., 1961.

of one hundred years or more — and then proceed to shorter and shorter periods.

The wholesale prices of farm products in the United States annually since 1800 are shown in Figure 1.1, along with the wholesale prices of nonagricultuarl products and the ratio of farm to nonfarm products. This graph shows how the credit expansions associated with four major wars threw up four sharp peaks in agricultural and nonagricultural prices alike.

Figure 1.1 shows how the long-time trend of agricultural prices, insofar as it can be distinguished through the four upheavals just mentioned, has been level or slightly upward for more than 150 years, while the trend of nonagricultural prices has been slightly downward. The trend of agricultural prices gradually rose, relative to the trend of nonagricultural prices, up to the time of World War I.

This relative rise in agricultural prices is shown in the lower section of Figure 1.1, where the agricultural price index each year is divided by the nonagricultural price index and the ratio between the two is plotted as so much below or above a straight base line running across the chart.

The chart indicates that up to 1920, the prices of farm products were rising relative to nonagricultural prices. After 1920, however,

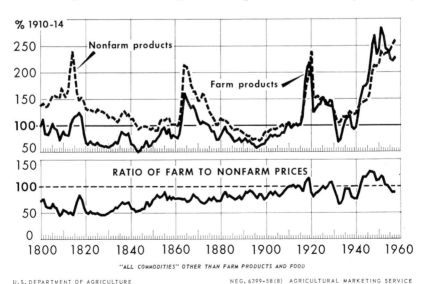

Fig. 1.1 — Wholesale prices of farm products and of all other commodities, United States, 1800–1958, and ratio of farm to nonfarm prices. Index numbers: 1910–14 = 100.

the opposite happened; agricultural prices began to decline relative to other prices. World War II brought agricultural prices up again, but only briefly. Since 1950 they have been declining.

What does this mean? Does it mean that agricultural prices have been below nonagricultural prices most of the past 160 years, or that agricultural prices struggled up for 100 years before attaining equality with nonagricultural prices in 1910–14, and then climbed above nonagricultural prices during the 1940's but have since fallen below nonagricultural prices again?

It does not mean this. The position of the agricultural price line as a whole, relative to the position of the nonagricultural price line, has no significance in itself. There is no way of measuring the inequality of these two groups of prices—no way of measuring whether one is "above" or "below" the other—except by reference to some base point. If the price of wheat is $2 a bushel, and the price of a plow is $400, one cannot say merely by direct comparison of the two prices that one is "higher" or "lower" than another. All that can be said is that one is higher or lower than its *usual or normal relation* to the other.

Strictly speaking, even this statement is open to question. It implies that things do or should stay put. But in a world so full of change as ours, what is *usual* or *normal*? If the attempt is made to define it objectively as *average,* then the question arises—average over what period of years? And the further question remains—can what is usual, normal, or average for one period of years be considered so for a later period?

Even loosely speaking, then, prices or groups of prices can be compared with each other only by reference to some *usual* or *normal* relationship between them. Strictly speaking, all that can be done is to compare them with respect to their relation in some other period, without implying that the relation should be the same now as it was then.

Where two groups of prices represented by index numbers (which are expressed in terms of some base year or period) are compared, that base year or period usually is taken as the basis of the comparison of two price series. In the case of the two price series shown in Figure 1.1, the base period is the same for both series; the average of the prices in 1910–14 is taken as 100, in each case. The two price indexes, therefore, necessarily stand at the same figure (100) in the base period. They are "equal" at that time, but only because that is their index base period when both are taken as 100.

If the same basic data were recomputed with some other year as the base, say the year 1800, the two indexes (agricultural and nonagricultural prices) would both stand at 100, i.e., be "equal," in 1800. The effect of this on the chart would be to leave the horizontal line representing nonagricultural prices where it is, but to shift the irregular line representing agricultural prices up about 40 points as a whole. Agricultural prices then would be "above" nonagricultural prices most of the years after about 1840—about 40 points above in 1910–14—and well above every year since. But this appearance would be as misleading as the appearance of the lower part of Figure 1.1. All that either chart shows is that agricultural prices are higher or lower in relation to nonagricultural prices *than they were in whatever year or period is chosen as a base.* The comparison is only as valid as the validity of the base period for representing equality or equilibrium today.

Relative Shifts in Supply and Demand Curves

Study of Figure 1.1 raises several questions. Why did agricultural prices rise, relative to nonagricultural prices, from 1800 to 1920, decline thereafter until World War II, and then rise and fall again?

The long-time movements in agricultural prices are caused, like any other price movements, by changes in supply and in demand. The extent of the price movements depends upon the elasticities of supply and demand, as well as upon the extent of the changes in the supply and demand.

For analytical purposes, it is essential to keep clearly in mind the distinction between supply and production, and demand and consumption. Supply is the whole series of quantities that would be offered for sale at different prices. It is the whole supply schedule; in graphic terms, it is the whole supply curve. A change in supply means a change in the location or position of the whole curve. But production is simply the quantity produced at a specified point on the supply curve. It is the horizontal distance from zero on the quantity axis to the point where the demand and supply curves cross at a particular point in time. Production may change while supply remains constant. The same sort of thing is true of demand as distinguished from consumption.

What happened after 1800 was simply this: Agricultural prices rose because the demand curve for farm products moved to the right more rapidly than the supply curve moved. But after 1950,

TABLE 1.1

INDEX NUMBERS OF FARM OUTPUT, CROP PRODUCTION PER ACRE, AND POPULATION, UNITED STATES, 1950–60 AND PROJECTED 1965*

Year	Population 1950 = 100	Farm Output 1950 = 100	Crop Production per Acre 1947–49 = 100
1950.	100	100	97
1951.	102	103	98
1952.	103	107	104
1953.	105	108	103
1954.	107	108	101
1955.	109	112	106
1956.	111	113	109
1957.	113	113	112
1958.	115	123	126
1959.	117	125	123
1960†.	119	127	126
1965.	129‡	133–138§	127–130‖

* Source: 1961 Agricultural Outlook Charts, USDA, 1960, p. 61.
† Preliminary.
‡ Based on Census Series II projections.
§ Based on alternative assumptions for crop yields and acreage, and projected outlets for livestock production.
‖ Based on alternative assumptions for crop yields at 1959 crop acreage compositions.

the supply curve moved to the right more rapidly than the demand curve moved.

It is difficult for economists to measure the movements of these curves directly, much as physicists cannot see and measure directly the movement of an electron. But physicists can see and measure the path an electron makes in a cloud or bubble chamber, and economists can trace the movements of the intersection points of demand and supply curves, and measure the chief factors that cause the curves to move.

Table 1.1 and Figure 1.2 show that United States farm output and total United States population increased at about the same rate from 1950 to 1957, but that after 1957 output rose to about 8 per cent higher than population.

The rapid increase in farm output after 1950, especially marked after 1957, did not result from an increase in acreage. Total acreage in the United States remained practically constant. The increase in farm output resulted almost entirely from the rapid adoption of new technology in agricultural production. This increased yields per acre dramatically; from 1947–49 to 1961, crop production per acre increased 30 per cent.[3]

---

[3] *Statistical Summary*, USDA, SS-226, Sept. 21, 1961, p. 4.

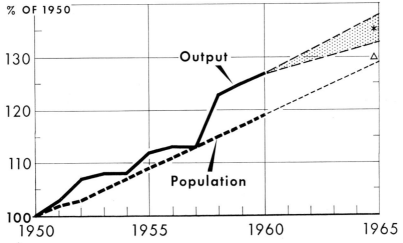

U. S. DEPARTMENT OF AGRICULTURE   NEG. 60 (10)-9003   AGRICULTURAL RESEARCH SERVICE

Fig. 1.2 — United States population and farm output, annually, 1950–60, and projected to 1965.

The effects of technological changes that increase yields without requiring extra labor, on the position of the supply curve, can be measured fairly accurately. If hybrid seed corn, for example, has increased yields per acre 20 per cent, it has shifted the supply curve 20 per cent to the right.

Technological changes that reduce the cost of producing the same yield, say 20 per cent, also can be measured; they shift the supply curve 20 per cent downward.[4] The difficulty comes in determining how much a technological change of this sort has decreased production costs. The job of adding up these effects for each product, and determining how much the supply curve for farm products as a whole has shifted, is almost impossible. Therefore, it is almost impossible to measure accurately how much the position of the supply curve for farm products has moved over the past 150 years. The relative rise in prices from 1800 to 1914 shows that up to World War I, the demand curve moved to the right faster than the supply curve did, so that the demand curve cut the supply curve at higher and higher points. It is almost impossible to say how much of the increase in production was the result of the demand curve's cutting

---

[4] See Chapter 7 and Appendix A for an elaboration of the distinction between vertical and horizontal shifts in the position of supply and demand curves.

the supply curve at a higher point, and how much was the result of the supply curve's moving to the right also. Conceivably, although not probably, the supply curve might have been very elastic and might not have moved at all.

The trend of agricultural prices between World Wars I and II declined; we deduce from this that the supply curve moved to the right faster than the demand curve. The trend of prices then rose rapidly during World War II, because of the rapid increase in demand. After the war, agricultural prices declined again; they reached a lower point relative to nonagricultural prices than the level reached in 1910–14.

Changes in Demand

Changes in demand are also hard to measure. Some of the chief factors that determine the demand can be measured, but not all.

The chief factor affecting the demand for farm products is the rate of population growth in the United States.

Population in the United States used to grow at such a steady rate that up to about 1920, forecasts of population growth up to the year 2,000 were made with considerable confidence.[5] One such forecast is marked A in Figure 1.3.

After 1920, however, immigration decreased, birth rates decreased, and the rate of population growth began to slow down. Population experts then began to revise their estimates downward. The downward decline in the rate of growth accelerated during the 1930's, to about 0.7 per cent per year. Projections were made then by responsible population experts that the decline in the rate of growth would continue until the population would level out at about 140 million by 1965, and actually begin to decline thereafter. This projection is shown by the curve marked C in Figure 1.3. Comparisons were made with the logistic curve shown in the lower part of the chart. O. F. Baker of the USDA, and others made many speeches about the dismal prospect for the United States and especially for United States agriculture.

These projections might well have been borne out if the depression conditions of the 1930's had continued. But the life of the forecaster is hard. In actuality, World War II and the prosperity that came with it reversed the decline in the birth rate and forced the experts to revise their projections upward. At first they merely raised the point at which the population would level out and postponed the date about 100 years. Some of these more recent projec-

---

[5] J. S. Davis, "Implications of Prospective United States Population Growth in the 1960's," *Milbank Memorial Fund Quarterly*, Vol. 2, April, 1961.

A.-U.S. POPULATION BY DECADES, 1800-1960,
WITH SELECTED PROJECTIONS

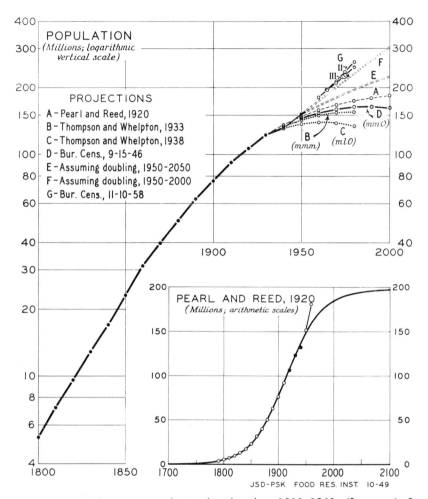

Fig. 1.3 — United States population by decades, 1800–1960. (Source: J. S. Davis in **Milbank Memorial Fund Quart.**, Vol. 2, Apr., 1961).

tions are shown in the upper part of the chart. They also turned out to be too low. The actual growth by 1950 and 1960, at the rate of about 1.8 per cent per year, is shown by the short straight line in the lower part of the chart.

Relation Between Income and Food Consumption

The relation between population and food consumption, other things (age distribution, income, etc.) being equal, is roughly 1 to 1.

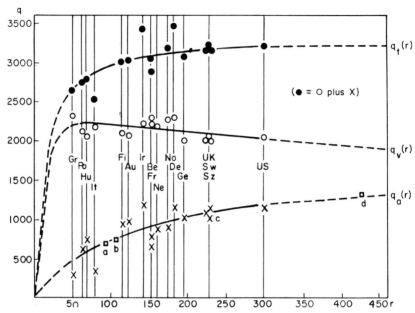

Fig. 1.4 — Relation between income and food consumption (measured by cal-orie intake) by nations. Countries are identified as follows: Gr = Greece, Po = Poland, Hu = Hungary, It = Italy, Fi = Finland, Au = Austria, Ir = Ireland, Be = Belgium, Fr = France, Ne = Netherlands, No = Norway, De = Denmark, Ge = Germany, UK = United Kingdom, Sw = Switzerland, and US = United States. Special points in the diagram are labeled as follows: **a** = farm and forestry workers; **b** = small farmers; **c** = industrial workers and low grade employees; and **d** = middle class.

Ten per cent more people demand 10 per cent more food. But the relation between income and food consumption — the income elasticity of the demand for food — is much less than 1 to 1. An increase of 10 per cent in income results in much less than a 10 per cent increase in food consumption.

This income elasticity of the demand for food can be measured by observing either the change in the *consumption* of food with a given change in income, or the change in the *expenditures* for food.

The relation between income and food consumption (measured by calorie intake) by nations is shown in Figure 1.4.[6] The curve in the lower part of the chart shows that the consumption of animal foods (meat, milk, etc.) increases with income, although at a de-

[6] L. Jureen, "Long-Term Trends in Food Consumption: A Multi-Country Study," *Econometrica*, Vol. 24, No. 1, Jan., 1956, pp. 1–22. The curves in Figure 1.4 are based on data before World War II. Curves based on 1949–51 data are closely similar.

clining rate. The curve in the middle shows that the consumption of other foods rises to a peak at the low-income end of the scale, and then *declines* slightly with further increases in income. The curve at the top, representing the sum of the animal and other foods, runs almost horizontal from the middle of the chart to the right-hand end; that is, total food consumption is almost unaffected by income above about 300 (the level in the United States); the income elasticity of food consumption above that level is almost as low as zero.

The income elasticity of the demand for one important food, meat, in the United States is shown in terms of quantities at three different times (1942, 1948, and 1955) in Figure 1.5. It is interesting to observe from this figure that the income-quantity elasticity of the demand for beef remained roughly constant over the years shown (the curve for 1955 is higher than the others, but it retains about the same slope), but for pork it changed from positive to negative from 1942 to 1955. It would be interesting to observe what changes have taken place in the years since 1955, but the 1955 data are the most recent available. They were obtained from a large and expensive United States survey of food consumption conducted in 1955 which has not been repeated since that date.

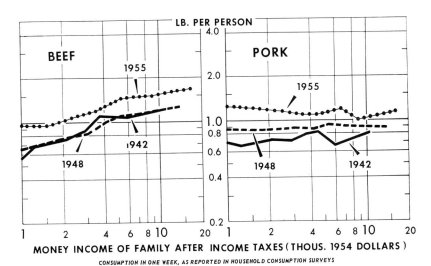

Fig. 1.5 — Urban per capita consumption of beef and pork as related to income in 3 specific years, 1942, 1948, and 1955.

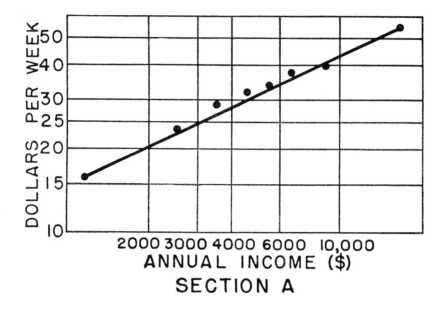

SECTION A

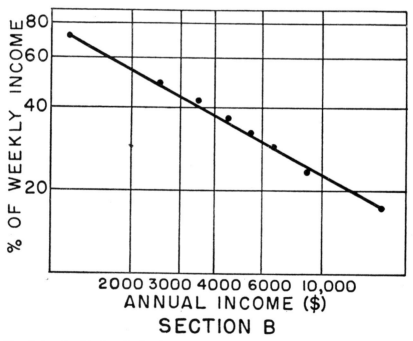

SECTION B

Fig. 1.6 — Weekly family food expense, April–June, 1955, by income groups: Section **A** in dollars; Section **B** as per cent of income.

Income Elasticity of Food Expenditures

The income elasticity of expenditures for food, measured in money, is higher than the income elasticity of the consumption of food measured in physical units (pounds, calories, etc.). The elasticity is less than 1 to 1 (it is therefore called "inelastic") but it is some distance above zero. The inelasticity of the income-food expenditure curve was first demonstrated by Ernst Engel in Belgium in 1895; it is referred to now as "Engel's Law."

Engel's work showed that high-income groups spent more money per capita for food than low-income groups; but the high-income groups spent a smaller *proportion* of their incomes for food than the low-income groups. A number of statistical studies since Engel's time have revealed similar relations between income and expenditures for food in other countries.

An income-food expenditure curve for urban consumers in the United States, based on the data given in Table 1.2, is shown in Figure 1.6. The upper part of the chart (Section A) shows that high-income urban groups spend more money for food per family than low-income groups. The straight line drawn through the dots shows that, on the average, a family with 1 per cent more income than another did not spend 1 per cent more money for food; it spent only 0.44 per cent more. The income elasticity of family expenditures for food, then, was 0.44.

The lower part of Figure 1.6 (Section B) shows that, although high-income groups spend more money for food per family than low-income groups, what they spend is a smaller percentage of their incomes. The general conclusion is this: The bigger the family income, the smaller is the percentage of the income that is spent on food.

The percentage spent on food per family by the high-income groups would be still lower than it is, were it not for the fact that families in the high-income groups are larger than families in the low-income groups, as Table 1.2 shows. The average family size of the highest income group ($10,000 and over) is 3.80 persons; this is larger than the size of the lowest income group family, 2.88 persons. It used to be said that "the rich get rich and the poor get children." This does not appear to be borne out by Table 1.2. The high-income groups have large families, however, not only because high incomes are conducive to fertility, but also because income and family size both increase with the passage of time. Normally a young couple begin married life at the bottom of the ladder with a small income and no children. Bigger pay checks and children come along together

TABLE 1.2

AVERAGE INCOME AND FAMILY SIZE, AVERAGE EXPENDITURES PER URBAN FAMILY IN THE U. S., FOR PURCHASED FOOD USED AT HOME AND AWAY FROM HOME, AND PER CENT OF INCOME SPENT FOR FOOD, IN A WEEK, APRIL–JUNE, 1955; BY FAMILY SIZE AND INCOME*

Family Groups According to Money Income After Income Taxes for Families of 2 or More Members (1)	Average Money Income After Income Taxes (1954) (2)	Average Family Size (Count) Members (3)	Money Value of Food† per Family in Week Purchased‡		Meals and other food eaten away from home			Per cent of income spent for food (9)
			Total (4)	Used at home§ (5)	Total (6)	Meals (7)	Others‖ (8)	
(dollars)	(dollars)	(persons)	(dollars)	(dollars)	(dollars)	(dollars)	(dollars)	(per cent)
All urban families	4,826	3.26	29.99	24.23	5.76	4.26	1.50	32.3
under 2,000	1,250	2.88	17.49	15.28	2.22	1.56	.66	72.7
2,000–2,999	2,511	3.28	23.20	20.24	2.96	1.69	1.26	48.0
3,000–3,999	3,517	3.60	28.63	24.51	4.11	2.46	1.65	42.3
4,000–4,999	4,500	3.65	31.63	26.17	5.46	3.71	1.74	36.5
5,000–5,999	5,444	3.62	33.92	28.64	5.28	3.84	1.44	32.4
6,000–7,999	6,766	3.62	37.52	29.35	8.17	6.07	1.20	28.8
8,000–9,999	8,860	3.77	39.44	30.39	9.04	7.17	1.87	23.1
10,000 and over	16,050	3.80	54.73	38.37	16.37	13.89	2.48	17.7

*Source: "Food Consumption of Households in the United States," *Household Food Consumption Survey 1955*, Rpt. No. 1, USDA, p. 11.

† Includes alcoholic beverages.

‡ Adjusted to exclude value food used at home by boarders, farm help, and members of secondary families. No inf. requested of respondents on expenditures for food away from home by these nonfamily members of households.

§ Includes packed lunches and other food carried from home.

‖ Between-meal snacks and beverages; supplements to packed lunches.

with the passage of time. If income and family size were not positively correlated, the income elasticity of expenditures for food would be lower than the actual figure, 0.44.

The influence of family size can be removed by expressing the urban data in the form of expenditures for food per person instead of per family. When this is done, the income elasticity per person is shown to be only 0.29. For the United States as a whole, it is 0.37.[7]

The income elasticity of the *consumption* of farm-produced food measured at the farm level is much lower than the income elasticity of *expenditures* for food given above. It is about 0.12. This is the figure for food from all sources. The figure for purchased farm food, however, is about 0.24.[8]

PROSPECTS FOR THE FUTURE

Is the long-run trend of agricultural prices likely to continue upward? Or is the opposite likely to happen? Is the recent short-run decline likely to persist and develop into a new long-run trend downward? The outcome will depend on the relative speed of the increases in supply and demand.

Prospects for Demand

The effect of a further increase in per capita income on expenditures for food is likely to be less in the future than it has been in the past.

Per capita income can be expected to continue to increase in the future. But this increase is likely to have less increasing effect on per capita expenditures for food than it has had in the past. The reason for this is that the higher the income, the lower is the income elasticity of the demand for food.

This is shown in Figure 1.7 taken from a special analysis of the data collected in the 1955 Household Food Consumption Survey. Separate analyses were made for farm and nonfarm households because of differences in food consumption patterns and income levels. In each case, households were ranked by family income and divided into three classes. Within each family income class, per person consumption of food at home was related to money income per person after income taxes and to size of household. Elasticities of demand with respect to income for total food and for the principal foods were computed as a measure of the relationship.

---

[7] See the fifth and eighth lines up from the bottom of Table 915, M. C. Burk, "Some Analyses of Income-Food Relationships," *Jour. Amer. Stat. Assn.*, Vol. 53, Dec., 1958, p. 915.

[8] Burk, *op. cit.*, p. 915.

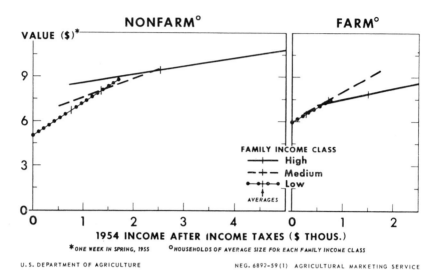

Fig. 1.7 — Per capita value of food and beverages consumed in 1955, by income groups: high, medium, and low. The lines overlap from one family income class to another because per person figures were computed within family income classes. Per person figures in a large, high-income household, for instance, might therefore be smaller than in a household with a medium or low income.

The rate of change in consumption per person as income per person increased, as measured by the elasticity of demand with respect to income at the point of averages, differed considerably among low, medium, and high-income classes, and between farm and nonfarm households. For all food and beverages taken as a whole, these rates of increase in consumption as income rose tended to be greater for nonfarm than for farm households, and for lower than for higher income classes. For each 1 per cent increment in income per person in nonfarm households the value of food and beverages used at home per person increased 0.25 per cent in low-income households, 0.21 per cent in medium-income households, and 0.15 per cent in high-income households. In farm households the value of food and beverages used at home per person rose 0.08 per cent in low-income households, 0.19 per cent in medium-income households, and 0.15 per cent in high-income households.[9]

Prospects for Supply

A USDA study of the farm production potential of the United States by 1975 in relation to needs[10] investigated whether the supply

[9] C. R. Rockwell, Jr., "Income and Household Size," Marketing Res. Rep't 340, USDA, June, 1951, pp. 1, 6.
[10] R. Rogers and G. T. Barton, "Our Farm Production Potential 1975," ARS, USDA, Agr. Ext. Bul. 233, 1960.

of farm products was likely to keep up with the demand. The study proceeded on the basis of several assumptions:

1. That United States population will be 230 million by 1975.
2. That per capita consumption of farm products will continue to increase moderately.
3. That exports will remain high, although below the exceptionally high year 1956.

On these assumptions, the study concluded that the present productive capacity of agriculture is sufficient to meet the projected 1975 needs of the United States population for food and fiber and to provide for a relatively high level of exports, at the same or lower relative prices than in 1951–53.

The projected attainable yields are indicated in Figure 1.8. This projection is based on the use of technology presently known by researchers or almost certainly expected to be available to farmers by 1975. The higher projection shown in Figure 1.8 is the "economic maximum" — if farmers made full use of available technology.

Substantial adjustments in crop acreages, however, would be required — less wheat acreage, for example, and more corn. The extent of these changes is indicated in Figure 1.9. This figure shows that if farmers attained economic yields by 1975, 20 million more acres would be needed; but if they attained maximum yields about 75 million fewer acres would be needed.

These conclusions appear to the present author to be conserva-

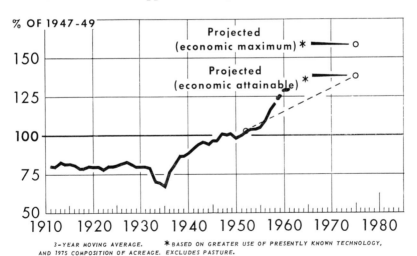

U. S. DEPARTMENT OF AGRICULTURE   NEG. 60 (6)-2907   AGRICULTURAL RESEARCH SERVICE

Fig. 1.8 — Crop production per acre, with projections to 1975.

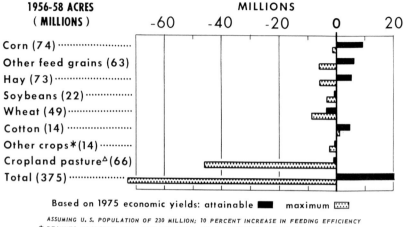

Fig. 1.9 — Harvested acres needed in 1975, showing change from 1956–58.

tive. Two years of additional data can now be added to the original figure taken from the study. These data show yields nearly 20 per cent higher than the "economic attainable" projections for those years. A part of this is due to good weather, but only a part of it.

The one point that is left open in the study is the number of acres that will be harvested. If programs like the Soil Conservation program and the feed grains and the wheat programs of 1962 are continued or expanded, the reduction in acreage may offset at least part of the projected increase in yields.

But if acreage is left uncontrolled, the prospects are that agricultural production will continue to be excessive, and this will exert a downward pressure on agricultural prices.

A final point needs to be kept in mind. The outlook for prices is not the only thing that concerns farmers. The outlook for costs is equally important. It appears very likely that, under the impact of new technology, costs per unit of product will continue to decrease in the future as they have since the early 1940's. The new technology in the past must have reduced costs or in other ways increased profits per farmer, or it would not have been adopted. It seems likely that this will continue in the future; so the prospects for agriculture are more promising than the prospects for agricultural prices alone.

2

Short-time Changes in Agricultural Prices

Over a long period of time, as Figure 1.1 shows, agricultural prices have gradually risen and then fallen, relative to nonagricultural prices. In addition to this long-time, gradual dissimilarity of price movements, there is a more marked dissimilarity within short periods of a decade or so in length. Over these shorter periods of time, agricultural and nonagricultural prices may move in opposite directions, or at least move different amounts in the same direction, more markedly than they do over long periods of time.

This dissimilarity of short-time movements is clearly revealed if attention is focused on the movements of agricultural and nonagricultural prices and production during the past 35 years. These movements are shown in Figure 2.1. The price data are the same as those shown in Figure 1.1, but on a 1947–49 index base.

Figure 2.1 shows that the chief difference between the movements of agricultural and nonagricultural prices since 1913 is the difference in the amplitude (size) of their movements. During World War I the two price series rose to about the same extent, but since that time agricultural prices have fluctuated about twice as much (that is, over about twice as great a range) as nonagricultural prices. This was true during World War II as well as during peacetime (nonagricultural prices were held down more by price controls during the war than agricultural prices were). It was true also during the post-World War II boom, when all prices were carried upward by general inflation.

WHY ARE INDUSTRIAL PRICES MORE STABLE THAN AGRICULTURAL PRICES?

Why are nonagricultural prices (or to use a less clumsy term, industrial prices) so much more stable than agricultural prices?

U. S. PRODUCTION AND PRICES
IN AGRICULTURE   IN INDUSTRY

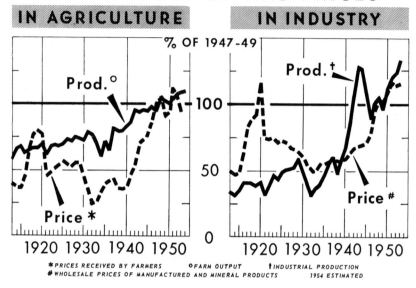

*PRICES RECEIVED BY FARMERS   ○FARM OUTPUT   †INDUSTRIAL PRODUCTION
#WHOLESALE PRICES OF MANUFACTURED AND MINERAL PRODUCTS   1954 ESTIMATED

U. S. DEPARTMENT OF AGRICULTURE   NEG. 1023-54(8)   AGRICULTURAL MARKETING SERVICE

Fig. 2.1 — United States production and prices in agriculture and in industry, 1913–54.

It is not because the demand for industrial products is more stable than the demand for agricultural products. The demand for industrial products fluctuates as much as the demand for agricultural products—perhaps more. The reasons for the comparative stability of industrial prices must lie in the conditions of supply.

Figure 2.1 shows that this is indeed true. The production of industrial products has fluctuated widely, while the total production of farm products, in spite of the effects of the record-breaking drouths of 1934 and 1936, varies very little from year to year.

These charts show that industrial prices are comparatively stable, in spite of the great fluctuations in demand that go with prosperity and depression, because industrial production fluctuates greatly and concurrently with those fluctuations in demand. The changes in demand are largely offset, in their effects on price, by corresponding changes in supply. The charts also show that agricultural prices are unstable because agricultural production remains comparatively constant in the face of great fluctuations in demand. The small changes in agricultural production that do take place result chiefly from changes in such physical things as weather, and show practically no correlation with fluctuations in demand, except for World

War II. Since agricultural supply is relatively constant, great fluctuations in demand cause great fluctuations in agricultural prices.

The question, therefore, boils down to this: Why is agricultural production stable, in spite of great cyclic changes in demand, and why is industrial production unstable, fluctuating with cyclic changes in demand?

WHY DOES AGRICULTURAL PRODUCTION REMAIN STABLE WHEN DEMAND FLUCTUATES?

It may seem strange that agricultural production remains stable when demand fluctuates greatly. Elementary economic theory teaches that under a freely competitive system, with positive sloping supply curves, a decrease in demand reduces prices; and this reduces production to the point where equilibrium between costs and prices is restored, at lower levels than before. An increase in demand brings about similar but opposite adjustments.

But this is true only of long-time changes and adjustments. Things work out differently when the changes in demand are severe and sudden. So high a proportion of the costs in agriculture are fixed that once the investment is made, when prices decline suddenly the farmer cannot reduce his costs much by reducing his production. In fact, in the face of falling prices he may attempt to meet his fixed costs by producing more, not less.[1]

The situation is complicated by the further fact that in the short run a farmer has even less control over the prices at which he sells his products than he has over his costs of production. If he does reduce production, as an individual act, that will have no appreciable bolstering effect on the prices of his products. If all farmers reduced production, that would at least reduce the fall in agricultural prices. But since no one farmer has any assurance that the bulk of his competitors (other farmers) will reduce their production, he dares not reduce his; so nobody reduces production.

Even nationwide programs for reducing agricultural production, organized by the federal government, have not been very successful. The AAA programs of the 1930's reduced the acreage of cotton, wheat, corn, etc., by percentages ranging from 10 to 40, but yields per acre increased, partly as a result of the reductions in acreage. Except for cotton, production was not reduced appreciably below previous levels. This was true in the 1950's also.

---

[1] D. G. Johnson explains the low elasticity of agricultural supply by the low elasticity of the factors of production—capital, land, and labor. See his "The Supply Function for Agricultural Products," *American Economic Review*, Vol. 40, No. 4, Sept., 1950, pp. 539–56.

Conversely, when agricultural prices rise, agricultural production as a whole cannot expand very much. The expansion during World War I was slight—only about 5 per cent. During World War II, the expansion was considerably greater—about 33 per cent—but a large share of this expansion was the result of good weather.

The plain fact is that agricultural production runs very close to capacity all the time, and cannot be expanded much under any circumstances. Livestock production, for example, is limited by livestock feed production, and that cannot be expanded much. Additional fertilizer can be applied if prices are high, and land farmed somewhat more intensively, but the agricultural "plant" cannot run more than twenty-four hours a day, and only very small additions to the plant can be made. To put it in a sentence: The short-time elasticity of agricultural supply is low—even lower than the long-time elasticity.

SHORT-TIME ELASTICITY OF SUPPLY

Technological improvements in agricultural production, which shift the whole supply curve to the right, make it difficult to determine the elasticity directly from price and production data. One attempt has been made to handle this problem by assuming that technological improvements have occurred in spurts, not at an even rate, over a period of years. On this assumption, four separate periods may be perceived—1912–17, represented in the right-hand section of Figure 2.2 by the curve AA; 1918–22, represented by BB; 1923–36, by CC; and 1943–46, by EE. During those periods productivity appeared to remain fixed. Between those periods (especially during 1937–42, represented by TT) productivity appeared to increase.[2]

There is some question whether improvements in productivity resulting from technological changes actually started and stopped as suddenly and frequently as this. Irregular variations in the weather also had something to do with it; bad weather in 1921, and again in 1934–36, for example, shifted the curve temporarily to the left. But be that as it may, the prices of food one year plotted against the production of food the next year are shown in Figure 9 to result in very inelastic supply curves, moving to the right as productivity increased over the period from 1912 to 1946.

This chart shows that the supply of farm products is inelastic with respect to changes in the prices of farm products, when those changes are accompanied by corresponding changes in the prices

---

[2] Willard W. Cochrane, "Farm Price Gyrations—An Aggregative Hypothesis," *Journal of Farm Economics,* Vol. 29, No. 2, pp. 383–408.

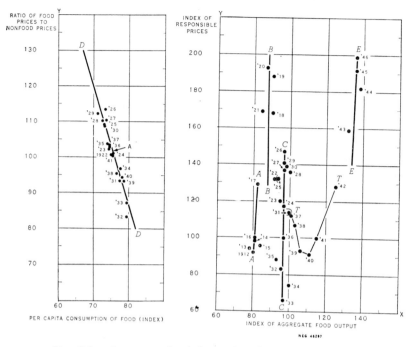

Fig. 2.2 — Aggregate food demand and output schedules.

of nonfarm products. The chart does not show that the supply of farm products is inelastic with respect to changes in the prices of farm products, *if other things (nonagricultural prices, especially) remain equal.* The elasticity of agricultural supply under those conditions is unknown. Undoubtedly it would be greater than the elasticity shown in Figure 2.2. It would vary directly with the length of time involved.

SHORT-TIME ELASTICITY OF DEMAND

An empirical demand curve for food also has been developed. The left-hand section of Figure 2.2 shows the relation between (1) the ratio of retail food prices to nonfood prices, and (2) the per capita consumption of food, after the net effects of income and trend have been removed from the consumption data.[3]

The elasticity of the curve shown in Figure 2.2 is about —0.3. That is, a 1 per cent increase in the retail price of food (relative to other prices, in this case) reduces consumption 0.3 per cent.

E. J. Working estimates the elasticity of the demand for food as

[3] *Ibid,* p. 403.

—0.251.[4] His equation, and the effect of different levels of income on the position of the demand curve, is shown in Figure 2.3.

Working illustrates the drastic effects of this low elasticity on prices by a concrete arithmetical example. During 1950, food exports, plus military and other government purchases, amounted to 9.9 per cent of the 1935–39 average food production. If they had been only 2.3 per cent, as in 1940, supplies available in the domestic market would have been increased by 7.6 per cent of the 1935–39 level of production. Such an increase of food supplies (assuming that it was not temporary so that its effect would be moderated by building up stocks) might be expected, based on the above elasticity, to decrease retail food prices by about 30 per cent. This illustrates how a comparatively small change in supply has a drastic effect on prices, because of the low elasticity of demand.

The corresponding elasticity of the demand for food at the farm (based on farm prices) must be lower still, because of the relative inflexibility of distributors' margins. If distributors' margins were absolutely inflexible, and the margins took half of the consumers' dollar, the corresponding elasticity of the demand for food at the farm would be just half of the elasticity at retail given above.

Agriculture, then, faces an inelastic short-time demand for its products with an inelastic short-time supply. Under those conditions, a small change in either demand or supply causes a large change in price. Until some means is found for keeping the demand for farm products more stable than it has been in the past, the short-time changes in agricultural prices are likely to continue to be violent.

FORECASTING SHORT-TIME CHANGES IN THE PRICE OF FARM PRODUCTS

Total agricultural production is comparatively stable from year to year, so forecasting short-time changes in the price of farm products as a group reduces chiefly to forecasting short-time changes in the demand for farm products. For this purpose the Agricultural Marketing Service of the United States Department of Agriculture has developed a system of relationships that provides a reasonably good basis for forecasting.

---

[4] E. J. Working, "Appraising the Demand for American Agricultural Output During Rearmament," *Journal of Farm Economics*, Vol. 34, No. 2, p. 221.

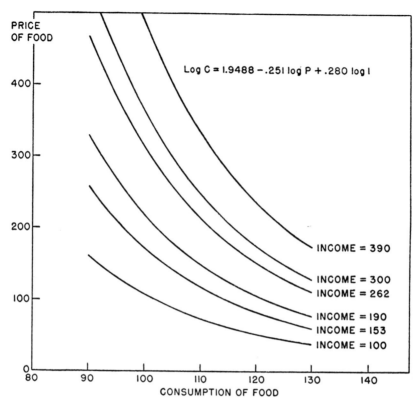

Fig. 2.3 — Demand curves for food at several income levels. (Average 1935–39 = 100.)

FORECASTING THE GROSS NATIONAL PRODUCT (GNP)[5]

The Economic Research Service of the USDA appraises general business conditions in order to analyze the impact of these changes on agriculture. Changes in economic activity affect the level of employment and consumer income, thus changing the demand for farm products. Although per capita use of farm products as a whole is influenced little by changes in consumer buying power, the impact on individual commodities varies. Rising incomes strengthen per capita demand for meats and high-protein food, for example, but tend to reduce the demand for cereals, potatoes, animal fats, and some other high-calorie foods. The farmer is also interested in

[5] The remaining pages of this chapter were prepared by Rex Daly, Chief, Outlook and Projection Branch, Economic and Statistical Analysis Division, ERS, USDA.

changes in business activity as they influence the general price level and the farmers' production costs.

There are no simple mechanical techniques of forecasting general economic activity accurately. A number of empirical frameworks are used but all are tempered by considerable judgment. Forecasts of business conditions are made in the framework of the national income accounts, appraising each major source of demand and its impact on output, employment, income, and the price level.

Major Sources of Demand

Figure 2.4 shows that consumer spending is the biggest source of demand. But nonconsumption outlays usually are the prime movers in changes in economic activity. They vary around a third of total spending for goods and services with government spending the more stable component of nonconsumption expenditures.

In building up estimates of demand or total spending, the plans of the government sector are first determined on the basis of the federal budget and programs of state and local governments. Business investment outlays are examined in relation to the investment cycle, trends in manufacturers' new orders relative to productive capacity, surveys of business investment intentions, and investment levels dictated by projected levels of demand, output rate, corporate profits, and funds for financing investment. Residential construction is also appraised in relation to new family formations, surveys of

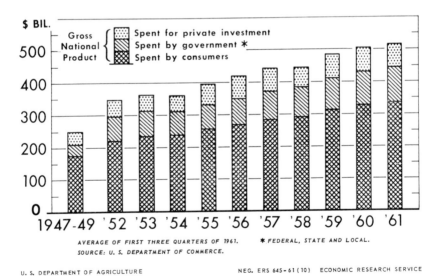

AVERAGE OF FIRST THREE QUARTERS OF 1961.   *FEDERAL, STATE AND LOCAL.
SOURCE: U. S. DEPARTMENT OF COMMERCE.

U. S. DEPARTMENT OF AGRICULTURE   NEG. ERS 645-61 (10)   ECONOMIC RESEARCH SERVICE

Fig. 2.4 — Comparison of the three sources of demand in the United States, 1947–61.

consumer home-buying plans, consumer incomes, and financing terms. Such investment outlays are prime movers influencing changes in output and employment, but they are also determined to a large degree by changes in demand. Consequently, investment must be simultaneously determined or related to the estimated economic framework.

In accordance with output and employment theory, nonconsumption outlays directly affect total demand and, at the same time, affect changes in the level of output, employment, consumer income, and the demand for food. These secondary impacts — the multiplier effect — multiply the impact of a given change in nonconsumption expenditures. These relationships vary widely with cyclical changes in economic activity. Historically in the United States an increase of $10 billion in nonconsumption outlays has usually been accompanied by an increase of around $20 billion in the gross product, as nonconsumption spending contributes to increased employment, income, and consumer spending. This is an obvious oversimplification. The flow of income to consumers will be influenced also by the tax rate structure and possible changes in it, by corporate dividend policy, government financing, consumer saving and credit, and a host of other factors.

It is not possible in the brief treatment of this subject to outline a sophisticated analytical framework. But a simple framework will indicate the nature of the relationships as well as provide some empirical measurements for the United States economy. Simple relationships can be used to illustrate the consumption function, the multiplier, and an indication of the leakage of the income flow into tax revenues and gross business savings.

Consider the following framework:

Y = Gross national product

C = Consumer expenditures for goods and services

N = Nonconsumption outlay — government expenditures and total domestic and foreign investment

T = Includes mainly taxes and gross business savings which divert out of the flow of income to consumers

$X = Y-T$ = Disposable personal income

u and v = Residuals reflecting the effect of omitted variables and random disturbances

$$Y = C + N$$
$$Y = X + T$$

and

$$\triangle C = a + b \triangle (Y - T) + u \quad (1)$$
$$\triangle T = k + t \triangle Y + v \quad (2)$$

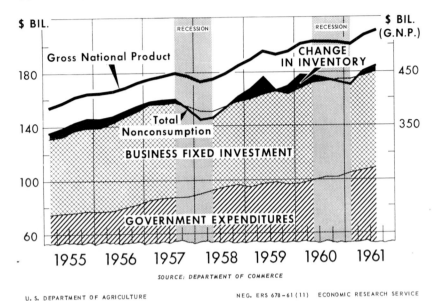

SOURCE: DEPARTMENT OF COMMERCE

U. S. DEPARTMENT OF AGRICULTURE   NEG. ERS 678-61(11)   ECONOMIC RESEARCH SERVICE

Fig. 2.5 — Comparison of Gross National Product with total nonconsumption
in the United States, quarterly, 1955–61.

In the years preceding World War II, year-to-year changes in equations (1) and (2) indicated a propensity to consume (b), the tendency for consumer to spend out of income, of around 0.73. That is, if a man's income increased by $1, his spending increased by 73 cents. The leakage of the income flow to government revenue and business savings represented by (t) was equal to about 0.3. The multiplier, which indicates the change in the gross national product associated with a change in nonconsumption outlays, was a somewhat more involved relationship of the two functional equations resulting in a multiplier of 2.0.

$$\text{Multiplier} = \frac{1}{1 - b\,(1 - t)} = \frac{1}{1 - .73\,(1 - 0.3)} = 2.0$$

The close relationship between changes in nonconsumption outlays and the gross national product are illustrated in Figures 2.5 and 2.6. On the upswing of the cycle, the multiplier effect appears somewhat greater, so that consumer income and buying tends to increase more than dictated by the framework. In a similar manner, consumer spending is "sticky" to downward adjustments in investment and other nonconsumption outlays. The consumer sector is also appraised in relation to surveys of consumer buying plans,

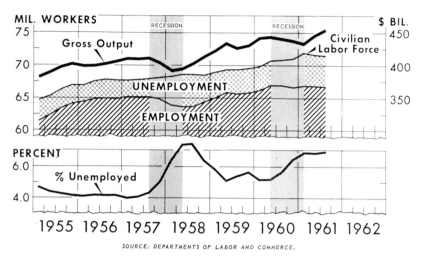

MIL. WORKERS $ BIL.

Fig. 2.6 — Comparison of gross output with employment and unemployment in the United States, quarterly, 1955–61.

credit availability, and separate appraisals for major groups of consumer goods such as autos, household goods, food, and services.

After a skeleton of the national accounts is developed with the aid of historical relationships, a knowledge of tax rates, capital consumption allowances, dividend policy, transfer payments and many other relationships in the economy are employed in building up in detail the expenditure side of the income accounts and the income flows to the business sector, government, and the consumer sector. These relationships are examined for internal consistency by analyzing the saving-investment balance in the accounts and the government revenue-expenditure balance. These calculations are based to a considerable extent on judgment.

Demand For Farm Products

Changes in expenditures for food are highly correlated with changes in consumer disposable income. In the postwar years, a 10 per cent increase in per capita income has usually been accompanied by an increase of about 5 per cent in per capita expenditures for food. But most of this increase in expenditures goes for the services involved in the processing and marketing of food (Figure 2.7). The farm share of changes in retail food expenditures is very small, particularly when supplies are very large. Price and income elasticity of demand for foods measured at the farm level were very

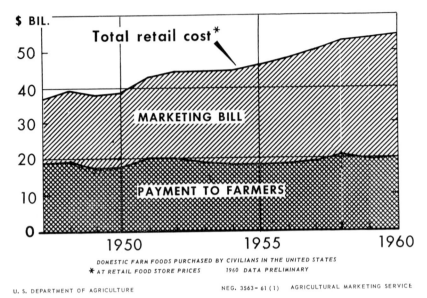

Fig. 2.7 — Comparison of total retail cost of domestic farm food products in the United States, with the marketing bill and the payments to farmers, 1955–60.

inelastic in the postwar period. Both may be as low as 0.1 — minus for price elasticity and plus for income elasticity of demand.

$$\triangle q = k - 0.1 \triangle p + 0.1 \triangle I \qquad (3)$$

In equation (3) a 10 per cent increase in real income per capita may increase per capita food consumption only around 1 per cent, or a price increase of 10 per cent may reduce per capita use of food, measured at the farm, by around 1 per cent. This is for food as a whole which reflects many offsetting trends — uptrends for meat, high-protein livestock products, and convenience foods, and downtrends for animal fats, cereals, and fresh use of many fruits and vegetables.

Prices of many farm products are determined to a considerable extent by the levels of price supports. This is especially true for crops. But crop prices also influence output and consequently, prices of those livestock products not under price support.

The output of farm products likewise depends on farm policy, including the level of farm price supports. Although analytical frameworks are used in appraising probable output and farm product prices, the estimates must allow for the influence of policy. The provisions of the 1961 Feed Grain Program were responsible for the cut in the 1961 feed grain crop. Consequently, it is helpful to supplement over-all appraisals with the judgment of experts intimately familiar with each commodity. This type of information also gives a basis for estimating marketings and total cash receipts for farm products. Analytical frameworks are continuously improved, but it is unlikely that economic forecasting for agriculture or for the general economy will ever become a mechanical process. This is not to imply, however, that statistical measurement and analysis are not helpful. They are essential. And such analytical work must continue in order to develop better tools and more accurate forecasts.

3

Cyclic Variations in Individual Agricultural Prices

Under conditions of atomistic competition, the price and production of a commodity are determined at the point where the supply and demand curves intersect. Under static conditions a disturbance that moves the price and production from that intersection point sets in motion forces which tend to bring them back to the original point.

Where there is a considerable time lag in the response of production to a change in price, however, the price and production may not return to the original equilibrium point; instead, they may circulate around it.

A drouth, for example, which reduces the size of the corn crop, will raise the price of corn. Ordinarily, this induces farmers to raise fewer hogs. When those hogs reach the market the small size of the market receipts raises the price of hogs. This rise in the price of hogs induces farmers to raise more hogs; then when this large crop of hogs reaches the market, it depresses the price of hogs below the equilibrium point. This leads farmers to produce fewer hogs, and so on. The price and production of hogs continues to swing round and round the equilibrium point rather than settle at it.

Figure 3.1 shows that this in fact is what actually takes place. The figure shows that the price of hogs in the United States moves in characteristic cycles averaging about four years in length. These cycles in hog prices are caused by opposite cycles in hog production.

The situation is shown in terms of supply and demand curves in the upper part of Figure 3.2.[1] The demand curve is represented

---

[1] Figures 3.2 and 3.3 are a part of the "Cobweb Theorem" as originally prepared by Mordecai Ezekiel.

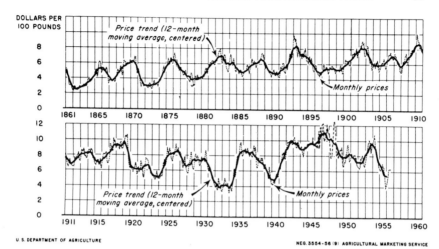

Fig. 3.1 — Cyclic changes in heavy hog prices at Chicago, 1861–1956, adjusted to 1910–14 price level.

by D_tD_t'. It shows the schedule of prices received for various quantities.

The supply curve is represented by S_tS_t'. It shows the quantities that farmers will produce in response to various prices. But these quantities do not reach the market until a production and marketing period has elapsed. OQ_1 is the quantity that sets the price in period 1 (the first crop-disposal year), but OQ_2 is the quantity produced in period 2 (the second crop-disposal year) in response to the price in period 1. These two quantities are by no means identical; they may be quite different, as they are in this case. The two curves shown in Figure 3.2 lie in two different planes reflecting two different time periods. They do not intersect; the one laps over the other.

THE "COBWEB THEOREM"

This situation has been given a generalized explanation, referred to as the "cobweb theorem."

Case 1: Continuous Fluctuation

In the lower portion of Figure 3.2, the series of reactions is portrayed for the curves shown in the upper portion of the figure. The quantity in the initial period (Q_1) is large, producing a relatively low price where it intersects the demand curve, at P_1. This low price, intersecting the supply curve, calls forth in the next period a relatively short supply, Q_2. This short supply intersects the de-

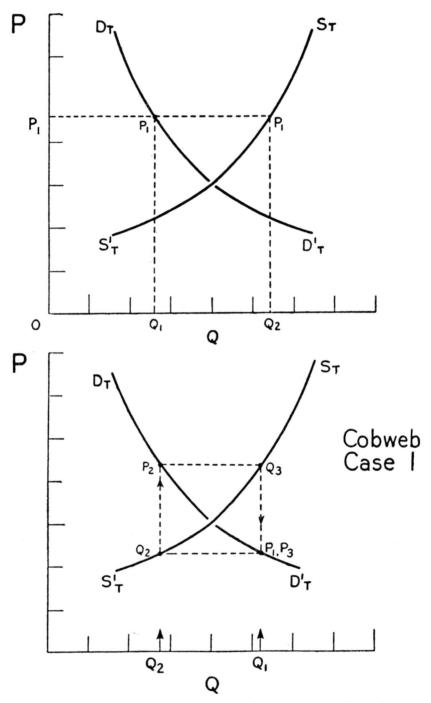

Fig. 3.2 — The mechanics of continuous cycles in prices and production.

mand curve at a high price point, P_2. This high price calls forth a corresponding increased production Q_3 in the third period, with a corresponding low price, P_3. Since this low price in the third period is identical with the original price in the first period, the production and price in the fourth, fifth, and subsequent periods will continue to rotate around the path Q_2, P_2, Q_3, P_3, etc.

As long as price is completely determined by the current supply, and supply is completely determined by the preceding price, fluctuation in price and production will continue in this unchanging pattern indefinitely, without an equilibrium being approached or reached. This is true in this particular case because the demand curve is the exact reverse of the supply curve, so that at their overlap each has the same elasticity. This is a case of "continuous fluctuation."

Case 2: Divergent Fluctuation

Where the elasticity of supply is greater than the elasticity of demand, the series of reactions works out as shown in the upper portion of Figure 3.3. Starting with the moderately large supply, Q_1, and the corresponding price, P_1, the series of reactions is traced by the dotted line. In the second period, there is a moderately reduced supply, Q_2, with the corresponding higher price, P_2. This high price calls forth a considerable increase in supply, Q_3, in the third period, with a resulting material reduction in price, to P_3. This is followed by a sharp reduction in quantity produced in the next period to Q_4, with a corresponding very high price, P_4. The fifth period sees a still greater expansion in supply to Q_5, and so on.

Under these conditions the situation might continue to grow more and more unstable, until price fell to absolute zero, or production was completely abandoned, or a limit was reached to available resources (where the elasticity of supply would change) so that production could no longer expand. This is a case of "divergent fluctuation."

Case 3: Convergent Fluctuation

The reverse situation, with supply less elastic than demand, is shown in the lower portion of Figure 3.3. Starting with a large supply and low price in the first period, P_1, there would be a very short supply and high price, Q_2, and P_2, in the second period. Production would expand again in the third period, to Q_3, but to a smaller production than that in the first period. This would set a moderately low price, P_3, in the third period, with a moderate reduction to Q_4

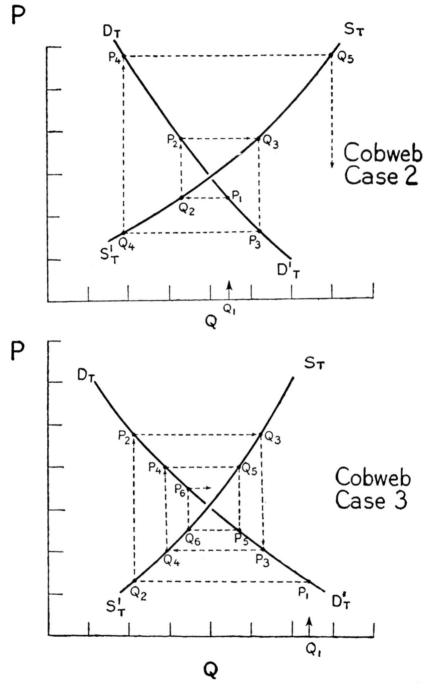

Fig. 3.3 — The mechanics of divergent and convergent cycles in prices and production.

in the fourth period; and a moderately high price, P_4. Continuing through Q_5, P_5, and Q_6 and P_6, production and price approach more and more closely to the equilibrium condition where no further changes would occur.

Of the three cases considered thus far, only this one behaves in the manner assumed by equilibrium theory; and even it converges rapidly only if the supply curve is markedly less elastic than the demand curve. This is a case of "convergent fluctuation."

LONG CYCLES

The cobweb theorem as developed above explains two-year cycles in production and prices, alternating up one year and down the next. It does not fully explain the longer cycles observed for some commodities; that requires a further extension of the cobweb analysis.

In the cases considered thus far, it has been assumed that a change of price in one period was reflected in a corresponding change in production in the next succeeding period. In some commodities (such as beef cattle and various fruits) two or more seasons may be required for the production process, so that two or more periods may elapse before the effect of price upon production becomes apparent. The cycles in these cases will be several years in length.

The same general "cobweb" analysis applies here. The exposition is more complicated, but the principles are the same.

ILLUSTRATIONS OF CYCLIC BEHAVIOR

The principles can be illustrated by the actual price and production cycles for several commodities where the lag between the price and the response of production to that price is longer than one year.

Hogs

The four-year hog price cycles for the years 1861–1956 were shown a few pages back in Figure 3.1. The regularity of the simple cycles that would result if production were determined entirely by price is affected, in actual life, by the irregular fluctuations in the size of the corn crop, which are due chiefly to irregular fluctuations in the weather. These irregular natural variations affect the regularity of the cycles that would result if production were determined entirely by price.

Even in commodities which follow the convergent pattern, the actual cycles may be quite similar to those of either of the other

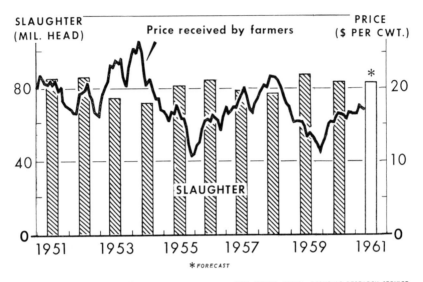

U. S. DEPARTMENT OF AGRICULTURE   NEG. ERS 134-61 (5)   ECONOMIC RESEARCH SERVICE

Fig. 3.4 — Cycles in hog slaughter and price, 1951–61.

types, if abnormally large or small crops occur frequently enough to cause a marked departure from normal and to start again a long series of convergent cycles before stability is again approached. The combination of "cobweb" reactions with occasional crop disasters or gluts may be sufficient to produce recurring cyclical changes in production and prices, rather than stability, as the normal situation.

Evidence in recent years, however, indicates that the four-year hog production and price cycles are inherent in the internal conditions of the hog industry and do not require shocks from outside to keep them going. After 1952, the stabilization operations of the CCC were conducted on so large a scale that they almost completely damped down year-to-year variations in corn prices. Yet hog production and prices continued their four-year cyclic movement much the same as before. The production (slaughter) and price cycles are shown in Figure 3.4; the pig crop cycles are shown in a different form in Figure 3.5. Their relation to the hog-corn price ratio the previous fall is evident.

LENGTH OF THE HOG CYCLE

The length of a cycle depends on the time required for a change in price to affect production. The time to produce an average market hog, from breeding to slaughter at about 230 pounds, is about 12 months. If the physiology of the hog were all that were involved,

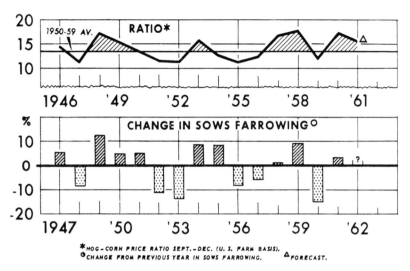

Fig. 3.5 — Cyclic changes in hog-corn ratio and spring farrowing, 1947–62.

the hog cycle would be two years in length. But actually it is about four years in length. Why is this?

The answer is that the psychology of the farmer is involved as well as the physiology of the hog. Farmers do not respond immediately to a change in price. The change in price might be only temporary; if it were temporary — say if it were a rise of $3 lasting only a month or two — farmers would be unlikely to breed many more sows, because even by the time the sows farrowed four months later, hog prices might have declined back to their previous levels. It is only after the price of hogs has remained high for a year or so that farmers pay enough attention to it to breed more sows, and six months more elapse before the pigs from this increase in the number of sows bred reach the market.

Apparently, farmers pay more attention to the length of time that a rise in prices persists than they do to the likelihood that when they do increase the number of sows they breed, other farmers will be doing likewise. The internal mechanism of the hog cycle is shown in Figure 3.6.[2]

Hog production and price cycles may decrease in the future. Farmers' reactions after 1950 were carried over from previous years,

[2] This figure and Figure 3.9 are taken from W. Maki, "Decomposition of the Beef and Pork Cycles," *Journal of Farm Economics,* XLIV, No. 3, August, 1962, pp. 731–43.

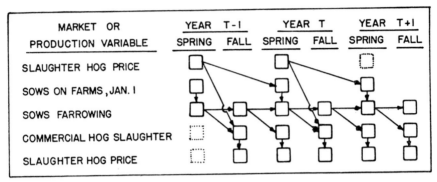

Fig. 3.6 — Internal mechanism of the hog cycle.

before corn prices became very stable. It may be that as farmers become adjusted to stable corn and other feed grain prices, and see the hog production and price cycle more clearly, that they will stabilize their hog production too. If not, it may be necessary to use more direct means to stabilize hog production, such as by making direct payments to farmers whenever hog prices fall cyclicly below a stable level.

Beef Cattle Cycles

The numbers of cattle on farms also move in cycles. These cycles are shown as a continuous series in Figure 3.7.

The cycles in beef cattle numbers are more than twice as long as the cycles in hogs, chiefly for physiological reasons. The gestation period for a cow is about 9 months, and a calf requires nearly two years to reach slaughter age.

The same data, carried back to 1896, are shown in a different form in Figure 3.8. In this figure, each cycle is plotted separately, beginning with the low point at the beginning of the cycle. This figure shows that the cycles have been getting shorter with the passage of time. It will be interesting to see whether this shortening of the cycle is only a temporary thing, or whether it continues in the future. It seems likely that it will continue, because beef cattle are being sold for slaughter now at a younger age than they were several decades ago—at one and one-half to two years of age, instead of two to three years. It will be interesting to see how the current cycle turns out.

The internal mechanism of the beef cycle is shown in Figure 3.9. The mechanism is a little more complicated than the mechanism of the hog cycle. The chain of events in the chart begins with feeder cattle prices. Changes in beef cow inventories January 1, listed

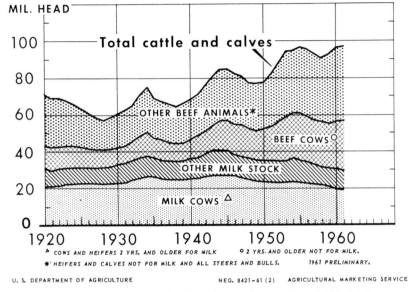

Fig. 3.7 — Comparison of all cattle on farms, Jan., 1920–1961.

under "other cattle on farms" (this means other than dairy cattle) play a critical role. A small decrease in beef cow inventories, for example, would signal a much larger increase in commercial slaughter during the next year. Moreover, beef cows on farms would decline in numbers because of an increase in cow and heifer slaughter during the preceding year.

CYCLIC SEASONAL MOVEMENTS

The prices of most farm products exhibit a regular cyclic movement within the season—from a low price point during the weeks of heaviest market receipts to a high price peak later in the season when supplies are at their lowest. On the average, the rise from low to high is about equal to the extra cost of producing the commodity "off-season"; or, in the case of annual crops, the rise in price is equal to the cost of storage from harvest time until later in the year. But there is much variation from year to year.

The average seasonal variation, independent of other kinds of variation—irregular year-to-year, cyclic, secular, etc.—can be measured by any one of several different methods.

The simplest method is to assemble the monthly data over a fairly long period, such as the twenty years between World Wars I and II, and compute the average for each month separately. The

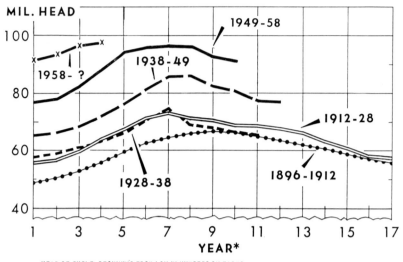

U. S. DEPARTMENT OF AGRICULTURE   NEG. ERS 19-61(4)   ECONOMIC RESEARCH SERVICE

Fig. 3.8 — Numbers of cattle on farms, by cycles, 1896–1960.

averaging process eliminates most of the non-seasonal variation. A more complicated method is to use link relatives; this is a laborious procedure, and the results usually are not much different from those obtained by the simple averaging process.

Still another method is to establish the trend of the series by computing a 13-month moving average of the monthly data, centered on the seventh month. The original value for each month is then expressed as a percentage of the moving average for that month. The average of these percentages is then computed for each month separately.

The variation or departure in individual years from the average seasonal variation can be measured by computing the average deviation of the percentage of trend for individual months about the value of the index of average seasonal variation for each month. This may be called the index of irregularity. A band of the size of this index on both sides of the index of average seasonal variation may then be plotted on a chart to show both the index of seasonal variation and the index of irregularity.

In a normal distribution, this band includes about 60 per cent of the individual items that make up the average. The narrower

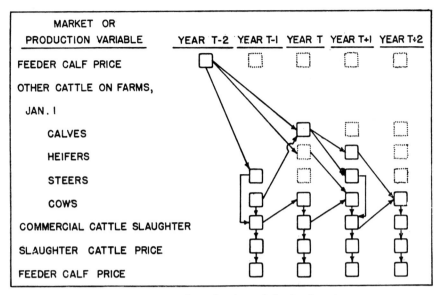

Fig. 3.9 — Internal mechanism of the beef cycle.

this band, the closer is the conformity of the individual years' seasonal movement to the average seasonal movement.[3]

It is also possible to measure the closeness of the conformity of the whole seasonal movement in a particular year to the average seasonal pattern. This conformity may be computed for individual years by the formula

$$a = \frac{\Sigma \, d \, s}{\Sigma \, s^2}$$

where d is the percentage deviation of the individual month from the value of the moving average for that month and s is the deviation of the index of average seasonal variation from 100. In a year when the seasonal pattern corresponded exactly with the average seasonal pattern, this ratio would have a value of one.[4]

The amount of seasonal variation in the prices of several farm products has been decreasing chiefly because the amount of seasonal variation in the production of those products has been decreasing. An illustration of this is shown in Figure 3.10. Another way of showing changes in seasonal patterns with the passage of time is shown

[3] *Marketing Farm Products: Economic Analysis,* Chapter 11, Iowa State University Press, 1962, by the present author; also R. J. Foote and K. A. Fox, "Seasonal Variation: Methods of Measurement and Tests of Significance," BAE, USDA, 1952.

[4] This measure was developed by S. Kuznets. See page 324, *Seasonal Variations of Industry and Trade,* Publ. 22, Nat. Bur. of Econ. Res.

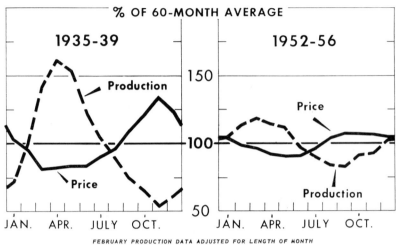

% OF 60-MONTH AVERAGE

1935-39   1952-56

FEBRUARY PRODUCTION DATA ADJUSTED FOR LENGTH OF MONTH

U. S. DEPARTMENT OF AGRICULTURE   NEG. 4459-57 (9)   AGRICULTURAL MARKETING SERVICE

Fig. 3.10 — Average seasonal egg production and prices, 1935–39 and 1952–56.

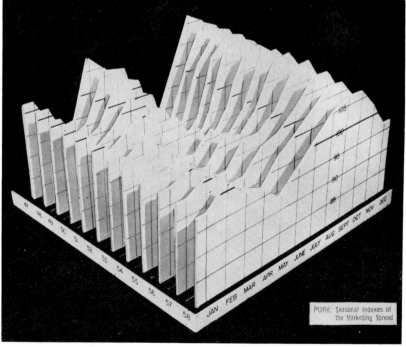

Fig. 3.11 — Monthly indexes of the farm-to-retail price spreads for pork, by years, 1947–58.

in Figure 3.11.[5] In cases like these, the average seasonal variation over the past five or ten years is not an accurate basis for estimating the seasonal variation over the next year or two.

To take this into account, elaborate methods have been worked out for projecting trends in seasonal variation into the future. Briefly, the procedure involves plotting on a separate time chart for each month, the ratio between the price for that month, say January, and the 13-month moving average price centered on January. A trend line is then drawn through the ratios. If, for example, the ratios for January are represented by a trend line declining at the rate of 2 per cent per year, the January ratio for next year (in the future) would be 2 per cent lower than the trend value for the last year.[6]

This is not a very reliable procedure in itself, for it assumes uncritically that recent trends will continue in the future as in the past. Whether this is likely to happen is something that has to be established separately for each product on the basis of knowledge of that product.

Some problems involved in the graphic presentation of seasonal patterns, however, are discussed in Appendix B.

[5] H. F. Gale, "Seasonal Variation in Farm Food Prices and Price Spreads," Misc. Publ. No. 840, USDA, 1961.

[6] H. F. Breimyer, and C. A. Kause, "Charting the Seasonal Market for Meat Animals," USDA Handbook No. 83, 1955.

Breimyer gives a broad treatment of the demand for meat in "Demand and Prices for Meat," USDA Tech. Bul. No. 1253, 1961.

two

MEASURING THE ELASTICITY OF DEMAND AND SUPPLY

4

Elasticity of Demand for Individual Farm Products

In most cases in economics, it is difficult to draw a sharp line between the long run and the short run. In agricultural economics, however, one kind of short run is clearly marked off. Most crops are produced once a year, and the yield per acre is determined chiefly by the weather. Variations in the weather from year to year are almost entirely random in character. A tendency toward cyclic variations has been "discovered" by a number of different investigators, but the length of the cycles differs so much among the different investigators that there is a real question whether there actually are any cycles at all. Crop production series show almost completely random variations from year to year. Each crop is like a flip of a coin or a roll of the dice—a new item, practically independent of the other items in the series. Crop production series, and other series closely associated with them (such as crop price series in times of stable demand, or independent of variations in demand), therefore lend themselves well to statistical analysis.

RELATIONS AMONG PRODUCTION, PRICE, AND INCOME

Each year farmers plant their crops, not knowing whether the weather will be good, bad, or indifferent; their crops accordingly large, small or average; and their prices accordingly low, high, or average.

Large crops bring low prices, and small crops, high prices. But will large crops bring high incomes, or low incomes?

The answer depends upon the extent to which prices vary (inversely) with variations in production. In the case of some crops, an increase in production of 10 per cent decreases price 20 per cent. The price falls twice as far as the size of the crop increases. In this case, a large crop brings a lower income than an average crop. In other cases, the price falls less than the size of the crop increases; a large crop then is worth more than an average crop.

This relation between the extent of the change in the size of the crop and the extent of the change in price is called the price elasticity of the demand. Each crop has its own price elasticity of demand, differing from the elasticity for other crops. It is important to measure this elasticity for each crop. In a free-market economy, it is important to know how much, and in which direction, variations in the size of the crop affect income as well as price. This knowledge is still more important in a controlled economy or sector of an economy, such as a price or income stabilization program.

MEASUREMENT OF THE ELASTICITY OF DEMAND

The concept of elasticity is basically simple. People will buy more carrots, for example, when they are cheap than when they are high-priced. A reduction in the price of almost anything ordinarily increases the amount of the thing that can be sold. This responsiveness of quantity to price is called the elasticity of the good in question.[1]

With some goods, for example peaches, a change in the price will result in a large change in the amount that can be sold. With other goods, for example, salt, the same change in the price has only a small effect on the amount that can be sold. In practically no case is the quantity of a good completely unresponsive to a change in price; that is, the demand is very seldom completely inelastic. With most goods a change in price has an appreciable effect upon the quantity that can be sold—a small effect in the case of some goods, a large effect in the case of some others.

This definition of elasticity of demand is phrased in terms of the change in quantity per unit change in price. This does not mean that the change in price is regarded as the cause, and the change in quantity as the effect. In many cases the line of causation runs the other way; in agriculture, farmers determine the acreage and the weather determines the yield of the crop, and the quantity produced "sets the price." But the term elasticity here as elsewhere refers

---

[1] The term elasticity is not very clear. Frank Knight believes that the term "responsiveness of consumption" expresses the concept better. (Frank H. Knight, "Demand," *Encyclopaedia of the Social Sciences*, Vol. 5, 1931, p. 70.) It makes clear that elasticity refers to the responsiveness of quantity to price, not vice versa (which Moore has called the "flexibility of prices"). Knight's term, "responsiveness of consumption," is clearer or at least more self-explanatory than "elasticity of demand"; but it has one shortcoming, namely that it cannot, strictly speaking, be applied to the purchases of dealers who do not consume the product, whereas "elasticity of demand" can be thus applied. The term "elasticity of purchases" would meet this objection, but it is not so clear as the other. In any case, "elasticity of demand" has become so well established in use that it probably will remain in use (like the established width of railroad tracks, even though a greater width would be better suited to present needs).

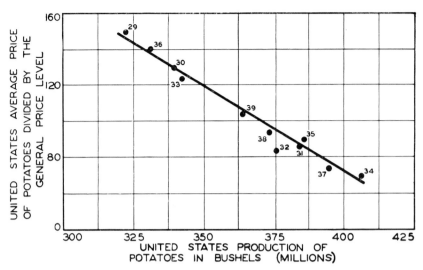

Fig. 4.1 — Potatoes: United States average farm price, December 15, and total production, 1929–39.

to the change in quantity, neither causing nor caused by, but *associated with* a given change in price.

The concept of elasticity has been familiar to economists for generations. Gregory King two or three centuries ago attempted to measure the elasticity of the demand for wheat in quantitative terms,[2] but nothing much else was done until Moore in 1914 published his empirical studies of the elasticity of the demand for corn, hay, and potatoes.[3] After World War I, a great increase took place in the quantity of statistical data available concerning production, prices, demand, and supply, and analytical statistical methods were applied to economic data on an extensive scale. Many studies of the elasticities of demand for different products have been published, and one of the first things a student of price analysis should be able to do is to measure the elasticity of the demand for a given product and interpret his results properly.

---

[2] "We take it, that a defect in the harvest may raise the price of corn in the following proportions:

Defect		Above the Common Rate
1 Tenth		3 Tenths
2 Tenths	Raises the	8 Tenths
3 Tenths	price	16 Tenths
4 Tenths		28 Tenths
5 Tenths		45 Tenths

so that when corn rises to treble the common rate, it may be presumed that we want above 1/3rd (one-third) of the common produce; and if we should want 5/10ths, or half the common produce, the price would rise to near five times the common rates." C. D'Avenant, *Political and Commercial Works*, Vol. II, 1771, p. 224, quoted in *Farm Economics*, Cornell Univ., May, 1939, p. 2758.

[3] Henry L. Moore, *Economic Cycles, Their Law and Cause*, Macmillan, 1914.

TABLE 4.1

POTATOES: UNITED STATES PRODUCTION AND AVERAGE FARM PRICE, DECEMBER 15, 1929–39*

Year	(1) Potatoes (000 bushels)	(2) Potatoes Average Price per Bushel December 15 (cents)	(3) Wholesale Price Index, All Commodities Dec. 1926 = 100	(4) [(3)×1.50−50]	(5) (2) ÷ (4)	Data in (1) and (5) Expressed in Percentages of Average	
						Production	Deflated Prices
1929........	322,204	134.6	93.3	89.95	149.6	88.1	144.5
1930........	340,572	89.8	79.6	69.40	129.4	93.1	125.0
1931........	384,125	45.0	68.6	52.90	85.1	105.0	82.2
1932........	376,425	36.8	62.6	43.90	83.8	102.9	81.0
1933........	342,306	69.2	70.8	56.20	123.1	93.6	118.9
1934........	406,105	44.9	76.9	65.35	68.7	111.0	66.4
1935........	386,380	63.7	80.9	71.35	89.3	105.6	86.2
1936........	331,918	106.3	84.0	76.0	139.9	90.7	135.2
1937........	395,294	53.0	81.7	72.55	73.1	108.1	70.6
1938........	374,163	61.3	77.0	65.5	93.6	102.3	90.4
1939........	364,016	70.8	79.0	68.5	103.4	99.5	99.9

* Sources of data: (1) and (2) *Agricultural Statistics*, 1940, pp. 262, 269; *Crops and Markets* (monthly); data from *Wholesale Prices* (monthly). (3) *Mimeo. 4313*, Bureau of Labor Statistics, U. S. Department of Labor.

Measuring Elasticity

Let us take a concrete example. The price and production data for potatoes for eleven years are given in Table 4.1. They are plotted in scatter-diagram form in Figure 4.1. The prices are the average United States farm prices December 15 each year, adjusted for changes in the general price level.[4] The production figures show the total production of potatoes in the United States.

The dots in Figure 4.1 fall closely around a sloping line, which can be fitted to the data mathematically by the method of least squares, or simply drawn in freehand. In either case, the investigator must decide whether to use a straight line or a curved line to fit the dots. The decision must be based on (1) the appearance of the data, (2) the investigator's knowledge of the particular product, and (3) his grasp of economic theory. That is, the line chosen should be a reasonable one from all three of these points of view. In Figure 4.1 the dots fall about a straight line, and in the absence of any reason for using a curved line, a straight line is chosen. The line in this case is drawn in freehand. It does not necessarily go through any of the dots, but merely represents the average relationship between production and price shown by the data. The line should not be extrapolated (extended) beyond the dots.

The job now is to measure the elasticity of the demand represented by this line—that is, to measure the change in quantity associated with a unit change in price.[5] Inspection of the chart

---

[4] These actual production and market price data are used so as to show that the concept of elasticity that we measure here is a concept that reflects and arises from what goes on in the world, and not merely from some economist's brain. Data for the pre-war period are used, because the data since that time are affected by additional war and post-war forces that can only be taken into account by complicated methods that still leave the dots with a rather wide scatter about the line.

The adjustment for changes in the general price level here consists in dividing the price data by the corresponding Bureau of Labor Statistics all-commodity wholesale price index inflated by 50 per cent (because the relation between the two is not 1 to 1 but 1 to 1.5). This procedure, probably not clear to the reader at this point, is explained in detail in Chapter 8, along with a general discussion of the adjustment of prices to take care of the effect of changes in demand.

The simple analytical methods used have resulted in the straight-line demand curve shown. More complicated and accurate analyses show that the demand curve has a concave curvature at the lower end.

[5] The computation of the elasticity of the demand should be based upon two points on the line rather than upon two actual data dots, because a line joining any two dots (1938 and 1939, for example, or still more obviously, 1931 and 1932) may have a different slope from the line representing the average relationship of all the dots, and it is the average relationship that is being measured. Furthermore, two points at the ends of the line shown in Figure 4.1 should be used, rather than two anywhere along the line, since it is the elasticity of the line as a whole that is to be measured, not just the elasticity of a part of it.

This concept of the elasticity of the line as a whole, or of a part of it, may be referred to as the average elasticity in much the same way that reference is made to one's average speed, say 50 miles an hour, on a trip. It is contrasted with point elasticity, as in physics the empirical concept of average speed is contrasted with the limiting concept of velocity. Point elasticity is taken up in the next chapter.

shows that a change in quantity from 325 million bushels to 400 million bushels (using round numbers near the ends of the line) is associated with a change in price in the opposite direction, from 144 to 70 cents per bushel. That is, a change in quantity of 75 million bushels is associated with an opposite change in price of 74 cents;

the change in quantity per unit change in price is $\dfrac{75}{-74} = -1.01$.

But this is not the elasticity of the demand for potatoes, for it is evident that the result is determined largely by the particular units in which the quantity and price changes are measured. If the quantity had been measured in bushels, for example, instead of millions of bushels, the answer obtained by the formula above would have been —1,013,389, clearly an absurd answer. Or if the price had been measured in English money, the change in price would have been about 3 shillings instead of 75 cents; and this again would have given a different answer. The basic situation remains unchanged when different units of computation are used, but the numerical results obtained above are quite different. This is not as it should be. What is needed is a measure of elasticity that will be unaffected by the units of measurement chosen—a coefficient of elasticity.

The Coefficient of Elasticity

One good way to compute such a coefficient of elasticity is to divide the observed change in quantity by the average of the two

quantities, i.e., divide 75 by 367.5 (400—325 by $\dfrac{400 + 325}{2}$).

The same thing can be done with the prices. The formula thus becomes a complex fraction,

$$\frac{\dfrac{change\ in\ quantity}{average\ quantity}}{\dfrac{change\ in\ price}{average\ price}}$$

Now the average is simply the total sum divided by the number of items. The number of quantity items is the same as the number of price items (in this case two) so the result will be the same if the sum of the quantities and the sum of the prices is used instead of the average prices and quantities (the 2's in the numerator and denominator cancel out). This will save some computation. The formula may then be expressed:

$$\frac{\dfrac{q_1 - q_2}{q_1 + q_2}}{\dfrac{p_1 - p_2}{p_1 + p_2}}$$

The same formula can also be written in the form

$$\frac{q_1 - q_2}{p_1 - p_2} \cdot \frac{p_1 + p_2}{q_1 + q_2}$$

This was substantially the form which Marshall used,[6] although he restricted the concept to infinitesimally small changes, in which case the change is represented by "d," and there is no need to use the average or the sum of the quantities and prices. His formula was merely $\dfrac{dq}{dp} \cdot \dfrac{p}{q}$. The complex-fraction formula is clumsier in appearance than the Marshallian form of the formula; it is superior to the other form for introductory expository purposes, because it shows more clearly just what elasticity is, but Marshall's form of the formula is standard and we will use it henceforth.

The data for potatoes substituted in this formula yield the following coefficient of elasticity:

$$\frac{400 - 325}{70 - 144} \cdot \frac{70 + 144}{400 + 325} = \frac{75}{-74} \cdot \frac{214}{725} = \frac{1605}{-5365} = -0.299$$

Exactly the same result is obtained when the original quantity data are expressed in tons instead of bushels. The figures then become

$$\frac{12 - 9.75}{70 - 144} \cdot \frac{70 + 144}{12 + 9.75} = \frac{2.25}{-74} \cdot \frac{214}{21.75} = \frac{481.5}{-1609.5} = -0.299$$

The same thing is obviously true if the prices are expressed in some other units.

We can now refine our definition of elasticity and make it more

---

[6] Alfred Marshall, *Principles of Economics*, 8th American edition, Macmillan, Mathematical Appendix, Note III, p. 103 n.

precise and definite, thus: *Elasticity is the proportional change in quantity associated with a proportional change in price.* The strict mathematical definition runs in terms of infinitesimals, but for students without mathematical training, the concept can be expressed in terms of percentages. The definition in that case is: *Elasticity is the percentage change in quantity associated with a 1 per cent change in price (other things remaining constant).* The computation for potatoes given above shows that a change in quantity of 0.299 per cent (roughly, 0.3 per cent) is associated with a 1 per cent change in price. That is, the elasticity of the demand for potatoes is − 0.3.

EFFECT OF CROP SIZE ON TOTAL INCOME

The chart discussed in the preceding pages shows the effect of the size of the potato crop upon the price of potatoes. Another question now arises. What is the effect of the size of the potato crop upon the *total revenue* from the crop? Does a large crop depress prices so much that the low price per bushel more than offsets the large number of bushels sold, or not?

It takes only a moment to answer this question. The smallest crop shown in Figure 4.1 was 322 million bushels; it sold at a price of $1.50 per bushel; the total revenue, therefore, was 322 million × $1.50, or *$483 million.* The largest crop was 406 million bushels; it sold at a price of 69 cents per bushel; the total revenue therefore was 406 million × $.69, or *$289 million.* The small crop was worth more than the large crop. The larger the crop, the smaller the total income. The demand in this case is said to be inelastic. In the case of some goods, a small reduction in price results in a larger increase, proportionally, in sales, and the larger the crop, the *larger* the total revenue. The demand in this case is referred to as elastic.

What these terms elastic and inelastic really mean is "relatively elastic" and "relatively inelastic." The term "relatively" is dropped only for brevity; it really belongs in. "Relatively" here means relative to *unit elasticity,* the borderline case between relatively elastic and relatively inelastic. If the elasticity of demand for a good were such that any percentage increase in supply depressed the price by an equal percentage, then the total value of a large crop would be the same as that of a small crop.[7] In fact, no matter

---

[7] Strictly speaking, this is true only when the percentage changes involved are infinitesimally small. Large changes introduce slight arithmetic discrepancies. For example, if the crop increased 10 per cent and the price decreased 10 per cent, the total value would be 90 × 110 = 9,900, not 10,000. This question is discussed fully in the next chapter.

what the size of the crop, it would be offset by an opposite change in price, so that the total value of the crop would be constant no matter what its size. In this case, in the formula presented a few paragraphs back, a 10 per cent (or any other) change would yield the following results:

$$\frac{10}{-10} \cdot \frac{100}{100} = \frac{1000}{-1000} = -1.0$$

This is called unit elasticity. It is the dividing line or borderline case between elastic demand and inelastic demand. If the elasticity is less than 1 it is called inelastic; if it is more than 1 it is called elastic. For technical accuracy, the terms, "relatively inelastic" (that is, less elastic than unity, inelastic relative to unit elasticity) and "relatively elastic" (more elastic than unity) should be used. But the word "relatively" is understood, and may be omitted in ordinary discussion.

In the illustration just given, an increase in quantity, a plus, is associated with a decrease in price, a minus. The measure of elasticity, therefore, carries a minus sign, as shown. Curves of this sort, with minus signs, all slope downward to the right, that is, from northwest to southeast. Practically all demand curves are of this character. If a case were found where increases in quantities were associated with *increases* in prices, the numerical expression of elasticity would have a positive sign and the curve would slope upwards to the right.

ELASTICITY GRAPHICALLY REPRESENTED

Elasticity can be represented graphically, but proper attention must be given to the scales of the charts. One might think that a demand curve of unit elasticity would be the hypotenuse of a right-angled triangle lying on one side, and that the slope of the curve would therefore be 45°; and, further, one might conclude that all curves that were more steeply sloped than 45°—say 50°, 60°, or 70° —would be inelastic, and all curves less steeply sloped than 45° would be elastic.

Reference back to Figure 4.1, however, shows that the demand curve for potatoes shown in that figure has a slope that is definitely less than 45°. It is about 30°. This would seem to place it in the elastic category. Yet the numerical computations a few pages back showed that the elasticity was −0.3°. This is clearly inelastic. Which is wrong, our graphics or our arithmetic?

A moment's reflection shows that it is our graphics that is at fault. The scales in Figure 4.1 are laid out in absolute, not percentage, terms. But elasticity is a proportional concept. The scales in the graph should run in percentage terms, and 10 per cent on the quantity scale should cover as much distance as 10 per cent on the price scale. If this procedure is followed, the chart will show elasticity correctly; the category into which the curve falls—inelastic or elastic—can then be determined directly from the chart by observing whether its slope is steeper or flatter than 45°.

The data, expressed in percentage terms and plotted on a properly scaled chart, are shown in the left-hand section of Figure 4.2. The curve in this chart is much steeper than the one in Figure 4.1. It is clearly in the inelastic category. The proper arrangement of scales for representing elasticity directly is that which is used in Figure 4.2, with the data expressed as percentages and the horizontal and vertical scales equal, so that 10 per cent on one scale equals the same distance as 10 per cent on the other.

It is not the conversion of the original data into percentage form alone that enables elasticity to be read directly from the slope of the line on a chart with arithmetic scales. It is this, plus the setting of the horizontal and vertical scales so that 10 per cent on the one scale is represented by the same distance as 10 per cent on the other scale, that does the trick.

This could be accomplished just as well by plotting the data in their original form, on a chart with the horizontal and vertical scales set so that the average price equals (say) 5 inches on the vertical scale, and the average production equals the same distance, 5 inches, on the horizontal scale. The elasticity could then be read directly from the slope of the line on a chart with arithmetic scales, regardless of what units the original data were expressed in. This sounds easier than converting the data into index form. But, as a matter of fact, it turns out that it is more trouble to do this than to convert the data into index form and plot them in that form. For suppose that the average price comes out to be 77 cents, or some other figure that is not an easy multiple of 5; the resulting scale is very awkward to plot, especially when the production scale is probably awkward too. It is easier after all to convert the data into index form (i. e., into percentages) and set the scales so that 100 per cent equals 5 or 10 inches, or some other easy divisor of 100.

Elasticity can also be shown graphically by plotting the data in their original form on double logarithmic paper, that is, paper in which both the horizontal and vertical scales are logarithmic. No matter what units the original data are expressed in—dollars, francs,

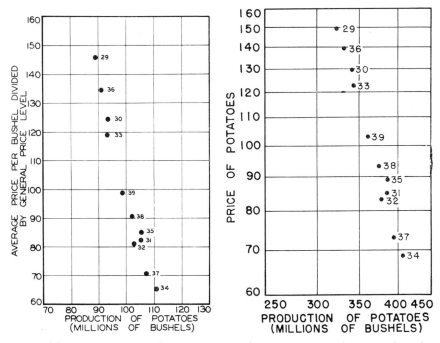

Fig. 4.2 — Potatoes: United States average farm price, December 1, and total production, 1929–39. Chart on left, data in percentage terms, arithmetic scales; on right, data in original form, logarithmetic scales.

pounds, ounces, etc. — when they are plotted on double logarithmic scales, the slope of the line shows the elasticity directly.[8] The data plotted in this manner are shown in the right-hand section of Figure 4.2. The slope of the curve here is identical with the slope of the curve in the left-hand section of Figure 4.2. This is really the simplest way to show the relation between price and production data; but most people are not familiar with logarithmic scales, so for purposes of presentation it is better to plot the data in percentage terms on ordinary arithmetic paper.

Considerations similar to those which hold for ordinary arithmetic paper rule here. It is not the plotting of the data on logarithmic scales that enables elasticity to be read directly from the chart; it is the fact that the horizontal and vertical scales are equal that does it.

---

[8] Technically speaking, the elasticity is not the same as the slope; it is the reciprocal of the slope. For the slope is the number of units that the curve rises per unit of horizontal run; it is $\dfrac{p}{q}$. But elasticity is $\dfrac{q}{p}$. The greater (i.e., steeper) the slope the less the elasticity. In addition, elasticity is expressed in proportions, while slope is usually expressed in absolutes, such as feet.

EFFECT OF MIDDLEMAN'S MARGINS ON ELASTICITY

The factors that determine elasticity are discussed in any good textbook on elementary economic theory, and there is no need to repeat the discussion here. But most discussions of this sort deal with the elasticity of demand at the retail store, or wherever the consumer buys the goods. The elasticity of demand at the farm is affected by still another thing in addition to these—by the size and stability of the middleman's charges, that is, the margins between the prices of goods at the farm and at the retail store.

Middleman's margins remain rather stable through periods of high prices and low prices resulting from fluctuations in supplies. They change from periods of prosperity to periods of depression (fluctuations in general demand) because wages, although comparatively stable, do change to some extent from peak to trough of industrial activity. But during periods of relatively stable industrial activity, the margin between potato prices at the farm and potato prices at the retail store, for example, remains much the same when potato supplies are short and prices high as when supplies are plentiful and prices low.

In that case, if the demand curves for potatoes at retail and for potatoes at the farm were plotted on the same chart with arithmetic scales, the two curves would be parallel, the one lying above the other. The curves would look something like those in Figure 4.3. This figure is based on hypothetical data, that enable the exposition to be made arithmetically simple.

In this chart the average price of potatoes at the retail store is 20 cents a pound, the average price of potatoes at the farm is 10 cents a pound, and the margin between the two prices remains fixed at 10 cents a pound. The elasticity of the demand for potatoes at retail is represented as unity. From the parallelism of the two curves, one might conclude that the elasticity of the demand for potatoes at the farm must be unity also.

But that would be a mistake. Application of the regular elasticity formula to these hypothetical data shows that whereas the elasticity of the demand at retail is unity, that at the farm is only -0.5. The two calculations, based upon figures read off the chart, follow:

For potatoes at retail $\qquad \dfrac{12-8}{16-24} \cdot \dfrac{20}{10} = \dfrac{80}{-80} = -1.0$

For potatoes at the farm $\qquad \dfrac{12-8}{6-14} \cdot \dfrac{10}{10} = \dfrac{40}{-80} = -0.5$

Looking at the two sets of calculations, we see that they are identical in all respects except the average price. For potatoes at retail, the average price is 20; for potatoes at the farm it is 10.

It is clear from this formula that if you halve the average price, other things being the same, you halve the elasticity. It shows that the width and fixity of the margin between farm prices and retail prices affects the elasticity of the demand at the farm. The wider and more stable the margin, the less elastic is the demand at the farm compared with the demand at the retail store.[9]

EFFECT OF TIME UPON ELASTICITY

Economists since at least as far back as Marshall have recognized that it is incorrect to speak of "*the* elasticity" of the demand for a commodity, for the elasticity differs according to the length of time involved. The subject has been given extensive theoretical discussion, with the aid of hypothetical data, but not much has been offered in the way of empirical demonstration. A few studies may be brought together to serve this purpose.

Short-time Elasticities

Estimates have been made that "*the* elasticity" of the demand for hogs at the farm is —0.46.[10] But all that this statement means is that the elasticity of the demand for hogs based upon annual data is (or, more accurately, was) —0.46. Other empirical studies have shown that the elasticity of the demand for hogs derived from weekly data is much greater than this, and that the elasticity

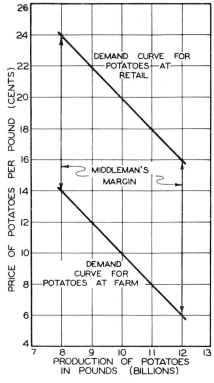

Fig. 4.3 — Hypothetical demand curves for potatoes at the retail store and at the farm.

[9] When a reduction is made in middlemen's margins, who gets the benefit — the producer, or the consumer? This question is answered in *Marketing Farm Products*, Iowa State Univ. Press, 1962, Chap. 9.

[10] G. E. Brandow, "Interrelations Among Demands for Farm Products and Implications for Control of Market Supply," Bul. 680, Aug. 1961, Pennsylvania State Univ., Agr. Exp. Sta., University Park, Pa.

derived from daily data is still greater. Stover[11] found that over a 7-year period the elasticities of the demand for hogs at Chicago based on daily, weekly, and yearly data were as follows:

Saturday . . . . —5.8
Wednesday . . . . . . —2.8
Week . . . . —2.5
Year . . . . —1.0

Among the various days of the week, the elasticity was greatest on Saturday and least on Wednesday; the elasticity on Wednesday was almost as high as the elasticity for the week as a whole.[12]

Similarly, the elasticity of the demand for eggs, based upon annual data, is about—0.3,[13] whereas the elasticity based upon monthly data would be higher. Other instances of this sort could be given. It is not surprising that the short-time elasticities differ from the annual-data elasticities; they refer to different demands. The short-time elasticities should be greater than the long-time elasticities, because a large part of the short-time fluctuations in supplies thrown on the market are absorbed by short-time storage operations. Dealers buy eggs, for example, for storage, whenever they believe that the price of eggs some time in the future (within the probable storage life of an egg) will be higher than it is at present — and higher by more than the cost of storage to that future time. The future changes in prices that dealers can predict most confidently are those associated with regular seasonal changes in egg receipts, so that storage is largely a seasonal phenomenon. At the time of large egg receipts and low prices, therefore, the storage dealer's demand for eggs is added to the consumer's demand; this keeps prices from falling as low as they would in the absence of purchases for storage. Later on in the season, when egg receipts are light and prices high, the storage dealer's eggs are added to the current receipts from producers. This keeps prices from rising as high as they would otherwise. Longer-time (annual) fluctuations in supplies, however, cannot be thus absorbed, because the commodity is too perishable to stand storage for more than a few months.

---

[11] Howard J. Stover, "Relation of Daily Prices to the Marketing of Hogs at Chicago," Cornell Univ. Agr. Sta. Bul. 534, p. 33.
[12] The elasticity he found for the yearly data was higher than that which was found in the more recent study referred to in the preceding footnote, because his data were Chicago (not national) data, and he found the gross regression of receipts on prices, not the net regression.
[13] G. E. Brandow, op. cit., p. 17.

Long-time Elasticities

The elasticities of demand based on daily, weekly, or monthly data are likely to be greater than for annual data. What about the elasticities based on items each of which covers more than a year, perhaps five or ten years?

There are reasons for believing that these elasticities based on long-time data may be greater than the elasticities based on annual data. These reasons are not the same as those which make the elasticities for weekly data greater than for annual data; they are related not to storage, but to the ease of substitution.

If some year the grapefruit crop is short, for example, consumers who have established a place for it on their breakfast table may bid grapefruit prices up to a high point in an attempt to keep it there. They know that grapefruit will probably be plentiful again within another year, and they dislike to change their consuming habits merely for a year only to change them back again when the year is over. But if grapefruit acreages were more or less permanently reduced and grapefruit rose to a place in the luxury price class, many consumers would replace it on their breakfast table with something else, and prices would not be bid so high as for a one-year shortage.

Another example is corn. The demand for corn, based upon annual data, is only about —0.5 at its lower end; but if large supplies and low prices seemed likely to persist for years in the future, power alcohol plants would be set up to use the cheap corn, and would open up a demand that would be very elastic indeed. Similarly, at the upper end of the scale, if scarcity and high prices appeared likely to persist for a decade or more, consumers would have time to cultivate new tastes and manufacturers would have time to bring new substitute products on the market, which would render the upper part of the curve more elastic also.

This boils down to the simple fact that the more time you give people to change their tastes, the more they will change them. This principle operates continuously, from the shortest periods of time, only a few moments long, up to the longest periods, decades and more in length. Within the short periods of time, however, the effect of this principle is more than offset by the opposite effect of storage and subsequent "unstorage" of temporary surpluses. The lowest elasticity of demand for a good, therefore, is that which is based on data each of which represents a period just a little longer than the storage life of that good. For extremely perishable goods like strawberries, this period is only a few days or weeks in length. For many farm products which are semiperishables, such as meat, eggs, and butter, this period is a year. Most analyses of the demand for farm products are based on annual data, and the elasticities found for the semiperishables are likely to be the minimum elasticities; both shorter-period and longer-period data yield higher elasticities than the annual data. For grains, which are stored to some extent for longer periods than one year, the minimum elasticity period is likely to be longer than one year. For cotton, which is stored for still longer periods than grain, the minimum elasticity period is likely to be still longer.

THE MEASUREMENT OF LONG-RUN AND SHORT-RUN ELASTICITY

It is difficult to measure "the" short-run elasticity of supply or demand directly, for through each point on a long-run supply or demand curve passes a fan of short-run curves, each one appropriate to a different interval of time.[14]

Figure 4.4, Section A, illustrates this point. The curve D_LD_L is the long-run demand curve. The point B on D_LD_L represents an equilibrium of demand and supply: At a price OA, the quantity AB is consumed each period. If the supply curve shifts so that the price is now OC, the quantity consumed does not increase immediately to CP, where P is a point on the long-run demand curve, but to CD, where D is a point on one of the short-run demand curves through B. If the price were to remain at OC, the quantity CE would be consumed the following period, then CF, then CG, CH, and so on. Each of the points, D, E, F, G, H, etc. lies on a different short-run demand curve through the point B. As time passes, the points gradually approach the point P which lies on the long-run demand curve.

In most situations, price will be changing constantly; hence, the points observed never lie on the long-run demand curve. Figure 4.4, Section B, illustrates this situation. We start out, as before, from an initial equilibrium point B on the long-run demand curve D_LD_L. Now, however, let supply shift in such a way that the price falls constantly, first to OC, then to OE, OG, OJ, and so on. When the price falls from OA to OC, consumers adjust their consumption

---

[14] The next few paragraphs, ending with Figure 4.5, are adapted from Marc Nerlove, "Distributed Lags and Estimation of Long-Run Supply and Demand Elasticities: Theoretical Considerations," *Journal of Farm Economics*, Vol. 40, No. 2, May, 1958.

from AB to CD. If the price remained at OC, they would consume CW the following period; but the price falls again to OE. Consequently they move along a new short-run demand curve through the point W to F. They consume slightly more than they would have, had the price remained at OC. Thus, as price falls, we observe a series of points, D, F, H, J, L, etc., which all lie on different short-run demand curves passing through different points on the long-run demand curve.

A curve passing through these points, $D_E D_E$, has neither the average elasticity of the short-run curves nor the elasticity of the long-run curve. The curve $D_E D_E$ is the sort of demand curve that would be estimated were we to neglect the whole problem of short- and long-run demand; i.e., it is the sort of demand curve which has usually been estimated. The position, elasticity, and even the shape of the estimated demand curve, $D_E D_E$, depend on the pattern of assumed price changes: if price had been assumed to fall more slowly, the elasticity of demand would be closer to the long-run elasticity. The measured elasticity could exceed the long-run elasticity or fall short of the shortest of short-run elasticities. The estimated curve is neither a short-run demand curve nor a long-run demand curve. In fact, it is not a demand curve at all.

THE ESTIMATION OF DISTRIBUTED LAGS

Whenever the effects of an economic change are not exerted all at once, but are distributed over time, we have what may be called a distributed lag.

The problem of estimating a distributiton of lag may be attacked in several ways: (1) We may make no assumption as to the form of the distribution. (2) We may assume a general form for the distribution of lag and estimate the parameters which define the exact distribution. (3) Finally, we may develop an explicit dynamic model of producer or consumer behavior which implies a distributed lag only incidentally. These models may be used directly in an analysis designed to estimate the long-run elasticity of demand or supply.

Because of the short length and degree of auto-correlation in most economic time series, the first approach where nothing is assumed is not always feasible. The error term is so large that the investigator gets erratic results if he tries to determine empirically from the data what the nature of the distribution of the lag is. The second approach necessarily contains a somewhat arbitrary assumption concerning the form of the distribution of lag. The investi-

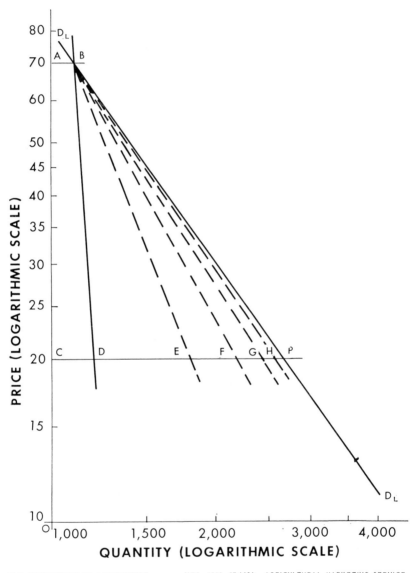

Fig. 4.4A — Adjustment of the quantity demanded to a once-and-for-all change in price.

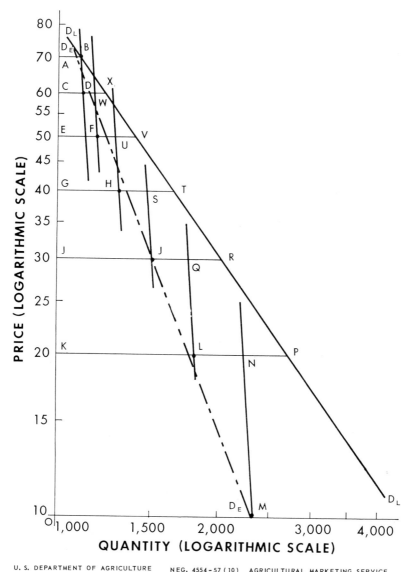

Fig. 4.4B — Adjustment of the quantity demanded to successive changes in price.

gator must assume in advance what the nature is, and then carry the analysis through on the basis of that assumption.

The second approach can be used with several different assumptions. One is that the lag is distributed like a normal distribution (when time is expressed logarithmically) the effect being small at first, rising to a peak, and then declining. A second assumption is that the effect is at a maximum at first and then declines at a constant rate. The second assumption is shown in graphic form in the upper section of Figure 4.5.

Berger used this second assumption in an empirical study of India's imports of glass from the United Kingdom.[15] He ran the following least squares regressions:

$$x_t = a + b \, \frac{(3p_t + 2p_{t-1} + p_{t-2})}{6} \quad (1)$$

$$x_t = a + b \, \frac{(4p_t + 3p_{t-1} + 2p_{t-2} + p_{t-3})}{10} \quad (2)$$

$$x_t = a + b \, \frac{(5p_t + 4p_{t-1} + \ldots + p_{t-4})}{15} \quad (3)$$

$$x_t = a + b \, \frac{(6p_t + 5p_{t-1} + \cdots + p_{t-5})}{21} \quad (4)$$

where x_t = the ratio of glass imports from the United Kingdom to total glass imports during period t, and p_t = the ratio of British glass prices to prices of competing glass. The simple correlations between the dependent variable and the weighted average independent variable were 0.858, 0.881, 0.836, and 0.751 for regressions (1), (2), (3), and (4), respectively. Regression (2), with the largest correlation, was selected as showing the "best" distribution of lag.

Working used a different assumption with respect to pork supplies (consumption) and prices. He assumed that pork supplies exerted the same effect on prices each year for 5 years and for 10 years, after which they had no effect. He found the short-run elasticity of the demand for pork to be about —0.75, whereas in the long run it was about —1.25.[16]

---

[15] J. Berger, "On Koyck's and Fisher's Methods for Calculating Distributed Lags," *Metroeconomica*, Vol. 5, pp. 89–90, 1953. Quoted from Marc Nerlove, "Distributed Lags and Demand Analysis," USDA, Agr. Handbook No. 141, p. 12. Beginning with the discussion of Koyck's assumption, the next several paragraphs are adapted from this Handbook, pp. 12–13.

[16] Elmer J. Working, "Demand for Meat," Univ. of Ill., 1954, pp. 13, 78–9.

FISHER'S SECOND DISTRIBUTION OF LAG

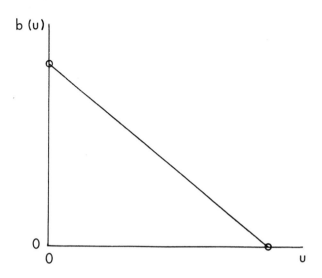

U. S. DEPARTMENT OF AGRICULTURE   NEG. 4409-57 (8)   AGRICULTURAL MARKETING SERVICE

KOYCK'S DISTRIBUTION OF LAG

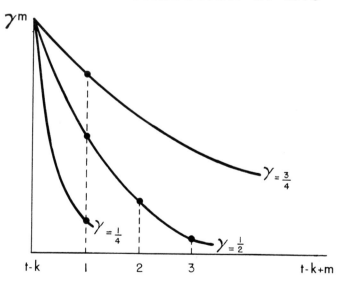

U. S. DEPARTMENT OF AGRICULTURE   NEG. 4410-57 (8)   AGRICULTURAL MARKETING SERVICE

Fig. 4.5 — Two distributions of lag: Upper section, effects decreasing by a constant amount each year; lower section, effects decreasing by a constant proportion each year.

Koyck[17] made a similar assumption to Berger's but assumed that the effect declined at a constant *proportional* rate. This distribution involves only one parameter and lends itself readily to statistical computation. It is shown graphically in the lower section of Figure 4.5.

Koyck's assumption is illustrated in the following type of formula:

Let time be measured as a discrete variable, in an equation such as

$$x_t = a + b_0 p_t + b_1 p_{t-1} + \cdots = a + \sum_{i=0}^{\infty} b_i p_{t-i} \quad (5)$$

where x_t is the quantity demanded in period t; p_t, the price in period t; p_{t-1}, the price in t $-$ 1; and so on, and the b_0, b_1, . . . are constants.

In equation (6), let ε_S be the short-run elasticity of demand (that is, the immediate effect of a one per cent change in price), and let ε_L be the long-run elasticity of demand (that is, the eventual effect of a one per cent change in price). Tinbergen proposed to interpret the short-run elasticity as

$$\varepsilon_S = b_0 \frac{\overline{p}}{\overline{x}} \quad (6)$$

and the long-run elasticity as

$$\varepsilon_L = \left(\sum_{i=0}^{\infty} b_i \right) \frac{\overline{p}}{\overline{x}} \quad (7)$$

where $(\overline{p}, \overline{x})$ is the point on the demand function at which we wish to evaluate the elasticity.

Koyck's assumption is that after a certain point, say i $=$ k, the series of coefficients b_i, i $=$ 0, 1, . . . , can be approximated by a convergent *geometric* series, so that

$$b_{k+m} = \delta b_{k+m-1} \quad (8)$$

where m $>$ 0 and 0 $\leq \delta <$ 1. From (5) and (8) it follows that

$$x_t = a + b_0 p_t + \ldots + b_{k-1} \, p_{t-k+1} +$$
$$b_k \, p_{t-k} + b_k \, \delta \, p_{t-k-1} + b_k \, \delta^2 p_{t-k-2} +$$
$$b_k \, \delta^3 \, p_{t-k-2} + \ldots + b_k \, \delta^m p_{t-k-m} + \ldots \quad .$$

$$= a + b_0 \, p_t + \ldots + b_{k-1} \, p_{t-k+1} + b_k \sum_{m=0}^{\infty} \delta^m p_{t-k-m} \quad (9)$$

[17] L. M. Koyck, *Distributed Lags and Investment Analysis*, North Holland Publ. Co., Amsterdam, 1954.

Thus, x_t is a function of $k - 1$ unweighted lagged prices and a geo-metrically weighted average of all other past prices. If time is treated as a continuous variable, Koyck's distribution of lag has the form shown in the lower section of Figure 4.5. This shows the dis-tribution plotted for different values of the parameter δ.

If $k = 0$, the long- and short-run elasticities and the exact distri-bution of lag are particularly easy to estimate if the distribution has the general form assumed by Koyck. Consider equation (9) with $k = 0$. Then

$$x_t = a + b_o p_t + b_o \delta p_{t-1} + b_o \delta^2 p_{t-2} + \cdot \cdot \cdot \cdot \quad (10)$$

If we lag (10) one period and multiply by δ, we get:

$$\delta x_{t-1} = a \delta + b_o \delta p_{t-1} + b_o \delta^2 p_{t-2} + \cdot \cdot \cdot \cdot \quad (11)$$

Now subtract (11) from (10) to get:

$$x_t = a(1 - \delta) + b_o p_t + \delta x_{t-1} \quad (12)$$

The distribution of lag is given by the estimate of δ, and the short-run elasticity of demand is given by $b_o \dfrac{\overline{p}}{x}$. The cumulative effect of a maintained price change is

$$b_o \sum_{m=0}^{\infty} \delta^m = \frac{b_o}{1 - \delta} \quad (13)$$

if $0 \leq \delta < 1$. Hence, the long-run elasticity of demand is given by

$$\frac{b_o}{1 - \delta} \cdot \frac{\overline{p}}{x} \quad (14)$$

The subject remains open for further exploration. Ladd and Ted-ford applied a generalized method to Working's data, and concluded that "the short-run and long-run elasticities of the demand for total meat are not significantly different on an annual basis."[18]

Brandow, in a comprehensive study of elasticities of demand for food, reached a similar conclusion for meats, and extended it to apply to other widely used foods. He also offered the criticism of Nerlove's methodology, that while it often shows market data to be consistent with the hypothesis of lagged price effects, it does not

[18] G. W. Ladd, and J. R. Tedford. "A Generalization of the Working Method for Estimating Long-run Elasticities," *Journal of Farm Economics* Vol. 38, No. 2, 1959, pp. 221–33.

I am indebted to George Ladd for checking the formulas on pp. 70–73.

exclude alternative, reasonable explanations for the behavior of the data.[19]

A study of the demand for beef and pork at retail, based on quarterly data and using distributed lag methods, revealed a significant difference between the short- and long-run price-elasticities of demand for these products.[20]

For beef, the short-run elasticity was estimated to be about —0.6; the long-run elasticity, about —1.0. The period of full adjustment to a price change was estimated to be three-quarters of a year.

For pork, the results were mixed; the short-run elasticity was —0.78 according to one formula and —0.74 according to another; the corresponding long-run elasticities were —0.75 and —0.83. The period of adjustment was about one-quarter of a year.

For meat (that is, beef and pork combined) the estimates were; short-run, about —0.3; long-run, about —0.54. The adjustment period was three to four quarters.

The authors therefore conclude that the adjustment period for these meats is less than a year. And since even the long-run elasticities that they found are —1.0 or less, they conclude that programs to reduce the supplies of these products would not reduce gross incomes to beef and hog producers, even in the long run.

They conclude, however, with a word of warning about this: "Over long periods of time a consistently high or low price relative to other prices may induce changes in tastes and preferences or influence the development of substitutes. This phenomenon might be called a price-induced change in tastes. Such changes may very well result in significant consumption changes. However, they involve modification of the static demand curve (i.e., a change in structure) and should not be confused with the rigorous concept of long-run elasticities developed in this article."

INCOME-ELASTICITY OF DEMAND

The elasticities of demand discussed above are all price-elasticities. Another kind of elasticity is *income*-elasticity.

It is a matter of common observation that consumers with high incomes spend more for food than do consumers with low incomes. Figure 1.7 in Chapter 1 showed this relationship for the United States in 1955. The income-elasticities shown in this chart are for three income groups.

---

[19] G. E. Brandow, "Interrelations Among Demands for Farm Products and Implications for Control of Market Supply," Bul. 680, Pennsylvania State University, Agr. Exp. Sta., University Park, Aug., 1961, p. 33.

[20] W. G. Tomek and W. W. Cochrane, "Long-run Demand: A Concept, and Elasticity Estimates for Meats," *Journal of Farm Economics*, XLIV, No. 3, August, 1962, pp. 717–31.

Note that these elasticities are positive. Note also that the elasticities are less than 1.0.

In price-elasticity charts, demand curves with elasticity less than 1.0 are steeper than 45°. Why are the inelastic *income*-elasticity curves shown in Figure 1.7 flatter than 45° ?

The reason is that most price-quantity charts show quantity plotted along the bottom and price up the side. They show the price-elasticity of demand or of supply, or both—that is, they show the responsiveness of quantity taken or produced, or both, to changes in prices. Income-food expenditure charts, however, show income plotted along the bottom and food expenditures along the side. They show the income-elasticity of the demand—the responsiveness of food expenditures to changes or differences in income.

The reason for plotting the scales this way in the two kinds of charts is that price analysts are usually interested in explaining prices. Prices, therefore, are regarded as the dependent variable. And the convention has become established that the dependent variable is plotted up the side. In the case of income-food expenditure charts, price analysts are interested in explaining food expenditures, so food expenditures are plotted up the side.

This is all logical and consistent. But it leads to one confusing result. We measure the price-elasticity of demand by dividing the percentage change in quantity (which is plotted along the bottom) by the associated percentage change in price (which is plotted up the side). But we measure the income-elasticity of demand by dividing the percentage change in food expenditures (which is plotted *up the side*) by the associated percentage change in income (which is plotted *along the bottom*). Accordingly, a demand curve that is steeper than 45° on equal proportional scales is called *inelastic*; but an income curve that is steeper than 45° is called *elastic*.

The same situation exists with respect to expenditures for food plotted as percentages of income. Ernst Engel was the first to measure this relationship and show that it was negative; consumers with large incomes spend more money for food, but their expenditures are a smaller percentage of their incomes than in the case of consumers with low incomes. The same basic data as those shown in Figure 1.7, plotted in this percentage-of-income form, yield curves with negative slopes.

The difference between the way income-elasticity curves and price-elasticity curves are plotted comes out most clearly when incomes are plotted against *quantities* of food purchased. In this case, incomes are plotted along the bottom, the same as with the income-expenditure elasticity curves discussed above. But the quantities of food are plotted up the side, instead of along the bottom as in the case of price-quantity elasticity curves.

These income-quantity elasticity curves are positive for food as a group, and for most individual foods taken singly. But they are negative for a few foods, such as potatoes, where consumers with high incomes eat less than consumers with low incomes. These foods are called "inferior goods." This term has no reference to their nutritional or other quality, but refers only to the negative slope of the curve.

Another form of elasticity is represented in Figure 4.6.[21]

This figure shows a statistical approximation to the partial indifference surface for beef and pork. It represents a horizontal slice through a three-dimensional solid, with pork consumption per person along one horizontal axis, beef consumption along another, and income per person up the vertical axis. The slice is taken at the $490.90 income level.

The slope of the heavy line drawn through each point of intersection in the chart represents the negative of the price ratio that year. The slope of the light line extending beyond the ends of the heavy line reflects the slope of the surface at other points. The lines conform to a characteristic feature of indifference curves in that they do not cross one another.

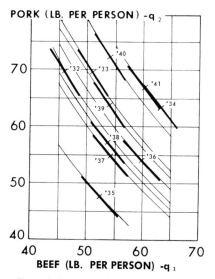

Fig. 4.6 — Partial indifference surface for beef and pork, based on capita consumption and adjusted price ratios. Slice taken at the $490.90 income level. (USDA, AMS.)

The own-price-elasticities and cross-elasticities of demand for the major farm products, based on annual data are brought together in Table 4.2.[22]

[21] Frederick V. Waugh, "A Partial Indifference Surface for Beef and Pork," *Journal of Farm Economics*, Vol. 38, No. 1, Feb., 1956, pp. 102–12.
[22] G. E. Brandow, *op. cit*, p. 17.

5

Point Elasticity, Total Revenue, Marginal Revenue

The discussion in the preceding chapter dealt only with the elasticity of the curve as a whole. But this is rather a rough-and-ready concept, for "*the* elasticity" of a curve is really a sort of average of the elasticities at different points along the curve. "*The* elasticity" we have been dealing with is often called *arc* elasticity, the elasticity of the arc of the curve. It is a sort of average elasticity. Whatever term is used (arc or average), it relates to the elasticity of the curve or arc as a whole. We come now to consider *point* elasticity, the elasticity at any point on a curve.

CURVES WITH AVERAGE ELASTICITY OF UNITY

Elasticity is a proportional concept, and the elasticity of a straight-line curve on a chart with arithmetic scales therefore is not constant from point to point along the line. It varies from point to point. This shows up most clearly in the simplest case of a straight-line curve with an average or arc elasticity of unity; such a curve is represented by the straight line marked *A* in section A of Figure 5.1.

This straight-line curve has an elasticity of unity at its central point where price $= 5$, and quantity $= 5$; for if $dx = dy$, as it does here when the slope of the line is 45°, then $\dfrac{dx}{-dy} \cdot \dfrac{5}{5} = -1.0$.

But at other points along the line the elasticity is not -1. At the point where price $= 6$, and quantity $= 4$, for example, the elasticity is $\dfrac{dx}{-dy} \cdot \dfrac{6}{4} = -1.5$. At the point where price $= 8$, and quantity $= 2$, the elasticity is -4.0. Conversely, at points below and to the right of the center of the line, the elasticities are less than -1.

What would a curve of constant unit elasticity at all points look like? It follows from the preceding paragraph that the slope of the line ($\frac{dy}{dx}$) at every point would have to be proportional to the relation between y and x at every point. A curve of this sort would be a rectangular hyperbola, approaching the x and y axes as asymptotes. Several constant-unit elasticity curves of this sort, lettered B, C, D, etc., are plotted in Section A of Figure 5.1 along with the straight-line curve A that has an average elasticity of unity.

This figure shows graphically how the elasticity of a straight line changes from point to point. It shows this by comparison of the straight-line curve, A, with the constant elasticity curves, B, C, D, etc., beside it. This comparison shows that the upper part of the straight-line curve is less steeply sloped than the constant unit elasticity curves; that is, it is more elastic than unity. Conversely,

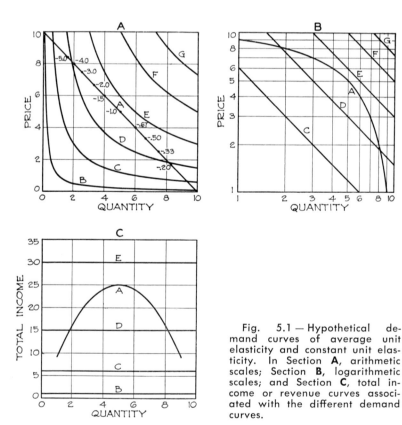

Fig. 5.1 — Hypothetical demand curves of average unit elasticity and constant unit elasticity. In Section **A**, arithmetic scales; Section **B**, logarithmic scales; and Section **C**, total income or revenue curves associated with the different demand curves.

the lower part of the straight-line curve is less elastic than unity. The elasticity is highest at the upper end and lowest at the lower end. It is higher than unity at the top, decreases to unity at the middle, and gets less and less than unity from there on down. The elasticity at different points along the straight line is shown by the series of figures written beside the line.

The situation can be shown on double logarithmic paper, as in Section B of Figure 5.1. The constant unit elasticity curves, C, D, E, etc., shown in Section A of Figure 5.1, become straight lines with slopes of 45° on the logarithmic paper used in Section B. The straight-line curve, A, on arithmetic paper in Section A undergoes the opposite change to become a curved line, convex from above,[1] on the logarithmic paper used in Section B.

TOTAL REVENUE OR INCOME

The total revenue (that is, total income) that would be realized from the sale of different quantities of a commodity depends upon the shape or curvature of the demand curve, as well as upon its elasticity. The total revenue curve is directly related to the demand curve (which is in other words the *average* revenue curve). They can be shown on similar charts, the only difference being that in the total revenue chart the vertical scale shows total revenues instead of average revenues (prices).

The total revenue curve associated with a straight-line demand curve on arithmetic paper, with an average elasticity of unity, is shown in Section C in Figure 5.1 This shows that with this sort of a demand curve the maximum total revenue is realized from an average crop. Large crops and small crops both bring in less money than average crops. The point of highest total revenue comes at the point where the elasticity of the demand curve is unity.

The total revenue curves derived from constant unit elasticity

---

[1] There are two ways of verbally describing the curvature of lines plotted on co-ordinate paper. Both of them are in common use. The one way is to describe curves as concave or convex from above (a basin with water in it is concave from above) while the other way is to describe them as concave or convex to the origin.

There are objections to both systems. The objection to the "from above" reference is that it cannot be applied to curves whose ends lie on the same vertical line. The objection to the "origin" reference is that it cannot be applied to curves that go through the origin. This objection is perhaps more important than the other, because some important economic curves necessarily start from the origin—total revenue curves, positive sloping curves of unit elasticity, etc. In addition, most mathematicians (although not R. G. D. Allen) and some economists use the reference "from above"—Joan Robinson in England, and Tintner, Waugh, and Thomsen in the United States, to name only a few. We are accordingly using the reference "from above" in the present work.

curves like B, C, D, etc., are horizontal straight lines. If the elasticity is unity at all points, the total revenue remains constant, whatever the size of the crop, as shown for the curves B, C, D, and E in Section C of Figure 5.1.

Concave demand curves with an average elasticity of unity, but less curved on arithmetic paper than the constant elasticity curves shown in Section A of Figure 5.1, undergo an interesting transformation when plotted on logarithmic paper. Their curvature is reversed. They are concave on arithmetic paper, but they become convex on logarithmic paper. The point of highest total revenue appears (in their case as in the case of straight-line curves on arithmetic paper) at the central point of the curve where the point elasticity is unity.

Concave demand curves with an average elasticity of unity, but more curved on arithmetic paper than constant-elasticity curves, lose some of their curvature when plotted on logarithmic paper. But they retain their concavity. Accordingly, with this kind of demand curve, the *minimum* total revenue is realized from the sale of an average crop. Large crops and small crops both bring in more money than an average crop. The point where the elasticity of the demand curve is unity is the point of lowest total revenue.

ELASTICITIES OTHER THAN UNITY

Demand curves whose elasticity is constant but higher or lower than unity are straight lines on logarithmic scales, like the curves C, D, etc., in Section B of Figure 5.1, but their slopes are other than 45°. The slopes of the inelastic curves are steeper than 45°, and those of the elastic curves, flatter than 45°.

The total revenue curves associated with these constant (but not unit) elasticity demand curves are sloping curved lines, not horizontal straight lines like the total revenue curves associated with constant unit elasticity curves. They are curved lines. The total revenue curves for constant but less than unit elasticity demand curves are rectangular hyperbolas like the curves of constant elasticity shown earlier in Section A of Figure 5.1. And like those curves, they would be straight lines with a negative slope on double logarithmic paper. A demand curve with constant elasticity of −0.5 is shown on arithmetic and logarithmic paper, together with the total income or revenue curve based upon it, in the four sections of Figure 5.2.

The total revenue curves for constant but more than unit elasticity demand curves are also curved, but they are parabolas,

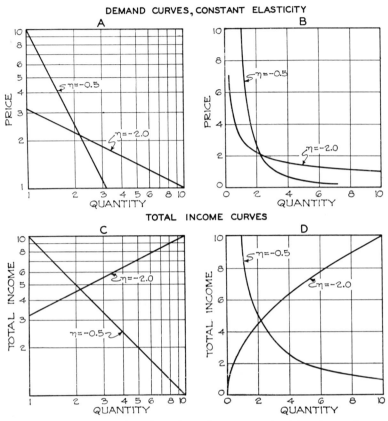

Fig. 5.2 — Sections **A** and **B**, hypothetical constant elasticity demand curves; Sections **C** and **D**, total income (revenue) curves associated with them.

with apex at the origin of the x and y axes. They, too, are straight lines on double logarithmic paper; but they have a positive slope. A demand curve with a constant elasticity of −2.0, and the total revenue curve based upon it, is shown also on arithmetic and logarithmic paper in Figure 5.2.

The elasticity figures given beside the total revenue curves in the lower sections of this chart are only identification-elasticities, showing in each case the elasticity of the demand curve from which the total revenue curve was derived, not the elasticity of the total revenue curve itself. That elasticity can be figured mathematically from the elasticity of the demand curve. The mathematical relationship between the elasticity of the demand curve and that of its associated total revenue curve is comparatively simple. If $E =$ the elasticity of the total revenue curve, defined in an analogous manner to the Marshallian definition of the elasticity of the demand curve

(i.e., as $\dfrac{dq}{d(pq)} \cdot \dfrac{pq}{q}$ or $\dfrac{dq}{q} \Big/ \dfrac{d(pq)}{pq}$) and e $=$ the elasticity of

the demand curve, the relationship[2] is $E = \dfrac{e}{e+1}$

This formula may be solved for e in terms of E, giving the elasticity of the demand curve in terms of the elasticity of the total revenue curve, as follows: $e = \dfrac{E}{1-E}$

THE MEASUREMENT OF POINT ELASTICITY

Point elasticity can be measured mathematically by the use of the same formula that was used for average or arc elasticity in the preceding chapter. If the demand curve is a straight line, the formula is merely the original Marshallian formula, with the p and q at the particular point used in place of the *average* p and *average* q over the range used when average elasticity is computed. If the

---

[2] This relationship may be derived as follows:

$$E = \frac{dq}{q} \Big/ \frac{d(pq)}{pq} = 1 / \frac{d(pq)}{pdq} = 1 / \frac{pdq+qdp}{pdq}$$

$$= 1 / \left(1 + \frac{qdp}{pdq} \right) = 1 / \left(1 + \frac{1}{e} \right) = \frac{e}{e+1}$$

It is interesting to observe that if E and e are both defined as reciprocals of the usual definitions, that is, as $\dfrac{d(pq)}{dq} \cdot \dfrac{q}{pq}$ and $\dfrac{dp}{dq} \cdot \dfrac{q}{p}$ respectively, then the relation between E and e is very simple. It is

$$E = \frac{d(pq)}{dq} \cdot \frac{q}{pq} = \frac{d(pq)}{dq} \cdot \frac{1}{p} = \frac{qdp+pdq}{pdq} = \frac{qdp}{pdq} + 1 = e+1.$$

(See R. G. D. Allen, *Mathematical Analysis for Economists*, Macmillan, London, 1938, p. 252.) That is, E as thus defined is always greater by 1 than e as thus defined.

If e is defined as usual (as $\dfrac{dq}{dp} \cdot \dfrac{p}{q}$) and E defined as above (as $\dfrac{d(pq)}{dq} \cdot \dfrac{q}{pq}$) then $E = \dfrac{1}{e} + 1.$

I am indebted to Gerhard Tintner and Adolf Kozlik for this footnote.

curve is not a straight line, then a tangent must be drawn to it at the point where the elasticity is to be measured. The $\dfrac{dq}{dp}$ is then computed from the tangent.

Point elasticity can also be measured graphically. The way to do it is shown in Figure 5.3. If the demand curve is a straight line and the elasticity at the point p is to be found, that can be done by laying a ruler along the demand curve and measuring the two distances (1) from p to the point where the ruler cuts the y axis (pc in the diagram) and (2) from p to the point where the

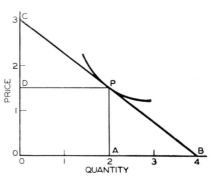

Fig. 5.3 — Diagram for the measurement of point elasticity.

ruler cuts the x axis (pb in the diagram). The latter distance divided by the former (that is, $\dfrac{pb}{pc}$) then gives the elasticity at the point p.

If the demand curve is a curved line, the procedure is the same, but the ruler is laid tangent to the curve at the point where the elasticity is to be measured. The ratio $\dfrac{pb}{pc}$ then gives the elasticity at that point.[3] It can then be shown that the elasticity at p is also given by $\dfrac{ab}{oa}$.

---

[3] The proof of these relations is simple. The elasticity, $\dfrac{dq}{dp} \cdot \dfrac{p}{q}$, is the change in quantity divided by the change in price, multiplied by the price divided by the quantity. In Figure 5.3, the first term of the elasticity formula, $\dfrac{dq}{dp}$, is $\dfrac{AB}{AP}$. The second term, $\dfrac{p}{q}$, is $\dfrac{AP}{OA}$. The formula as a whole then is $\dfrac{AB}{AP} \cdot \dfrac{AP}{OA}$. This reduces by cancellation of the two AP's to $\dfrac{AB}{OA}$.

Since a line parallel to the base of a triangle divides the other sides proportionally, $\dfrac{AB}{OA} = \dfrac{BP}{PC}$.

I am indebted to A. G. Hart for this proof, which is simpler than Marshall's. (Marshall, *Principles of Economics*, pp. 102–3, footnote 1, and the mathematical appendix, note 3, p. 839.)

MARGINAL REVENUE

The preceding sections have shown the relation between elasticity and total income or revenue. We turn now to a third concept, marginal revenue.

The concept or definition of marginal revenue is perfectly clearcut. The total revenue (or total income, which means the same thing) is the total revenue from the sale of a given amount of the product, say x bushels. It is computed by multiplying x bushels by the price at which that number of bushels can be sold. This total revenue may be compared with the total revenue from the sale of $x + 1$ bushels; this is computed by multiplying $x + 1$ bushels by the price at which that number of bushels can be sold. The difference between the two total revenues is the marginal revenue.[4]

For example, a dealer may be able to sell 10 boxes of apples a day for $2.00 a box. His total revenue from the sale of apples then is $20.00. Suppose now that more apples come on the market; he now has 11 boxes a day to sell. He has to cut the price to move them all. He cannot merely cut the price of the eleventh box; the buyers of the 10 boxes would object; so he has to cut the price of all the boxes of apples. If he has to cut the price to $1.90 per box, his total revenue then is $1.90 × 11, which is $20.90. What is the marginal revenue, then? It is the difference between $20.00 and $20.90; it is 90 cents.

Suppose then that still more apples come on the market, so that the dealer now has 12 boxes a day to sell. If he has to cut the price perhaps another 10 cents a box, to $1.80, what is the marginal revenue in that case? The total revenue now is $1.80 × 12, which is $21.60. If we subtract from this the total revenue from the sale of 11 boxes, which is $20.90, we see that the marginal revenue in this case is 70 cents.

For brevity, we say that the marginal revenue from the sale of the twelfth box of apples was 70 cents, whereas in the previous case, the marginal revenue from the sale of the eleventh box was 90 cents. But we must be careful to remember that it was not the sale of the twelfth box that brought in 70 cents, for actually that

---

[4] R. G. D. Allen, *Mathematical Analysis for Economists*, pp. 152–53: "It is clear that a marginal concept is only precise when it is considered in the limiting sense, as the variations in X are made smaller and smaller. It is then to be interpreted by means of the derivative of the function which relates X and Y . . . Marginal revenue is thus an abstract concept only definable for continuous variations in revenue and output. But it is always approximately equal to the added revenue obtained from a small unit increase in output from the level x."

twelfth box brought in $1.80 like all the other boxes. It was *the increase in total revenue when 12 boxes were sold, over the total revenue when only 11 boxes were sold, that was 70 cents.*

The marginal revenue, then, ordinarily changes as more and more units are sold. The changes in total revenue, average revenue (i.e., price), and marginal revenue for various numbers of boxes of apples are shown together in Table 5.1. The data are plotted in Figure 5.4. This figure shows the simple case where the demand curve (or what may be called the average revenue curve, to give it a name analogous to the marginal revenue curve) is a straight line on arithmetic paper, with an average elasticity of unity.

It is clear from this figure that the slope of the marginal revenue

TABLE 5.1

APPLES: TOTAL, AVERAGE, AND MARGINAL REVENUES FROM THE SALE OF
VARIOUS QUANTITIES
(Hypothetical Data)

Boxes of Apples	Price (and Average Revenue)	Total Revenue	Marginal Revenue (Successive Differences in Totals)
1...............	$1.90	$1.90	
			$1.90
2...............	1.80	3.60	
			1.70
3...............	1.70	5.10	
			1.50
4...............	1.60	6.40	
			1.30
5...............	1.50	7.50	
			1.10
6...............	1.40	8.40	
			.90
7...............	1.30	9.10	
			.70
8...............	1.20	9.60	
			.50
9...............	1.10	9.90	
			.30
10...............	1.00	10.00	
			.10
11...............	.90	9.90	
			−.10
12...............	.80	9.60	
			−.30
13...............	.70	9.10	
			−.50
14...............	60	8.40	
			−.70
15...............	.50	7.50	
			−.90

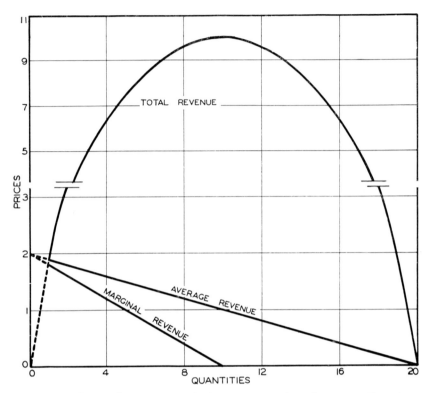

Fig. 5.4 — Relations between marginal, average, and total revenue. Hypothetical data.

curve is twice as steep as the slope of the average revenue curve. If the average revenue curve is a straight line, the location of the marginal revenue curve can be determined graphically without going through the calculations given above as follows: at any point on the average revenue curve, a horizontal line may be run across to the y axis. Then the marginal revenue curve cuts this line at the midpoint of the line. This holds true no matter what the elasticity of the average revenue curve may be. It also holds true for curved average revenue curves as well as straight ones, but applies in that case to the tangents to the curves.[5]

---

[5] Care is needed in this application, for where the average revenue curve is curved, the midpoint of the horizontal line from the point of tangency to the y axis does not lie on the marginal revenue curve. It is the line running through that point from the point where the tangent cuts the y axis, extended "southeast" until it cuts a line dropped from the point of tangency to the x axis that gives the marginal revenue at the point of tangency. This may be explained more clearly by reference to Figure 5.3. Obviously, the marginal revenue when 10 units are sold, at an average revenue (price) of $1.00, is 0; that is where a line dropped from the average revenue point ($1.00) when 10 units are sold, is cut by the line running from $2.00 and a quantity of 0 through the midpoint of the horizontal line from the point $1.00 at quantity 10, and the y axis.

It is also clear from the chart that the values of the marginal revenue curve are positive or plus (the curve lies above the x axis) wherever the elasticity of the average revenue curve is greater than unity. (We know from previous discussion that this elasticity is greater than unity in the upper half of this particular curve.) Conversely, the values of the marginal revenue curve are negative or minus (the curve lies below the x axis) wherever the elasticity of the average revenue curve is less than unity (as it is in the lower half of this particular curve). And finally, the value of the marginal curve is zero at the point where the elasticity of the average revenue curve is unity; and at that point the total revenue reaches its maximum.

The mathematical relation between the elasticity of the average revenue curve and the values of the average and marginal revenue curves is expressed by the formula:

$$e = - \frac{AR}{AR - MR}$$

In this formula,

$e =$ Elasticity of average revenue
$AR =$ Value of the average revenue
$MR =$ Value of the marginal revenue

PLOTTING DISCRETE SERIES

When discrete quantity and price series are plotted so as to show the average, total, and marginal revenue curves, the plotter may be puzzled by the fact that the marginal revenue curve apparently falls half a unit too far to the right on the chart.

This results when the curve is plotted incorrectly. The marginal revenue and average curves appear similar, but actually the two curves show not merely different things but different kinds of things.

The average revenue curve (actually, series of steps) shows the upper right-hand corners of a series of rectangles each extending to the x and y axes. The area of each rectangle shows the total revenue for each quantity and price in the series. Each figure in the scale along the bottom of the chart should be put under the mark representing the right-hand edge of each rectangle. A line drawn through the extreme point of each corner represents the average revenue curve. This curve remains the same (in the same place) for different size units of production and price.

The marginal revenue curve or series of steps, however, shows merely the tops of successive vertical bars, each one only one unit wide, showing the marginal revenue at each successive scale of production. Each figure in the scale along the bottom of the chart should be put under the center of each vertical bar. A line drawn through the center of the top of each vertical bar represents the marginal revenue curve. This line remains the same no matter how large or small the units are.

The total revenue curve is similar in kind to the average revenue curve. It should be handled in the same manner.

FORMULA FOR DETERMINING THE PRODUCTION THAT WILL BRING THE MAXIMUM TOTAL REVENUE

The size of the crop or production that will bring in the highest total revenue can be computed quickly and easily by means of a simple formula. The derivation of this formula can be visualized by remembering that if the data are plotted in index form, so that the base is 100 = the average of the series, a tangent to the demand curve would cut the x axis to the right of 100 at a point equal to the coefficient of elasticity (ignoring sign) multiplied by 100.

If, for example, the elasticity were —0.5, the tangent would cut the x axis at 150. The marginal revenue curve then would cut the x axis halfway between 0 and 150, that is, at 75. This would be the size of crop or production that would bring in the maximum total revenue.

$$\text{The formula is } P = \frac{(1 + e)\ 100}{2}$$

where P is the production that maximizes total revenue, and e is the coefficient of elasticity of demand, with the sign ignored.

BEARING UPON AGRICULTURAL POLICY

The relations between elasticity and total revenue shown above have a great deal of significance for agricultural policy.

The AAA production control program during the 1930's was designed to increase agricultural income by reducing agricultural production.

The program actually was only an acreage control program. Except in the case of cotton, it failed to reduce production below previous levels, because farmers offset the reduced acreage by recourse to production practices which increased yields. This left total production as high as before, or higher.

Even if the program had succeeded in reducing agricultural production, that would not have had much effect on agricultural income. The smaller supplies would have raised prices, but the effect of the higher price upon income would have been partially offset, completely offset, or more than offset, by the smaller supplies, depending upon the elasticities of the demand for the products concerned.

Statistical analyses have shown that the elasticity of the demand for corn in the United States, based on annual data, is about —0.65. This is shown in Figure 8.3 at the end of Chapter 8. The elasticity for hogs is about the same. Analyses of the data since World War II indicate lower elasticities for the postwar period. Whether this decrease in elasticity is temporary or permanent is not known.

The general relation between hog supplies, prices, and total income, can be set forth as in Table 5.2. For simplicity, the figures used are percentages, with 100 representing average size. The relation between hog supplies and prices is shown in Section A of Figure 5.5; the relation between hog supplies and total hog income is shown in Section B of Figure 5.5.

Table 5.2 shows that a large crop of hogs is worth less than a small crop. It shows that a 110 per cent crop, for example, brings a total income only 92 per cent of average, but a 90 per cent crop brings a total income 104 per cent of average. The large crop of hogs is worth 12 per cent less than the small crop.

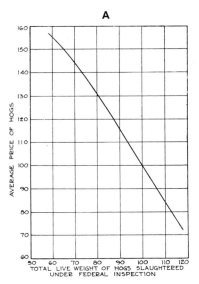
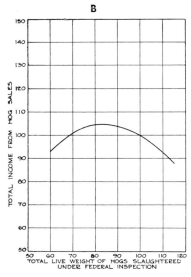

Fig. 5.5 — Relation between total live weight of hogs slaughtered under federal inspection: Section **A**, average hog prices; Section **B**, total revenue from hog sales.

TABLE 5.2

RELATION BETWEEN HOG SUPPLIES, PRICES, AND TOTAL INCOME*

(Percentage of average)

Hog Supply	Hog Price	Total Income
65	150	97
70	144	101
75	138	103
80	131	105
85	124	105
90	116	104
95	108	103
100	100	100
105	92	97
110	84	92
115	76	87

* This table is based on data in Table 9.2 and the accompanying discussion.

The difference between the total values of still larger and smaller crops is still greater than this. A 115 per cent hog crop brings an 87 per cent income. This is 18 per cent less than the income from an 85 per cent crop, which is 105 per cent of average. The rise in total income with decreasing size of crop, however, stops below crop sizes of about 83 per cent. A reduction in the size of below 69 per cent of normal would reduce the total value of the crop below the value even of an average crop.

The demand curve for hogs is compared with a demand curve of constant unit elasticity at every point (which would result in a constant income no matter what the size of the crop) in Figure 5.6. The figure shows how the upper parts of the two curves, over the range shown, lie close together. The lower parts of the curves diverge strongly, the divergence increasing with the size of the crop. The bigger the crop, the farther does total income decline.

The conclusions given above are based upon the relations between annual data. If longer periods of time were used, the elasticity would increase and the maximum increase in total value that could be brought about by reductions in supply would decline to less than 5 per cent.[6]

[6] E. J. Working in his bulletin "Demand for Meat," Institute of Meat Packing, Univ. of Chicago, 1954, marshals statistical evidence to show that "the long-run elasticity of the demand for pork is greater than the short-run elasticity" (p. 78). He uses logarithmic functions as well as linear (straight-line) functions; the former give demand curves with a slight concave curvature, which would be closer to the constant income curve shown in Figure 5.6 than the straight-line market demand curve shown in the figure.

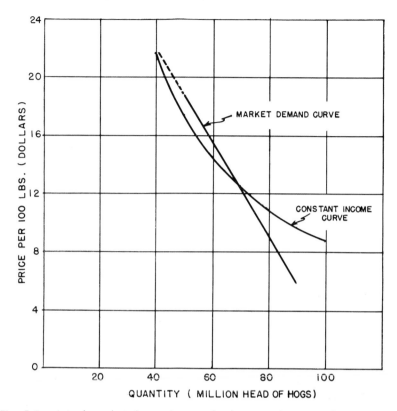

Fig. 5.6 — Actual market demand curve for hogs, and constant-income curve.

It is evident, therefore, that programs to restrict the production of crops with demand curves like those for corn and hogs could increase gross incomes only to a small extent in the short run, and probably not at all in the long run.

Elasticity of the Supply of Individual Farm Products

Supply curves are more difficult to measure than demand curves. Many statistical studies of demand have been published, but statistical studies of supply are not so numerous.

The nature of the difficulties, and their effects on the results, are well shown in the work of the pioneers in this field.

Warren and Pearson at Cornell derived coefficients of elasticity of supply for pre-World War I data which were all lower than 0.2 (some were negative) and probably were statistically not significant.

Later investigations constitute interesting background for current analyses, revealing how some of the difficulties were overcome or at least partially solved. These studies are grouped under two heads: Short-time elasticities of supply, where the supply represents market supply — the supply already produced, or in some stage or other of production — and long-time elasticities of supply, where the supply represents the quantities which farmers produce (plant or breed) in response to a change in price.

SHORT-TIME ELASTICITIES OF SUPPLY

DAY-TO-DAY CHANGES

O. V. Wells[1] investigated the effect of changes in hog prices upon the market receipts of hogs. In a study of short-time, day-to-day changes in prices and receipts of hogs at Sioux City in 1929–30, he found a positive relation between changes in price from Monday to Tuesday, and changes in truck receipts from Tuesday to Wednesday. A change of 10 cents per 100 pounds in hog prices was followed,

[1] O. V. Wells, "Farmers' Response to Price in Hog Production and Marketing," USDA Tech. Bul. 359.

on the average, by a change in the same direction of 15 per cent in hog receipts. At Chicago, served mainly by railroads that bring in hogs from longer distances than the trucks that serve Sioux City, a longer lag between changes in prices and changes in receipts was observed; the effects of price changes from Saturday to Monday showed up most strongly on receipts from Monday to Thursday. At this market and with this lag, a change of 10 cents in prices was followed, on the average, by a change of 10 per cent in receipts.

The price of hogs during 1929–30 averaged, in round figures, $10.00 per 100 pounds. The change of 10 cents per 100 pounds was, therefore, a change of 1 per cent. The elasticity of supply (short-time supply) at Sioux City, therefore, was 15, and at Chicago, 10.

H. J. Stover found that a change in the price of hogs at Chicago from Saturday to the next Monday had a direct effect on hog receipts at Chicago on the later days of the week.[2] The elasticity of this response of hog receipts to changes in prices was as follows:

Tuesday	4.4
Wednesday	8.8
Thursday	12.0
Friday	7.2
Saturday	4.4
Monday (one week later)	7.6

YEAR-TO-YEAR CHANGES

How do these short-time elasticities compare with the elasticities based upon longer periods? Wells also investigated that question and found that whereas the elasticities of supply of hogs based on daily data were high (much higher than unity, as we have just seen), the elasticities based upon annual data were low, only a fraction of unity. He used data for various states and markets, among them the average western Corn Belt corn-hog price ratio for October through March for the preceding two years (instead of the price of hogs) and the western Corn Belt hog marketings (October through September) as the measure of receipts. The elasticity of supply based upon the changes in these annual data (from the year before in each case) was only about 0.56. For Iowa data the elasticity was about 0.50; for Ohio and Missouri data the elasticities were nearly as high as unity; for the other states the elasticities ranged between 0.5 and 1.0.

This is interesting. It was shown in Chapter 5 that the elasticity

---

[2] Howard J. Stover, "Relation of Daily Prices to the Marketing of Hogs at Chicago," Cornell Univ. Agr. Exp. Sta., Bul. 534, pp. 46–48.

of demand for hogs, based on daily data, ranged from 5.8 on Saturdays to 2.8 on Wednesdays, whereas the elasticity based on annual data was about 0.6. Apparently, the elasticity of supply and demand for hogs is both high in the short run (day-to-day), and low in the long run (year-to-year).

Less is known about other products. Louis Bean found that the elasticities of supply for several other agricultural products were all less than unity, although his curves were less steeply sloped in their central parts, and in those parts the curves for rye, flax, and watermelons were more elastic than unity. The elasticity of the supply of broomcorn (acreage) is reported to be about 0.9, and of sweet potatoes, 0.5. The elasticity of the supply of cotton also appears to be about 1.0.[3] Pubols and Klaman[4] found that a change of 10 per cent in the (deflated) price of potatoes in the United States was associated with a change in the same direction of 2.3 per cent in acreage one and two years later.

LIMITATIONS OF SHORT-TIME STUDIES

The results of these studies are open to some question. The chief cause of variations in potato prices from year to year is variation in the size of the crop, caused chiefly by good or bad weather. Bad weather and a resulting short crop and a high price for potatoes one year should not induce much increase in potato acreage the next year. The new crop could only be expected to be average in size; this would bring only an average price, not a high price like the preceding year's short crop. High prices resulting from a strong demand should result in an increase in acreage, but high prices resulting merely from a short crop should not.

LONG-TIME SUPPLY SCHEDULES

The elasticity of supply curves is greatly affected by "the element of time, the source of many of the greatest difficulties in economics."[5] Ever since Marshall illustrated the effect of time upon production-response by reference to short, medium, and long-time changes in the demand for fish,[6] economists have been conscious of its importance. There is no curve which can be regarded as the *one-and-only* supply curve for any particular commodity. The character of each

---

[3] F. L. Thomsen and R. J. Foote, *Agricultural Prices*, McGraw-Hill, 1952, pp. 484–85.

[4] Ben H. Pubols and Saul B. Klaman. "Farmers' Response to Price in the Production of Potatoes, 1922–41," BAE, USDA, processed, 1945.

[5] Marshall, *Principles of Economics*, p. 109.

[6] *Ibid.*, pp. 369–71.

depends on the time specifically allowed for variations in output to take place. What we have, as a matter of fact, is a whole series of supply curves for each commodity representing all possible conditions between the most perfect long-run normal adjustment and most rigid momentary fixity of supply. Graphically speaking we may think of the supply curve for the very shortest period as a vertical line on the familiar two-dimensional chart and the supply curve for the very longest period as a line approaching the horizontal. Then, between these two extremes there will be a fanlike system of curves, each with a slope of its own, representing the various conditions of supply when adjustment periods of intermediate lengths are allowed for.

Accordingly, the length of time involved should be carefully noted in studies of the elasticity of supply, by the investigator so that he can adapt his methods to them, and by the reader so that he can appraise the results. The statistical supply curves discussed in this chapter so far have been mostly short-time curves. We will turn next to long-time supply curves.

It is difficult to derive long-time supply schedules. If each item in the series is to be the average of five years, or ten years, the conditions of supply may change (the whole supply curve may shift up or down). If production has changed, the investigator may not be able to tell how much of the change is due to a change in price and how much is due to the change in supply. The same difficulty is present in the derivation of demand schedules, but it is easier to solve, because fairly adequate measures of changes in demand exist (changes in the total national income, or in the general price level, for example). Measures of changes in supply of a similar sort are difficult to work out. Many variables have to be taken into account, and not all of them can be measured quantitatively—changes in the prices of various cost-items, in rents and interest, in technological production processes, and the like.

One possible way of getting around these difficulties is to analyze data on a geographical basis. If several different areas can be found with similar conditions of production but different prices, and if these price differences have persisted long enough for the production in the different areas to become adjusted to them, then the prices and production per square mile in the different areas can be used as points on a long-time supply curve. One illustration of this is the differences in the prices for fluid milk at various distances from the market, which result in great differences in output from different farms that are otherwise quite similar.

Another possibility is the experimental method. It would cost too much to guarantee certain farmers higher prices than the regular market prices for their products over a period of ten or fifteen years in order to measure the resulting changes in their production, but some research can be done on the physical relations which underlie the responses of production to price. An example of the latter is Einar Jensen's study of the response of dairy cows to varying inputs of feed.[7] Similar studies could be conducted with the feeding of hogs and cattle, and the application of fertilizer and different cultural practices to crops.

Still another possibility is the budget method. This method is based upon the study of individual records from representative samples of farms. It consists in going over the records for each farm and working out budget estimates of production for each farm separately, ten years hence, under several different price situations— higher prices for the product (say 15 per cent higher), constant prices, and lower prices. These estimates, added up, then provide three points on a long-time supply curve.

This method presents difficulties of its own, and involves a good deal of estimation, but it is realistic and shows promise. The results of applying this method to a study of milk production in the Cabot-Marshfield area of Vermont are shown in Figure 6.1. The heavy solid line BAC shows the estimated responses of production ten years later to milk prices 15 per cent higher, constant, and 15 per cent lower than they were originally. A short-term (three-month) supply curve for the same area, worked out by another investigator by other methods, is shown by the curve SS, shifted over to S' S' in order to allow closer comparison with BAC. The long-time curve is more elastic than the short-time curve, as would be expected.[5]

SUPPLY CURVES, "OTHER THINGS BEING UNEQUAL"

Most of the supply curves reported above represent the supply curves of economic theory—that is, they show the response of producers to changes in the price of a particular commodity, "other things being equal." They show what happens when a short crop, for example, raises the price of potatoes. Even though farmers know that the price is as likely to be low again as it is to be high when the new crop is harvested, still they increase their acreage of potatoes in response to the temporarily higher price.

---

[7] Einar Jensen, "Determining Input-Output Relationships in Milk Production," *Journal of Farm Economics*, Vol. 22, No. 1, pp. 249–58.

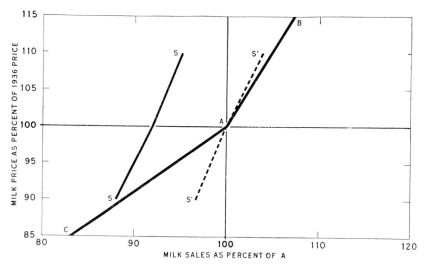

Fig. 6.1 — Long-time and short-time responses of milk production to price changes. (From USDA Tech. Bul. 709.[8])

This type of supply-response should be carefully distinguished from another type that results when all prices move up and down more or less together, as they do in periods of prosperity and depression. The supply curves derived above, "other things being equal," do not hold when "other things" (prices) are changing too, even though the periods of time involved may be similar.

Most demand curves are free from this sort of complication. The fluctuations in supply that make it possible to measure demand curves for agricultural products are fluctuations in the supply of individual products. They are large, rapid, and random, because they result chiefly from changes in weather. Moreover, the fluctuations in the supply of any one product are usually independent of those of other products. It is not often that shortages in one food are accompanied by shortages in another. Even in the record-breaking widespread drouth of 1934, total agricultural production fell only 3 per cent from the year before; and in the drouth year of 1936, it rose 3 per cent. The condition *caeteris paribus* (other things being equal) of classical economic theory is usually well fulfilled in the case of fluctuations in the supply of agricultural crops; the effect of

[8] R. H. Allen, Erling Hole, and R. L. Mighell, "Supply Responses in Milk Production in the Cabot-Marshfield Area, Vermont," USDA Tech. Bul. 709.

The subject is pursued further — although dealing mostly with physical relationships — in C. R. Hoglund *et al.*, *Nutritional and Economic Aspects of Feed Utilization by Dairy Cows*, Iowa State Univ. Press, 1959.

changes in the supply of one commodity can be measured "other things being equal" (i.e., unchanged), or at least having changes that are uncorrelated with the changes in the particular commodity being studied.

By contrast, the big fluctuations in demand that make it possible to measure supply curves are those that come with prosperity and depression; they affect all goods (not identically, but similarly). Other things do not remain equal; they change too. A decrease in demand for hogs is accompanied by a decrease in the demand for beef, lamb, poultry, butter, and eggs. The only changes in demand that affect one particular farm product and not others (like fluctuations in supply) are usually slow and gradual changes in consumers' tastes that take years to express themselves in sizeable figures. We now eat less starchy foods than our ancestors did, and more vegetables; but it has taken two or three generations to effect the change.

When a sudden change in *supply* takes place, as for instance when severe drouth cuts the production of butter 10 or 20 per cent, prices rise and less butter is bought; consumers eat something else instead. The readjustment in consumption takes place at once. But if an industrial depression comes, and the *demand* for butter declines 10 or 20 per cent, producers cannot make adjustments in production quickly. They are all set up to produce butter, and they cannot readily turn to produce something else. Even if they could change their setup rapidly and easily, it would do them no good; for the demand for other goods they might produce instead has also fallen.

Statistical demand curves show or at least purport to show what happens to prices when the supply of one product changes, the supplies of other products either remaining unchanged or else undergoing changes uncorrelated with the changes in the supply of the first product. But during periods of rapid change in general demand, statistical supply curves show what happens to prices when the demand for a specific product changes, *the demand for other products changing too and in a similar manner to the changes in the demand for the specific product.* This sort of supply curve is considerably less elastic than the supply curve "other things being equal."

One-Way Curves

There is an additional complication. When a general change in demand takes place, the supply curve is a more complex thing than the supply curve of classical economic theory. The situation is simple enough when the demand for butter, for example, is increasing in response to growth in human population, increase in per capita purchasing power, or a reduction in the costs of distribution. The demand curve shifts to the right and/or upwards, the price of butter rises, and butter production goes up. These things take place without much friction; agricultural production expands easily.

But when the demand for butter decreases, the situation is different. Farmers do not decrease their production of butter as readily as they formerly increased it. Their investment has been made, their plant is a going concern; it cannot be shut down without loss of the time and money invested. Most of the labor is supplied by the farmer and his family, and they cannot be discharged. It does no good to turn to some other farm products instead, for the demand for those products would have fallen too. Farmers take a lower return than they anticipated, rather than take no return at all. They continue to produce, perhaps almost as much as before, perhaps even more, but at lower prices than before. The path marked out by the intersection points of the demand and supply curves when the demand for butter increases is not retraced when the demand for butter declines.

Figure 6.2 represents the situation. The demand is shown as

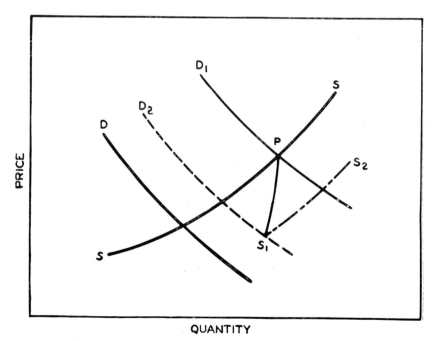

Fig. 6.2 — "One-way" supply curves. Hypothetical data.

increasing from D to D_1 and then decreasing to D_2. The curve SS is the supply curve under conditions of increasing demand. The other curve, running from P to S_1, is the supply curve established under conditions of decreasing demand. It is highly inelastic.

We saw in the section dealing with demand curves that *"the elasticity"* of the demand for a product varies according to the length of time represented by each unit in the series. The same phenomenon exists in the case of supply curves. But the complication shown in Figure 6.2 is a different and additional complication; it results not from different lengths of time (for it is revealed by annual data throughout) but from different directions of change in demand.

The one-way nature of the supply curves for most agricultural products is shown in the statistics of crop acreage and livestock population or slaughter, both after World War I and after the beginning of the industrial depression in 1929. In the case of most products, the production increased, rather than decreased, when prices fell; the supply curve actually had a slight negative slope for a time, as farmers attempted to offset lower prices by increasing production.

As to the effect of the passage of time on the difference between the elasticities of a supply curve "going up" and "coming down" on the curve, the evidence is inconclusive. After a few years of low prices after World War I, large wheat areas in the northwestern states—the "black triangle"—were abandoned. But by 1938 wheat acreage in the United States was the largest in history, with the single exception of 1919. Corn acreage in 1932 was also almost the largest in history, being only slightly exceeded in one previous year, 1917. It was reduced after 1932 only under the combined influence of two record-breaking drouths and the AAA programs. Hog and beef cattle production also held up. But so many other variables are also involved—changes in production costs, changes in domestic human population and in export demand—that clear-cut, simple conclusions can hardly be drawn.

It may be possible to derive useful supply curves for different farm products by what are essentially budgeting methods. One such supply curve, for hogs, derived by the application of linear programming methods to a typical 160-acre dairy farm in northeastern Iowa, is shown in Figure 6.3. Note that this chart is made, as so many are, to fit a pre-conceived shape of space on a page, rather than to show elasticity directly by having both scales run down to zero, and set proportionally equal in length. A little arithmetical compu-

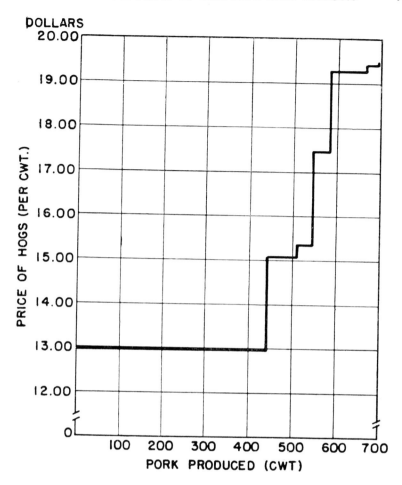

U. S. DEPARTMENT OF AGRICULTURE NEG. ERS 719-61 (12)   ECONOMIC RESEARCH SERVICE

Fig. 6.3 — Supply function for pork.

tation shows that the curve, upward and to the right of the $13 and 400 cwt. point, has an elasticity of about 1.2.[9]

Another study of supply curves, in this case for cotton in the rolling plains area of Oklahoma-Texas, derived a "reversed S" curve. This curve is inelastic close to zero, curves over to become

[9] R. D. Krenz, R. V. Baumann, and E. O. Heady, "Normative Supply Functions by Linear Programming Procedures," *Agricultural Economic Research*, USDA, Vol. 14, No. 1, Jan., 1962, p. 17.

highly elastic in the central part, and then curves upward to less than unit elasticity at right-hand end.[10]

GRAPHIC REPRESENTATION OF ELASTICITY OF SUPPLY

An interesting feature of the graphic representation of the elasticity of supply is the fact that two straight lines such as A and B in Figure 6.4, which have obviously different slopes, have the same elasticity, namely, $+1.0$. As a matter of fact, all straight lines passing through the origin have the same elasticity, $+1.0$.

A moment's reflection, however, shows that this is necessarily true, from the definition of or formula for elasticity. The figures for a line with a 1 to 1 slope (where $y = x$) at the point where $x = 10$ and $y = 10$, give the following result:

$$\frac{1}{1} \cdot \frac{10}{10} = 1.0$$

The figures for a 2 to 1 slope (where $y = \dfrac{x}{2}$) at the point where $x = 10$ and $y = 5$, give the same result:

$$\frac{2}{1} \cdot \frac{5}{10} = 1.0$$

All that this shows, however, is that elasticity is a proportional concept, as we found earlier in the study of demand. All it means is that if the second case just given ($y=2x$) were plotted in its original data form, on arithmetic paper, the diagram would be twice as high as it was wide. If the diagram were squashed down (scales, supply curves, and all) until it were square, it would then be identical in appearance with the first case given above ($y = x$). The slope of the supply curve would be the same as in that case ($45°$). True, the slope of the curve would still be expressed numerically, as

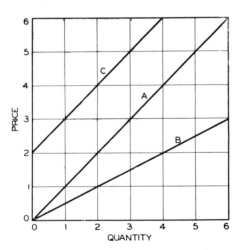

Fig. 6.4—Supply curves of different slopes and elasticities. Hypothetical data.

[10] John William Goodwin, "Aggregation of Normative Microsupply Relationships For Dry-Land Crop Farms in the Rolling Plains of Oklahoma and Texas," Ph.D. Thesis, Oklahoma State University, May, 1962, p. 105.

$y=2x$, but $2x$ in the second case means the same thing proportionally as x in the first case. That is, $2x$ would equal, for example, 10 per cent (of the average) in the one case, and x would equal 10 per cent (of the average) in the other, so the two elasticities should be the same, as in fact they are. This is shown clearly enough if the two cases are plotted on double logarithmic paper, which as we saw earlier is the proper paper for representing elasticity accurately. The curves then appear as two parallel lines, with identical slopes (45°).

The discussion above does not mean, of course, that all straight-line, positively sloping curves have an elasticity of unity. It is only straight lines that go through the origin that do so. Straight lines that cut the Y axis at some positive value (i. e., above zero), like the line C shown in Figure 6.4, all have elasticities that are greater than unity. Conversely, lines that cut the Y axis at some negative value below zero (or, to put the same thing in other words, that cut the X axis at some positive value, to the right of zero) have elasticities that are less than unity. As with straight line demand curves (with negative slopes), the elasticity varies from point to point along any straight line positively sloping curve, if it does not go through the origin.

three

MEASURING CHANGES IN DEMAND AND SUPPLY

7

The Measurement of Changes in Demand and Supply

The demand curve for potatoes portrayed in Chapter 4 clearly shows how a large crop of potatoes depresses the price of potatoes, and a short crop raises it. It shows how the large crop of 1935, for example, depressed the price of potatoes to 90 cents per bushel, and the short crop of 1936 raised the price to $1.40.

Exactly what was the change that took place from 1935 to 1936? We know that prices change in response to changes in demand, or supply, or both. In this case, did the demand decrease, increase, or remain constant? And what about the supply?

Looking at the small crop in 1936 one might say that the price rose and cut off part of the demand; that is, demand decreased. But looking at the high price, one might say that the demand must have *increased*. Which is right?

As a matter of fact, both of these statements would be wrong, for demand is the whole series of prices at which different quantities can be sold (or, the whole series of quantities that can be sold at different prices). The series of prices at which different quantities of potatoes can be sold was shown in Table 4.1. This whole table shows the demand for potatoes. In graphic terms, the demand is a line or curve, not just a single quantity and price; that is only a point on a demand curve.

The demand for potatoes, then, is the whole series of prices and quantities represented by the demand curve in Figure 4.1. Different-sized crops merely cut the curve at different points. From 1935 to 1936 it may be assumed for our purposes here that the demand did not change at all; only the supply changed; the two different-sized crops simply cut the (stationary) demand curve at two different points.

To some people this concept of demand as a whole series of prices and quantities seems unduly complicated. They ask: "When a large crop comes on the market, why not say simply that the price fell, and that brought more buyers into the market, i. e., increased the demand, which thereupon was great enough to take the large crop off the market? That is, why not simply say that the demand increased in 1935 (when the crop was large) and decreased in 1936 when it was small?"

But you can soon see the difficulties you would get into using this concept of demand. For then you would say that the demand decreased from 1935 to 1936 when prices rose. You would say that the rise in price reduced the demand, or, as some of the earlier elementary textbooks used to say, inaccurately, "Demand varies inversely with price."[1] But that would be a flat contradiction of everyday experience embodied in the elementary law of supply and demand, for everybody knows that a decrease in demand *lowers* prices, and an increase in demand raises prices; we know that demand varies *directly* with price.

WHEN DEMAND CHANGES, THE WHOLE CURVE SHIFTS

The only way to keep from contradicting yourself like this is to recognize that demand is the whole series of prices and quantities, the whole curve, in graphic terms. From 1935 to 1936 the demand remained constant (the curve remained stationary); all that happened was that the supply changed, and cut the demand curve at a different point.

This definition of demand as the whole series of quantities that can be sold at different prices is unequivocal. In the light of this definition, it is clearly inaccurate to say, "The demand is greater than the supply," or less than the supply, or equal to it. Each is a whole series of prices and quantities, which are usually negatively corre-

---

[1] ". . . popular thought and usage do not distinguish between demand as the actual quantity of a commodity bought, which 'under given conditions' depends on the price, and the 'given conditions' which determine how much the market will take at any named price. Thus in general usage demand is, as J. S. Mill remarked, both the effect and the cause of price. In scientific usage the term is now defined in the latter sense only. Thus a change in price occurs only when there is a change in sales without a change in price alone. When the reference is to actual quantity bought as a result of a certain price, the term to be used is sales or consumption, but this distinction in terminology is not always carefully observed."—Frank H. Knight, "Demand," *Encyclopaedia of the Social Sciences*, Vol. 5, 1931, p. 69.

Even some rather advanced books on economics use the term demand erroneously. Strangely enough, British writers are the worst sinners in this respect. *See* R. G. D. Allen, *Mathematical Analysis for Economists*, p. 117, where the statement is made, "Since price decreases as demand increases . . ." where the author clearly means output or production, not demand. Similar misuses of the term occur in pp. 254–58. *See also* J. R. Hicks, *Value and Capital*, Oxford, The Clarendon Press, 1939, at numerous points throughout the book.

lated in the case of demand and positively correlated in the case of supply. What is meant by the quotation just given is that the amount demanded at a certain price is greater or less than the amount offered at that price. If the amount demanded at $1.00 is more than the amount supplied at $1.00, some buyers will offer more than $1.00 (say $1.05); no seller then will sell for less than $1.00, so one or two buyers will drop out (the amount demanded at $1.05 is less than the amount demanded at $1.00) and one or two new suppliers will come in (the amount supplied at $1.05 is higher than the amount supplied at $1.00) until a price will be reached somewhere between $1.00 and $1.05, at which the amount demanded will just equal the amount supplied.

A change in demand has taken place only when the whole price or quantity series changes. If some years later than those shown in Table 4.1 you found that the quantities of potatoes given could be sold only at 25 cents per bushel less than the series of prices given in Table 4.1 (that is, if you found that you had to set up a new price series 25 cents per bushel less than the series of prices given in Table 4.1), then you could say that the demand for potatoes had decreased. The whole curve would have shifted downward.[2]

SHIFTS IN DEMAND AND SUPPLY CURVES

It is easy to discover the elasticity of the demand for a product when the demand remains constant and only the supply changes. It is much more difficult, however, when the demand is changing (the demand curve is shifting) as well as the supply. For in that case the intersection points of the shifting demand and supply curves are likely to be scattered all over the chart, and the shifts are mixed up with the elasticity so that it is impossible to measure the elasticity directly.

The sort of price-quantity scatter-diagram the investigator gets out of his figures depends upon the shiftiness or instability of the demand and supply. This can be illustrated by the use of real production and market price data. But during World War II, and in the cold war period since, the demand and supply for most products have been continually shifting, both at once, and in many cases under government controls, so that it is difficult to sort out the effects of the one from the other. Before World War II, however, there was one period when the demand was relatively stable (1921–29) and another when it was very variable (1930–39) and the situation approached "open-market" conditions. Empirical data from

---

[2] A distinction between vertical and horizontal shifts in demand curves is elaborated in Appendix A.

those periods can be plotted directly on simple two-dimensional diagrams to show the behavior of demand and supply curves under different conditions. Four broad classifications of these conditions may be made.

Demand Constant and Supply Fluctuating

In Figure 7.1 the chart on the left shows a typical scatter diagram for an agricultural product when demand remains fairly constant. (The series is entirely too short for analytical purposes; the chart is used here only for illustration. It is, as a matter of fact, difficult to find any longer series of years when demand was stable.) Changes in the weather from one year to another cause rather marked changes in supply, but if the demand remains fairly constant, the dots will cluster along a line with a negative slope; for each dot is the intersection of the demand and supply curve of that year. If demand remains absolutely constant, the supply curve, shifting back and forth from year to year, leaves its intersection points with the demand curve scattered along a single line; this line is the (stationary) demand curve. If, as is more likely, the demand is not absolutely constant, but changes slightly from one year to another, then the

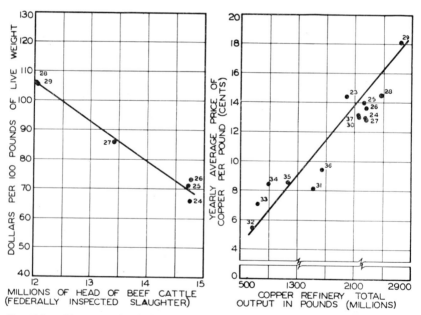

Fig. 7.1 — Chart on the left shows average price and federally inspected slaughter of beef cattle for 6 years (data from Table 7.1); chart on the right, average price and total refinery output of copper for 15 years (data from Table 7.2).

TABLE 7.1

CATTLE, UNITED STATES PRODUCTION AND PRICES, SIX CONSECUTIVE YEARS*

Year	Beef Cattle, Number Head Federally Inspected Slaughter	Average Cost of Cattle Slaughtered, Live Weight Basis
	(000)	*Dollars per 100 lbs.*
1924...........................	14,750	6.64
1925...........................	14,704	7.11
1926...........................	14,766	7.32
1927...........................	13,413	8.62
1928...........................	12,028	10.59
1929...........................	12,038	10.58

* *Livestock, Meats, and Wool Market Statistics, 1939*, AMS, USDA, pp. 21, 91, and 93.

dots will be scattered along a path or band about the average demand curve. A single line drawn along the middle of this pathway will represent the average demand curve closely, if the pathway is narrow.

Supply Constant and Demand Fluctuating

The chart on the right in Figure 7.1 shows the reverse situation, found in the case of some industrial products. The relation between production and price here is positive. The supply remains constant or nearly constant, but the demand shifts violently. This sort of diagram used to puzzle the early investigators. Thus Moore, in 1914, finding that the scatter diagram for steel looked like the scatter diagram for copper shown on the right, concluded that the demand curve for steel was positively sloped.[3] But actually what he had found was something approximating the supply curve for steel. Henry Wallace a few years later, pondering over Moore's results, began to grumble about the law of supply and demand. There was one law of supply and demand for farm products, he said—the higher the supply, the lower the price—and another law for industrial products—the higher the supply, the higher the price.

What Wallace had really found was that the two cases illustrated the two parts of the law of supply and demand. Most agricultural products illustrate the one part—that if the demand is constant, the price varies inversely with the supply. Many industrial products illustrate the other part—that if the supply is constant, the price

[3] "Our representative crops and representative producers' good (pig iron) exemplify types of demand curves of contrary character. In the one case, as the product increases or decreases the price falls or rises, while, in the other case, the price rises with an increase of the product and falls with its decrease."— Henry L. Moore, *Economic Cycles, Their Law and Cause*, Macmillan, 1914, p. 114.

TABLE 7.2

COPPER, UNITED STATES PRODUCTION AND PRICES, 1923–38 *

Year	United States New Copper (Refinery Output) Total	Copper (Electrolytic) New York Yearly Average Price
	Millions of lbs.	*Cents per lb.*
1923	1,980	14.421
1924	2,260	13.024
1925	2,205	14.042
1926	2,322	13.795
1927	2,326	12.920
1928	2,488	14.570
1929	2,740	18.107
1930	2,157	12.982
1931	1,501	8.116
1932	681	5.555
1933	742	7.025
1934	891	8.428
1935	1,178	8.649
1936	1,645	9.474
1937	2,134	13.167
1938	1,585	10.000

* *Statistical Abstract of the United States*, 1939, pp. 728 and 747.

varies directly with demand. The two groups of products are represented by the two sets of conditions shown in both sections. In
the one case, the demand remains constant and the supply changes,
while in the other, supply remains constant and the demand changes.

Correlated Shifts in Demand and Supply Curves

When the supply and the demand are both changing, the situation is more complicated. The changes in demand and supply may
have no relation to each other, or they may be correlated, either
positively or negatively. If they are correlated, care must be exer-
cised in interpreting results.

Let us take an extreme case for illustration. The annual price
and quantity data for sulfur for an 11-year period are shown in
the chart on the left in Figure 7.2. It should be noted that the price
and production scales in the chart both run down to zero. The dots
show that during this period the production of sulfur changed
greatly from year to year, but the price remained absoltuely constant. The data all fall on a horizontal straight line. What does that
line represent — a demand curve, a supply curve, or neither one?

The dots almost certainly do not represent a demand curve. It
does not seem reasonable that the demand for sulfur would be

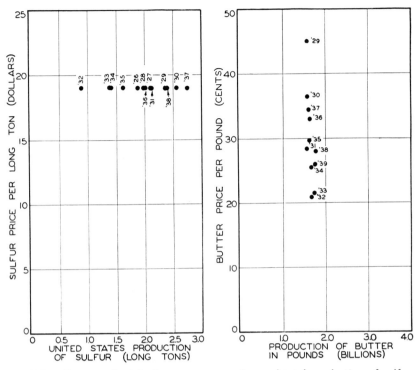

Fig. 7.2 — Chart on the left shows average price and total production of sulfur for an 11-year period; (data from Table 7.3); and on the right, average price and total production of butter, for a similar period (data from Table 7.4).

infinitely elastic over the range shown. It seems very unlikely that consumers would pay as much per ton for sulfur when 2,741,970 tons are offered for sale as when less than a third of that quantity, 890,440 tons, is offered, unless their demand curve shifted its position meanwhile. It must have shifted to the right when larger quantities were offered (or larger quantities must have been offered when the demand curve shifted to the right) and conversely. The dots must represent not a demand curve, but a series of inter-sections of a negatively sloping demand curve with a supply curve or series of supply curves.

Do the dots therefore represent a supply curve—an infinitely elastic supply curve? This also seems unlikely; but the question should be answered on the basis of a knowledge of the industry rather than any deductive reasoning. It is possible that the industry is a constant cost industry—that all that needs to be done when demand increases is (1) to run the plants more shifts per day, the

TABLE 7.3

SULFUR, UNITED STATES PRODUCTION AND PRICES, 1926–37

Year	Sulfur Produced *	Price †
	Long tons	*Dollars per ton*
1926..........................	1,890,027	18
1927..........................	2,111,618	18
1928..........................	1,981,873	18
1929..........................	2,362,389	18
1930..........................	2,558,981	18
1931..........................	2,128,930	18
1932..........................	890,440	18
1933..........................	1,406,063	18
1934..........................	1,421,473	18
1935..........................	1,632,590	18
1936..........................	2,016,338	18
1937..........................	2,741,970	18

* Production data for 1927 from *The Mineral Resources of the U. S.*, U. S. Bureau of Mines, 1929, Part II, p. 176; for 1928–32, from *The Minerals Yearbook*, U. S. Bureau of Mines, 1932–33, p. 671; for 1933–36, same yearbook, 1937, p. 1303; for 1937, same yearbook, 1939, p. 1245.

† Price data, 1927–37, "The price of sulfur was reduced in 1938—the first change in the quotations since 1926. The price at the mines dropped from $18 to $16 per long ton at the beginning of the last quarter (of 1938)." Quotation taken from *The Minerals Yearbook*, U. S. Bureau of Mines, 1939, pp. 1243–44.

higher labor costs exactly offsetting the lower overhead costs per unit, or else (2) put up new plants with the same costs as the old. However, there is some question about this. Sulfur is produced under oligopolistic conditions, and the stability of its prices probably results from this rather than from cost considerations.

The chart apparently represents a high short-time elasticity of supply, or, what amounts to the same thing, a succession of intersection points of a negatively sloping demand curve with a positively sloping, long-time supply curve, the changes being positively correlated. It should be emphasized that the interpretation of the chart has to rest upon knowledge of the industry and economic reasoning, not merely upon the data themselves.

The opposite situation—a high negative correlation between changes in supply and demand—existed in the case of many agricultural products during the 11 years from 1929 through 1939. The price and production data for butter are plotted in the chart on the right in Figure 7.2. The dots fall closely about a practically vertical line. It is obvious that the elasticity of the demand for butter cannot be practically zero. It is also obvious that the demand for butter declined greatly during the first few years of the depression that began in 1929, and recovered during the latter part. The vertical scatter

TABLE 7.4

BUTTER, UNITED STATES PRODUCTION AND PRICES, 1929–39 *

Year	Creamery Butter Produced in Factories	92-Score Creamery New York
	Millions of lbs.	*Cents per lb.*
1929.	1,597	45.01
1930.	1,595	36.51
1931.	1,667	28.31
1932.	1,694	21.00
1933.	1,763	21.66
1934.	1,695	25.70
1935.	1,632	29.79
1936.	1,629	33.05
1937.	1,624	34.39
1938.	1,786	27.97
1939.	1,759	26.00

* Source of data: *Agricultural Statistics*, USDA, 1940, p. 449.

of the dots, therefore, must represent a series of intersection points of a negatively sloping demand curve with a supply curve or series of supply curves.

Again the question arises—is there a single supply curve, practically a vertical line in this case, or a series of different supply curves? Do the dots all fall about a single supply curve of practically zero elasticity, or do they represent a succession of intersection points with a series of sloping supply curves?

It seems obvious enough that the long-time supply curve for butter must have some positive elasticity. The vertical supply curve shown on the right in Figure 7.2 must show merely the short-time elasticity of supply from plant and equipment already in production and unlikely to be shut down or junked during a short-time decrease in demand. It is a case where a short-time decrease in demand causes a short-time increase in supply; the correlation between changes in demand and supply here is high, and negative.

It goes without saying that most commodities do not fall neatly in one or the other of the classes indicated above—constant demand, constant supply, positive correlation between changes in demand and supply, negative correlation, or no correlation at all. Most commodities fall somewhere along the lines between the several extremes, and care must be taken in the interpretation of all charts and statistical analyses of this character.

The quantity-price curves for many farm products have a negative slope, and it is easy to suppose that they show the demand

TABLE 7.5

Hogs, United States Production and Prices, 1940–60*

Year	Total Hog Slaughter	Slaughter Hog Price
	Thousand head	*Dollars per 100 lbs.*
1940.....	77,610	$ 5.67
1941.....	71,397	9.42
1942.....	78,547	13.57
1943.....	95,226	14.11
1944.....	98,068	13.43
1945.....	71,891	14.55
1946.....	76,021	18.01
1947.....	74,001	24.60
1948.....	70,869	23.56
1949.....	74,997	18.31
1950.....	79,263	18.30
1951.....	85,540	20.24
1952.....	86,572	17.96
1953.....	74,368	21.72
1954.....	71,495	21.72
1955.....	81,051	15.09
1956.....	85,064	14.62
1957.....	78,636	18.02
1958.....	76,822	19.96
1959.....	87,606	14.27
1960.....	84,196	15.73
1961.....	82,057	16.89

* Source: "Livestock and Meat Statistics," Stat. Bul. 230, USDA, Supplement for 1957, p. 103 for 1940–57 slaughter data, and p. 235 for 1940–57 price data. Supplement for 1961, p. 64 for 1955–61 slaughter data, and p. 117 for 1956–61 price data.

curves for those products. Actually, as the charts on the preceding pages show, the curves may have very little relation to demand curves. It is fairly easy to keep from misinterpreting the curves in clear-cut cases like those shown in these charts. It is more difficult in the majority of cases, which lie somewhere between the extremes. Many "demand curves" are not demand curves at all, but only mixtures of demand and supply curves that move with some degree of positive or negative correlation and leave a track of intersection points that represents neither a demand curve nor a supply curve.

This does not mean that such curves are not useful. They may in fact be more useful than demand curves. If changes in demand cause changes in supply, or vice versa, it may be more useful to know what the price-quantity relationship is, under those conditions, than to know what the elasticity of demand or supply is.

A concrete illustration may make this clear. The price-quantity relationship for corn shows an elasticity of —0.65, but the demand curve for corn is probably less elastic than this. A short crop of corn lowers the hog-corn price ratio and leads to a considerable reduction in hog production. This reduces the demand for corn, so that the price of corn rises less than it would if the demand for corn had remained constant. The opposite happens in years of large corn crops; hog production increases—i. e., the demand increases—and this causes prices to fall less than if hog production (the demand for corn) had remained constant. Thus the demand for corn, "other things being equal," is less elastic than the demand for corn, "other things changing as they do when the supply of corn changes." But

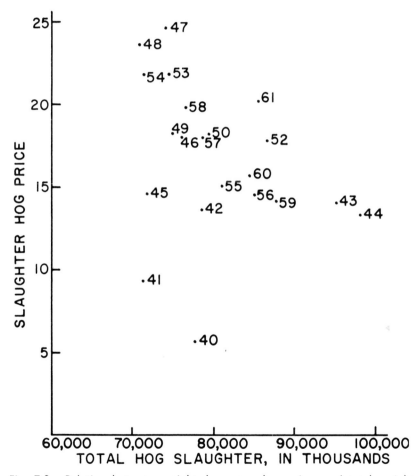

Fig. 7.3 — Relation between weighted average hog prices and total weight of hogs slaughtered, 1940–61 (data from Table 7.5).

it may be more useful to know the elasticity of the latter kind of demand than the former.

Uncorrelated Shifts in Demand and Supply Curves

In many cases, particularly with agricultural goods, the changes in demand and supply are uncorrelated.

This was particularly true during World War II, and has continued to be true during the cold war period that has followed. The demand for most farm products during these war and postwar years has fluctuated violently and sometimes simultaneously. The intersection points of the supply and demand curves for hogs in the United States, for instance, lie scattered all over the page, as shown in Figure 7.3.

When this happens, how can the investigator sort out the shifts in demand from the shifts in supply and determine the elasticities of each? On the face of it, it looks like an impossible job. But methods have been worked out to handle it. They are presented in the next two chapters.

The Measurement of Changes in Demand: Deflation

If the position of the demand curve remains constant, it is easy to determine the elasticity; one simply plots the price data against the production data in an ordinary scatter-diagram, and draws in the demand curve through the dots. But in actual life, demand curves constantly shift their position—sometimes only to a small extent, but sometimes violently. These shifts in demand curves scatter the intersection points all over the scatter-diagram, so that the dots do not fall on a single negatively sloping line; they may even cluster around a positively sloping line, or show no tendency to cluster around any line at all.

This caused the early price analysts a good deal of trouble. They were well aware that the demand for most of the products they were working with showed an upward trend with the passage of time, resulting from the steady increase in population if from nothing else. They knew that rising trends in prices and production both, such as are shown by the data for many commodities in the United States from 1893 to 1914, may be strong enough to convert a normal negative relation between prices and production to the appearance of a positive relation on a simple price-production chart; or at the least, it may obscure the normal negative relationship. Accordingly, they used two or three methods to take these rising trends into account. They recast their data in the form of ratios or percentages of the preceding year's data, or expressed them as ratios of their trends (usually straight line or slightly curved trends fitted by the method of least squares).[1]

---

[1] Charles F. Roos, *Dynamic Economics,* Principia Press, 1934, pp. 4 and 14: "In the older type of statistical study of demand, the chief purpose was the determination of 'the demand curve,' or in some cases the more limited purpose

It is instructive to review their experience with this problem, because it is still with us, only partially solved. The violent changes in price levels during World Wars I and II and the intervening periods of peace, with severe depression during the latter part of the period, provided a sort of laboratory in which different partial solutions were developed.

DEFLATING PRICES

After World War I, economists became acutely conscious of the changes in demand associated with inflation and deflation. For a time they attempted to take these changes into account by "deflating" the original prices by an index of the general price level. Most economists used this deflating procedure with misgivings.[2] They knew that changes in demand could take place (in fact were taking place from 1933 to 1939) without causing much change in the commodity price level. They knew, furthermore, that even if changes in demand were always associated with changes in the commodity price level, there was no reason to believe that these changes were associated in 1 to 1 ratio. The ratio was just as likely to be 1 to 0.8, or 1 to 1.5, or some other figure; and furthermore, it was likely to differ from one price level to another.[3]

SHORTCOMINGS OF DEFLATING

The shortcomings of this deflating procedure (and of the mathematical trend fitting procedure also) were illustrated even in the

---

of determining the percentage decrease in demand corresponding to a 1 per cent increase in price (elasticity of demand). From the standpoint of such studies all factors other than price were regarded as 'disturbing factors' whose effect should be eliminated. Various devices invented for performing this elimination included the method of trend ratios, of link relatives, and of first differences. On the whole this older type of study proceeded on the assumption that changes in demand due to factors other than price were of a gradual nature due to changes in habit, customs and the growth of population. Under the assumptions it appeared to be desirable to remove the effects of trends.

"But by 1934 it is more and more being recognized that the use of a trend in statistical analysis of economic relationships is a confession of ignorance of some of the important factors involved or is a desire to discuss these factors without identifying them."

[2] Henry Schultz, in his *Theory and Measurement of Demand*, University of Chicago Press, 1938, devotes most of two pages to a discussion of the shortcomings of deflation, but finally adopts it because it reduces the number of variables. He then compares his results with those based on undeflated data in an appendix.

[3] George J. Stigler, "The Limitations of Statistical Demand Curves," *Journal of the American Statistical Association*, Vol. 24, Sept., 1939, pp. 472–73:

"The rationale of this sort of 'deflation' (to remove the effects of changes in the general price level) is not clear: either the statistician adheres to the quantity theory in a form that even Jean Bodin would not accept, or else he meticulous work of Henry Schultz, in his monumental *Theory and Measurement of Demand*. He fitted trends to the data for the annual per capita consumption of corn (corrected for size of crop and real, i. e., deflated price) for three periods of time, the last one being 1915–29, excluding the war years of 1917 to 1921. The straight-line trend in this last period[4] shows a sharp decline, and Schultz regarded this decline in the demand for corn as the most important finding in his corn chapter.

Actually, however, the downward slope of the trend results almost entirely from the inclusion of the two prewar years, 1915 and 1916, with the postwar years, 1922 to 1929. The whole price level for corn shifted suddenly downward during the postwar deflation in 1920. If 1915 and 1916 are left out, as they should be (since they belong to the prewar period), the postwar trend of the demand, from 1920 on, is practically horizontal.

By calculations based upon the later year, 1934, Schultz attempted to check the accuracy of his conclusion that the trend had declined. These calculations confirmed his conclusion. But it is a curious fact that this check was itself erroneous, and instead of revealing his previous error, merely covered it up. The 1934 data "confirmed" Schultz's results merely because his deflator was inaccurate. The Bureau of Labor Statistics index of the general wholesale commodity price level in December, 1934, had fallen to 75 (base, 1926=100). It is well known that when the general price level changes, the accompanying percentage changes in prices at the farm are greater than the percentage changes in the general price level, because of the comparative fixity of middleman's charges between producer and retailer. This is shown by the fact that while the Bureau of Labor Statistics index of the general level of prices was 75 in December, 1934, the index of the prices of farm products at the farm was 62 (base in both cases, 1926=100). The general relation between the two series for the period 1921 to 1944 is shown in Figure 8.1 to be 1 to 1.5.

believes that some, perhaps most, of the monetary disturbance is somehow removed.

"The former alternative cannot charitably be attributed to anyone; the latter alternative seems to me to rest on a rather futile hope. Monetary changes come about through changes in the monetary funds of individuals within a community. The nature and extent of these monetary changes depend largely on who gets the 'money,' when it is received, and how and when it is spent. Only by examining the detailed structure of monetary relationships is it possible to isolate the effects of monetary policy on specific demand curves. And even if this is possible, the resultant demand curve is applicable to future periods only if detailed forecasts of monetary policy are also made. It is not surprising that blanket 'deflation' of prices does not improve the statistical demand curve, judged even by statistical criteria."

[4] Schultz, *op. cit.*

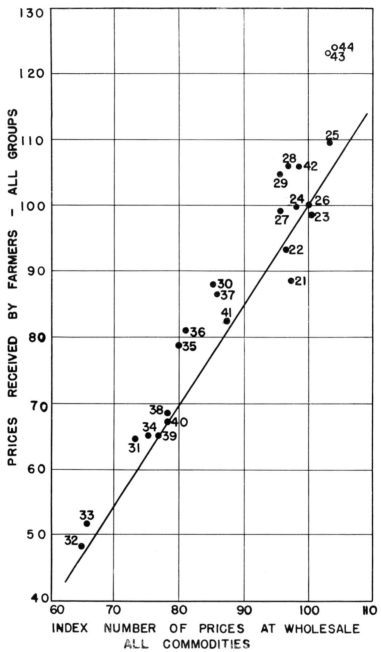

Fig. 8.1 — Relation between the index of prices received by farmers and the Bureau of Labor Statistics index of all commodity prices at wholesale, 1922—44. (Source, **Statistical Abstracts of the United States, 1944—45**, USDC, p. 417.)

The price of corn in 1934 was lower than a 1 to 1 relationship with the general price level, not because the trend of the demand for the corn had declined, but because the general price level had declined during the depression and this had caused a greater than proportional decline in corn prices. The second error happened to be in the same direction as the first. If the general price level in 1934 had been *higher* than in 1926, the deflated price of corn would have been higher than the size of the crop would have indicated, and this would have seemed to indicate a rise in the trend of the demand for corn. But this would have been just as erroneous as the downward trend which Schultz believed he had found.

The general price level may be used as a deflator for corn prices, without leading to this sort of error, if its movements are first "inflated" by the actual relation between those movements and the movements in the price of corn. An analysis of corn prices, in which the Bureau of Labor Statistics index of the general price level at wholesale is used as a separate variable, shows that corn prices are related to the general price level in the ratio not of 1 to 1, nor even of 1 to 1.5 (the relationship shown in Figure 8.1), but of about 1 to 1.7. Corn is farther from the consumer, economically speaking, than the average of the products used in the farm products price level index. If the investigator wishes to divide his corn price series through by the index of the general price level, he should multiply that index throughout by 1.7 and subtract 70 from the products, and use that index to deflate his corn prices, in order to do the job properly.[5] The correlation between corn supplies per animal unit and corn prices deflated by the index of the general price level is 0.79; when the same index is "inflated" as described above, the correlation rises to 0.93. This is shown graphically in Figure 8.2.

DEVELOPMENTS IN THE 1930'S

In spite of the shortcomings of the early methods for removing the effect of trends and fluctuations in demand, a good deal of useful work was done during the 1920's with their aid. Then several forces combined to bring about a change. They were (1) the popu-

---

[5] This, of course is still not a satisfactory procedure. It is only one step better than deflating by the original general price level directly. It assumes that the changes intervening between the corn producer and the general wholesale market (itself an ambiguous term) remain fixed when the general price level changes, not only for a year or two, but for periods five or ten years long. This is not true. Some of the important charges, such as railroad freight rates, change only slightly, and only after a period of years; but many other charges give way more readily. I do not know of any simple arithmetical method for taking this into account. The problem is not solved even by using the general price level as a separate variable instead of as a deflator; the same difficulties remain.

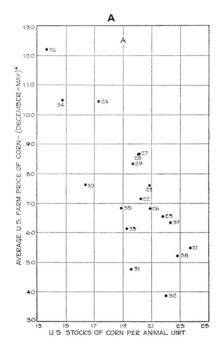

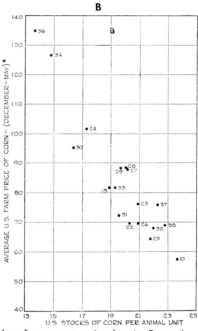

Fig. 8.2 — Relation of United States stocks of corn per animal unit, December 1, to the average United States farm price of corn, December-May, deflated by (A) the Bureau of Labor Statistics index of the general level of wholesale prices, and (B) that index multiplied by 1.7, minus 70, 1921–38.

larization of multiple correlation methods, (2) the development of labor-saving mechanical calculating machines and graphic methods, and finally (3) the onslaught of the great depression in 1929. The overwhelming importance of changes in demand became clear; economists realized that trends could not only rise, they could flatten out, and violently fall. No longer could trends be easily fitted as straight lines. And even if properly curved lines could be fitted, and the trend thus "removed," economists began to realize that they did not want to "remove" one of the main characters in the cast; they wanted to measure it, not in order to throw it away, but in order to include its influence in the analysis.

Furthermore, as the depression deepened, the disparity in the rates at which different prices fell became more and more striking, and the inaccuracy of deflating price series (or inflating them, as the process actually became) by division by an index of the general price level, or any other over-all index, became more and more apparent. The necessity of measuring changes in demand directly, and using that measure as a separate variable, became clear, and the spread of the use of labor-saving computing machinery and graphic methods made the use of additional variables in multiple correlation studies easier. The lengthening of the postwar series with the passage of time also permitted the use of larger numbers of variables. Today, therefore, many price analysts prefer not to fit trends or deflate prices in their analytical price studies, but to use some measure of changes in demand as a separate variable.

TWO KINDS OF CHANGES IN DEMAND

But this has not solved the problem of measuring changes in demand; it has merely revealed it more clearly. The problem thus revealed is: What variable or variables should be used to measure (in the earlier terminology, "remove") changes in demand?

This problem consists of two parts:

1. What variable or variables should be used to measure changes in demand affecting all commodities over the country as a whole, the sort that take place when the country swings from prosperity to depression and back? This kind of change can be referred to as a change in the general demand.

2. What variable or variables should be used to measure changes in demand for the specific commodity being investigated, independent of changes in the general demand which affect all commodities? This kind of change can be referred to as a change in the specific demand for the commodity.

These two kinds of changes in demand are discussed in order below.

Changes in General Demand

The most accurate and current measure of demand in the United States is "disposable personal income." This is total national personal income minus personal income taxes. This series goes back to 1921. It is published monthly in the Survey of Current Business of the United States Department of Commerce.

The relation between this series and the price of farm products, over the period since World War I, was about 1 to 1.2. This is not far from 1 to 1. But the relation of disposable income to expenditures for food at retail, as shown in Figure 1.6, is only 0.4. Deflation in this case would produce very inaccurate results.

Specific Changes in Demand

An analysis that is based on general demand factors only is deficient in two respects: (a) The connection between the general change in demand and the price of the particular commodity is not direct; there may be a good deal of loose play between the two. (b) Changes in the demand for the particular product only—what may be called specific changes in demand—are left out of account.

Specific changes in demand are more concrete and definite than the general changes in demand discussed in the preceding section. For example, whenever the price of livestock rises, Corn Belt farmers are willing to pay more per bushel for corn to feed to that livestock. This may be regarded as causing the demand curve for corn to rise. Whenever the number of livestock increases, farmers need more corn to feed them. This may be regarded as causing the demand curve for corn to shift to the right.

A rough price analysis for a specific commodity can be made by taking into account only those general changes in demand for all commodities represented by changes in the general price level. A more thorough analysis should include some additional factors representing changes in specific demand. It would be possible to deflate the price series for these other factors by dividing it through in turn by each of these other factors. But the shortcomings of the deflating procedure when only one deflator is used would be multiplied if several deflators were used; the errors resulting from the true relationships not being 1 to 1 would cumulate. A much better procedure is to use the method of multiple correlation analysis, which enables the investigator to determine what each of the true relationships is.

The use of two demand factors, one reflecting changes in gen-

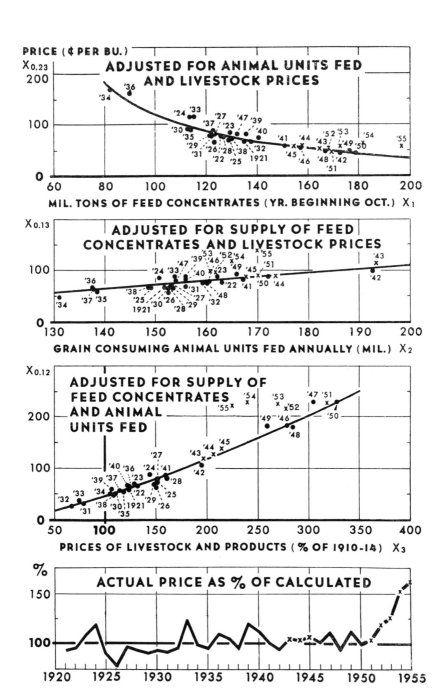

Fig. 8.3 — Corn prices received by farmers, November to May, in relation to specified factors. From an analysis based on logarithms for 1921—42 and 1946—50.

TABLE 8.1

PRICE RECEIVED BY FARMERS FOR CORN, NOVEMBER TO MAY: ACTUAL AND COMPUTED
PRICE PER BUSHEL AND RELATED VARIABLES, 1921–55

Period Beginning	X_0, Price of Corn			X_1, Supply of Feed Concentrates ‡	X_2, Grain-consuming Animal Units Fed Annually ‡	X_3, Price Received by Farmers for Livestock and Products (Nov.– May)§
	Actual	Computed *	Difference †			
	Cents	Cents	Cents	Million tons	Millions	
1921.....	51	54	−3	136	152	123
1922.....	73	77	−4	126	163	132
1923.....	76	70	6	129	162	128
1924.....	108	91	17	114	151	144
1925.....	69	76	−7	129	149	151
1926.....	66	85	−19	123	152	150
1927.....	83	87	−4	123	153	151
1928.....	83	89	−6	126	153	160
1929.....	78	86	−8	122	154	148
1930.....	60	65	−5	113	152	110
1931.....	33	36	−3	122	156	78
1932.....	24	25	−2	138	159	67
1933.....	45	37	8	115	154	74
1934.....	83	84	−1	82	131	106
1935.....	56	59	−3	114	138	118
1936.....	106	97	9	90	138	123
1937.....	51	49	2	123	138	114
1938.....	44	47	−3	130	148	108
1939.....	55	46	9	136	156	107
1940.....	58	52	6	140	156	122
1941.....	74	75	−1	151	167	159
1942.....	90	97	−7	172	192	194
1943.....	112	108	4	164	193	196
1944.....	107	104	3	158	173	206
1945.....	115	108	7	155	168	215
1946.....	138	137	1	158	160	278
1947.....	220	199	21	133	154	305
1948.....	120	127	−7	167	160	285
1949.....	118	108	10	176	166	258
1950.....	155	154	1	179	172	329
1951.....	167	163	4	169	172	318
1952.....	147	128	19	168	164	278
1953.....	142	121	21	173	161	271
1954.....	138	92	46	181	166	240
1955.....	121	76	45	196	171	223

* From an analysis based on logarithms for 1921–42 and 1946–50.
† Actual minus computed price.
‡ Year beginning October.
§ Index numbers (1910–14 = 100).

Table from R. J. Foote, "Statistical Analyses Relating to the Feed-Livestock Economy," USDA Tech. Bul. 1070, June, 1953, p. 6, brought up to 1955 by Foote.

eral demand, and the other reflecting changes in the specific demand for the product concerned, is shown in Figure 8.3. The data for this illustration are presented in Table 8.1. The figure is a graphic multiple correlation analysis. The dependent variable here (the one being explained) is the price of corn. The first independent variable is the total supply of feed concentrates, including corn. The next independent variable is the number of grain-consuming units fed; this is the specific demand factor for corn. The third independent variable is the price of livestock and livestock products. This is chiefly a general demand factor, since it reflects changes in the general price level, general economic activity, and other general factors affecting the economy as a whole. It also reflects, more directly but less importantly, changes in the specific prices of livestock and livestock products; it reflects them less importantly, because their effects as specific demand factors are highly correlated, inversely, with the number of animal units fed, which is already included as the second independent variable.

The method of multiple correlation is a little complicated. The graphic approach is explained in the next chapter.

9

The Measurement of Changes in Demand:
Multiple Correlation

The graphic method of multiple curvilinear correlation is, as it were, an F_2 product. It is an offshoot of an offshoot of the standard mathematical method of linear multiple correlation.

The first important offshoot was developed originally in the fertile mind of Mordecai Ezekiel.[1] He was working with the problem of curvilinear regressions (curved lines of relationship between different series of data). The simplest form of the standard mathematical method involves the assumption that the data are related in straight-line fashion. If this assumption is not valid—if the regressions are actually curvilinear—the standard method yields inaccurate results; before accurate results can be obtained, the curves must be represented by mathematical equations incorporated in the basic formula.

But the regressions cannot be determined accurately until the nature of the curvature is known, and the nature of the curvature cannot be determined accurately until the regressions are known. Ezekiel broke through this impasse by the method of successive approximations, starting with mathematically determined straight lines and adjusting them by graphic methods.[2]

---

[1] Mordecai Ezekiel, "A Method of Handling Curvilinear Correlation for any Number of Variables," *Journal of the American Statistical Association*, Vol. 19, No. 148, p. 441. See also: M. Ezekiel and Karl Fox, *Methods of Correlation and Regression Analysis*, Wiley, 1959, Chap. 14.

[2] Ezekiel and Fox, *op. cit.*, p. 210:

"The linear partial regressions are . . . computed [by the standard mathematical correlation method]. Then the dependent variable is adjusted for the deviations from the mean of all independent variables except one, and a correlation chart, or dot-chart, is constructed between these adjusted values and that independent variable. This provides the basis for drawing in the first approximation curve for the net regression of the dependent variable on that

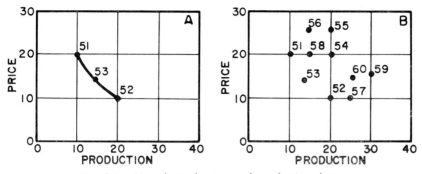

Fig. 9.1 — Hypothetical price and production data.

This first offshoot of the standard mathematical method of linear multiple correlation, therefore, was a hybrid, a combination of mathematics and graphics. Then Louis Bean developed the second offshoot. This second offshoot shed the mathematics inherited from its grandparent completely and became entirely graphic. In effect, Bean said, it is a waste of time to fit straight-line curves mathematically, and then modify them graphically, freehand, to make them fit any curvature existing in the regressions. Don't bother with any mathematics, he said; put the regression lines in freehand in the first place, curves and all.

But how does one know where to draw in the regression lines right off? The essence of Bean's contribution is his simple answer to this question.

In simple correlation, the dependent variable, for example price, is related to one independent variable, for example production. One simply plots price against production in a scatter diagram, and draws in the regression line, straight or curved, wherever the dots indicate that it should go. This is illustrated in section A of Figure 9.1, based upon the first three price and production items in Table 9.1.

In the simplest case of multiple correlation, the dependent var-

independent variable. . . . The dependent variable is then corrected for all except the next independent variable, the corrected values plotted against the values of that variable, and the first approximation curve determined with respect to that variable. This process is carried out for each independent variable in turn, yielding a complete set of first approximations to the net regression curves. These curves are then used as a basis for correcting the dependent factor for the approximate curvilinear effect of all independent variables except one, leaving out each in turn; and second approximation curves are determined by plotting these corrected values against the values of each independent variable in turn. New corrections are made from these curves, and the process is continued until no further change in the several regression curves is indicated."

TABLE 9.1
PRICE, QUANTITY, AND DEMAND SCHEDULE
(Hypothetical Data)

Year	Price	Production	Index of Demand
1951.	20	10	10
1952.	10	20	10
1953.	14	14	8
1954.	20	20	20
1955.	25	20	25
1956.	25	15	20
1957.	10	25	15
1958.	20	15	15
1959.	15	30	25
1960.	15	25	20

iable price is related to two independent variables, for example production and demand. Two scatter diagrams are required here —one to show the regression of price on production (or in more everyday language, the influence of production on price) independent of the influence of demand on price; and the other to show the influence of demand on price independent of the influence of production on price.

In handling a multiple correlation problem of this sort, the first thing to do is to plot the dependent variable price with one of the independent variables, say production, in a simple scatter diagram. The price and production data from Table 9.1 are thus plotted in Section B of Figure 9.1.

The dots in this Section B are scattered about with no evidence of any relationship. But this may be because the influence of production on price is obscured by the coexisting influence of demand on price. What we want is the *net* influence of production on price— the influence of production on price independent of the influence of demand on price.

This word "independent" is the key to the graphic method. One way to determine the influence of production on price independent of the influence of demand on price is to choose two years in which the values of the demand variable are identical. Any change in price from one of these years to the other then must show the influence of production on price independent of the influence of demand on price, since demand did not change from the one year to the other. A line connecting these two years would then be a preliminary indication or estimate of the influence of production on price independent of the influence of demand on price.

Inspection of Table 9.1 shows that there are several pairs of years in which the values of the demand variable are identical (within each pair). The years 1951 and 1952, for example, both carry demand values of 10. The dots for these two years may therefore be connected by a light line, as shown in Section A of Figure 9.2.

This is a beginning. If now another pair of years can be found in which the demand values are identical, another line can be drawn in connecting these two years. Two such years are 1954 and 1956. This provides a second estimate of the influence of production independent of the influence of demand. Additional pairs of years, in each of which the demand values are identical, may also be connected, providing additional estimates.

By now the chart looks like a piece of prehistoric bedrock with scratches on it showing the direction in which a glacier passed over it. A long heavy line can now be drawn in freehand, passing through the dots with a slope representing the general average slope of various short lines on the chart. It should go through the general mean. This line is shown in Section A of Figure 9.2. It is a first approximation to the net regression line desired.

The determination of the net influence of demand on price is then simple. If the heavy line just drawn in shows the net influence of production on price, the vertical distances of the individual dots above and below this line must show the net influence of demand on price. The way to reveal this net influence clearly is to take these vertical distances or residuals and plot them against demand in a second chart. In this chart, the demand scale runs along the bottom, like the production scale in the first chart. A horizontal line is drawn across the middle of the chart (about half way up). This line is regarded as zero on the vertical scale. The vertical distances of individual dots above or below the preliminary regression line in the first chart are then plotted above or below the horizontal line

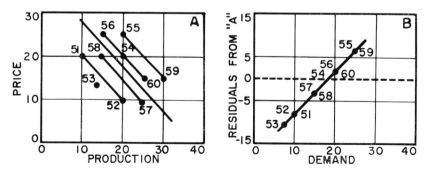

Fig. 9.2 — Hypothetical price and production data. Net regression curves.

across the middle of the second chart against the respective demand readings along the bottom of the second chart. A line drawn through the dots in the second chart then represents the net influence of demand on price—net, because the dots were plotted from the regression line on the first chart which showed the net influence of A on X.

If the first approximation line in the first chart is correct, and if the dependent variable price is completely determined by the two independent variables, production and demand, the line drawn through the dots in the second chart will pass through all of them. This is the situation shown in Section B of Figure 9.2.

If, however, some scatter still remains, either the first approximation line in the first chart was not correctly placed, or one or more additional independent variables need to be taken into account.

The test to determine whether additional variables are needed will also show whether the first approximation line was correctly placed. It consists in taking the residuals from the second chart (the vertical distances above and below the net regression line) and plotting them in red or in some other distinguishing manner, above or below the first approximation regression line in the first chart. (Or this first regression line may be traced on a new clean sheet of graph paper, with the same scales as the original chart). If they fall uniformly about this first approximation line, then a second approximation is not required; what is needed is one or more additional variables. If, however, the dots do not fall uniformly about the first approximation line, but have a different curvature or slope, this indicates that the first approximation line was incorrectly drawn. A second approximation line must be drawn, passing as nearly as possible through the red dots, and the residuals of the *original black dots* from that line plotted in a new second chart (or in different color in the old one) against demand. This may show that the regression line in the second chart needs to be revised. The process is repeated back and forth until the scatter is reduced to the minimum. If some scatter still remains, it means that the study should be extended to include one or more additional variables. In that case the residuals remaining in the second chart should be plotted against a third variable, and so on.

EMPIRICAL ILLUSTRATION

The preceding example, based upon hypothetical data with straight-line relationships and perfect correlation among the variables, serves to illustrate the principles of the graphic method under the simplest conditions. A second illustration based upon actual

TABLE 9.2

FARM PRICES OF CORN (PER BUSHEL) AND RELATED VARIABLES, 1936–51 *

| Period Beginning | Price Received by Farmers (Nov.–May) | | Supply of Feed Concentrates Per Animal Unit † |
	Corn	Livestock and products	
	Cents	*Per cent of 1910–14 prices*	*Tons*
1936.	106	123	0.65
1937.	51	114	.89
1938.	44	108	.88
1939.	55	107	.87
1940.	58	122	.90
1941.	74	159	.90
1942.	90	194	.90
1943.	112	196	.85
1944.	107	206	.91
1945.	115	215	.92
1946.	138	278	.99
1947.	220	305	.86
1948.	120	285	1.04
1949.	118	258	1.06
1950.	155	327	1.03
1951.	167	318	.97

* Source: F. V. Waugh, "Graphic Analysis in Economic Research," USDA, AMS, Agr. Handbook No. 84, June 1955, p. 37. Computed from data in Richard J. Foote, "Statistical Analyses Relating to the Federal Livestock Economy," USDA Tech. Bul. 1070, 1953, p. 6.

† Year beginning in October.

empirical data—"real data"—will now be used. The data for this illustration are given in Table 9.2.

The object here is to explain the variations in the price of corn. "You have to have an idea (hypothesis) to test before you can test it." Our present analysis starts with the hypothesis suggested by economic theory, that variations in the price of corn are caused by changes in demand and supply of corn.

There are several kinds of changes in demand. Two of the most important are:

1. The change in general demand that results from such things as changes in the general price level, changes in population, changes in per capita income, etc.

2. The change in specific demand for the specific product considered, independent of the change in general demand.

Similarly, there are several different kinds of changes in supply.

An analysis involving four variables—two demand variables and two supply variables—becomes a little difficult to explore by graphic methods. For our purposes here, we will use a little ingenuity and reduce the four variables to two which reflect both general and specific changes in demand and supply.

The prices of livestock and livestock products are carried up and down with general changes in demand; they also reflect changes in the specific demand for corn as a feed for livestock (about 90 per cent of the corn crop is fed to livestock). Accordingly, the average United States farm price of corn from November to May (this 7-month average price is used because it is not directly affected by the size of the preceding and succeeding corn crops as a 12-month average price would be) can be plotted against an index of the prices of livestock and livestock products, in order to reveal the effects of this combined reflector of general and specific demand on corn prices. This is shown in Section A, the upper part of Figure 9.3. In this chart, the prices of corn, regarded as the dependent variable, are plotted up the side. The prices of livestock, regarded as the independent variable, are plotted along the bottom. The data are given in Table 9.2.

The dots in the chart are scattered in a general southwest-northeast direction, indicating that there is some positive relationship between changes in demand (as reflected by livestock prices) and the price of corn. But the dots do not lie closely about any single positive line. Evidently, some other factor was at work, causing variations in the price of corn, in addition to changes in demand.

Economic theory suggests that this other factor is likely to be changes in supply. Here again we can combine two factors into one by expressing the supply of feed concentrates (corn is the principal feed) as supply per animal unit. This makes economic sense, because a large supply of corn would depress the price of corn more if the numbers of livestock were small than if they were large. This factor, the supply of feed concentrates per animal unit, is given in the right-hand column of Table 9.2.

Now we come to the essence of the graphic method of multiple correlation analysis. If we can find two different years when the values of this second independent variable, feed supply, were identical, we can say that changes in supply were not exerting any effect on corn prices, because there were no changes in supply. Any changes in corn prices from the one year to the other, then, must be entirely due to changes in demand. They must show the pure, or net, effect of changes in demand, independent of any change in supply, because the supply was constant.

Looking down the right-hand column of Table 9.2, we can find two years when the supply of feed per animal unit was almost exactly the same. The years are 1948, when the supply was 1.04, and 1950, when it was 1.03. We can connect the dots for these two years by a light line. This line shows the net effect of changes in the price of livestock on the price of corn, independent of changes in the supply of corn and other concentrate feeds.

Similarly, the values of the feed variable were nearly identical in 1946 and 1951. We can connect those years too, by a line which turns out to be parallel with the line connecting 1948 and 1950. We can do the same thing for 1940, 1941, and 1942, when the supply stood unchanged at .90.

A heavy straight line is then drawn in through the dots with approximately the average slope of these light lines. In the estimation of this average slope, each light line should be given an importance proportional to its length. The reason for this is that if the dots in one pair are only an inch apart, let us say, and one of the dots has been pulled up or down by some other influence a distance of half an inch, the slope of the light line connecting the pair will be very much affected. But if the pair had been four inches apart, the half inch displacement of one of the dots would have only a slight effect on the slope of the line connecting them. The longer the light line, the more likely it is to show the net influence of the variable correctly; the longer lines, therefore, should be given more weight than the shorter.

In Figure 9.3 the heavy straight line fits the slope of the drift lines pretty well; in some cases, a curve would be better. Perhaps the left-hand half of the line in Figure 9.3 could be curved upward a little from the straight sloping line shown, to fit better with the drift lines in the left-hand part of the chart, but for our purposes here we will use the simple straight line shown.

Plotting the Residuals

The next step is to plot the residuals from the heavy sloping line in Section A of Figure 9.3 against the second independent variable, the supply of feed. The theory behind this plotting is that since the heavy sloping line in Section A measures the influence of changes in demand on the price of corn, the residuals (residual differences) from that line reflect changes in supply. The dot for 1936, for example, is about 4.5 points above the heavy sloping line in Section A; it is accordingly plotted 4.5 points higher than the horizontal zero line in Section B, against the value of the feed supply variable that year, 0.65. The same sort of thing is then done for the other years.

A heavy sloping line is then drawn in through these dots as shown. There is still some scatter of the dots along this line, and it

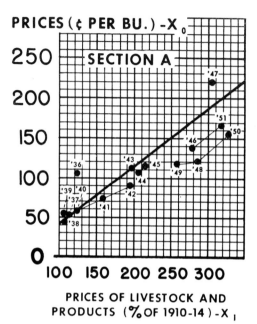

PRICES (¢ PER BU.) -X₀

SECTION A

PRICES OF LIVESTOCK AND
PRODUCTS (% OF 1910-14) -X₁

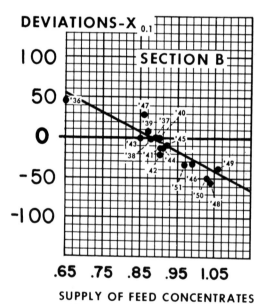

DEVIATIONS-X₀.₁

SECTION B

SUPPLY OF FEED CONCENTRATES
PER ANIMAL UNIT (TONS) -X₂

Fig. 9.3 — November—May corn prices received by farmers in relation to
specified factors. (Section A above, Section B, below.)

would be possible to plot the residuals or departures of these dots from the heavy sloping line against another independent variable in order to get a more complete explanation of variations in the price of corn. But for the present expository purposes, the two steps shown in the two sections of Figure 9.3 are sufficient.

The scatter of the dots about the heavy line in the second section of a graphic analysis of this sort could result from an incorrect slope of the heavy line in the first section. In order to test whether this is true, the residuals from Section B of Figure 9.3 should be plotted back against the heavy sloping line (as so much above or below the line) in red or some other distinguishing manner, as explained on page 136. If these dots fall about a line with a somewhat steeper or flatter slope, or with some curvature, a new heavy line should be drawn through the dots in Section A, and residuals from that new line should be plotted against the second independent variable in Section B. This procedure continues until no closer approximations can be made.

X-Ray Vision

One of the great advantages of the graphic method of analysis is that it reveals the anatomy of the subject, like an X-ray photograph, and shows more clearly than any blind application of mathematical methods just what went on during the period covered by the analysis.

A good example of this is shown in Figure 9.4. This figure shows the retail price of beef (divided by per capita income in order to get away from the complicating effects of changes in income) plotted against per capita beef consumption from 1926 to 1955.

It is clear from this chart that if these two series were thrown into a calculating machine, they would yield a very low correlation coefficient. The dots do not fall at all closely around a single line sloping downwards to the right. Yet economic theory suggests that a negative relationship would be expected to exist.

Inspection of the chart reveals that the lowest price years were all war years, when rationing and price ceilings reduced prices below their normal relation to incomes and supplies. Accordingly, we may run a ring around these years and remove them from consideration as abnormal.

Further inspection of the chart reveals that the remaining dots fall, not along one negatively sloping line, but along two. The dots for the later years fall along a line that lies to the right of the earlier

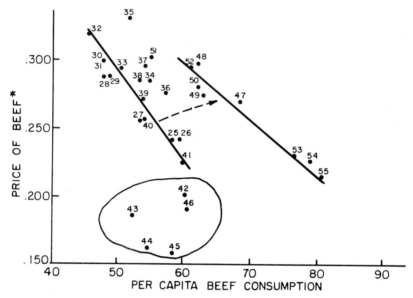

* Price in each case is retail price divided by per capita disposable income.

Fig. 9.4 — Retail price and per capita consumption of beef, 1925–55.

years. The demand for beef appears to have increased with the passage of time.

Figure 9.5 is similar to Figure 9.4, but it shows the situation for pork instead of for beef. This chart for pork shows a movement of the demand curve to the left—that is, a decrease in demand.

Furthermore, study of the two charts together shows that some of the phenomena in one throw additional light on the other. The dot for 1935 in the beef chart, for example, lies some distance above the line for the earlier years, while the dots for 1936, 1937, and 1938 subside back toward it, and the dots for 1939, 1940, and 1941 return all the way down to the line. Study of the pork chart shows that 1935 was the year when supplies of pork were very short, and that they gradually increased back to normal in the later years. The increase in the demand for beef in 1935, lasting with reduced effect through the next few years, apparently was induced by the severe shortage of pork in those years. The increase in the demand for beef after the war, however, cannot be attributed to shortages of pork, for pork supplies then were about average. It can be explained on other grounds.[3]

---

[3] G. S. Shepherd, J. C. Purcell, and L. V. Manderscheid, "Economic Analysis of Trends in Beef Cattle and Hog Prices," Agr. Exp. Sta. Res. Bul. 405, Jan., 1954, p. 736.

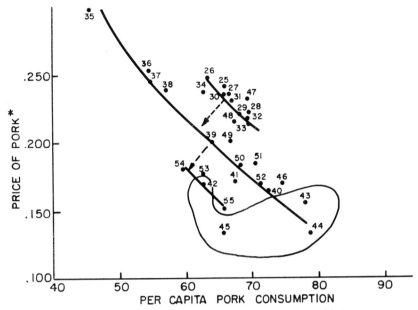

* Price in each case is retail price divided by per capita disposable income.

Fig. 9.5 — Retail price and per capita consumption of pork, 1925–55.

The pork chart similarly shows some effects of changes in the supply of beef. When the charts were first published, they showed the data only up through 1952. Later, the dots for 1953, 1954, and 1955 were added. On the pork chart, they fell on a third line, below and to the left of the other two. A major part of the reason for this decline, however, is shown in the chart for beef. The dots for 1953, 1954, and 1955 all fall far to the right of the others, reflecting the very large consumption of beef in those years, resulting of course from the very heavy production of beef then.

These relationships and inter-relationships are all revealed and shown more clearly in the two charts than they could have been shown by any other method that has come to the author's attention.

APPRAISING THE RESULTS OF GRAPHIC PRICE ANALYSES

The validity of price analyses of this sort should be judged by three criteria, (1) the closeness of fit of the dots about the lines of net regression, and the conformity of the results (2) with economic theory, and (3) with what is already known about the characteristics of the commodity. None of these tests alone is adequate. An analysis that yielded a positively sloping demand curve, no matter how closely the dots lay about it, would at least call for further investigation, if not rejection; so would an analysis that yielded a demand curve with the expected negative slope but a wide scatter of the dots. A careful worker tests his analyses by these three criteria, subconsciously, as he goes along.

Some controversy arose at one time over the question whether the investigator should follow "the procedure of determining in advance to fit a specific type of curve or set of curves," or should "more nearly allow the data to determine the shape of the curves by fitting a set of curves of minimum residuals." Most of this controversy seems unnecessary; no sensible person follows either procedure alone. It is easy to carry the spirit of determining what to do in advance so far as to make it unnecessary to make the analysis at all, if the investigator already knows all he will permit himself to learn from it. On the other hand, Bean exposed himself to later criticism because in his earlier work he let his curves follow his data too closely to conform well with economic theory.

In presenting their results, some workers show a final chart in which the prices estimated from the regression lines are plotted along with the actual prices in an ordinary time chart (with the price scale running up the side and time along the bottom). This shows nothing about the amount of the difference between the estimated and actual prices that is not already shown in the final regression chart. The scatter of the dots about the line in the final regression chart is the same as the "scatter" of the actual prices about the estimates in the time chart.

It is worth while for purposes of further analysis, however, to plot the residuals from the final regression chart against time treated as an additional variable. This will reveal any serial correlations (cycles or waves) in the residuals, and any trends that may exist. It may be that the residuals gradually rise, or fall, with the passage of time, or show some sort of cyclic movement. If so, plotting them against time will reveal it. If the residuals do rise or fall, the investigator may be tempted to use time as an additional independent variable. But that would be a mistake. Time of itself does not cause residuals to rise or fall; some variable associated with time does it, and the variable itself should be isolated and used, not merely time as such. Otherwise the results may be disastrous, since a variable — such as the displacement of horses by tractors — that moves in one direction over a certain period of time may cease to move, or reverse the direction of its motion, in another.

THE ORDER OF PRESENTATION

The results attained will be the same no matter what the order in which the variables are worked through. The results will be attained more quickly if the variables are taken in the order of their importance, for in that case the first approximation lines are most likely to be accurate. But the lines will be the same whatever the order of the variables may be.

For purposes of presentation, however, one order may be better than another. In some cases attention is being focused in the discussion upon the effect of one particular variable, for instance quantity, upon price. In that case it may be advisable for presentation purposes to use that variable last (even if it is the most important) because the average nontechnical reader is more convinced by the close scatter of the dots around the final variable than by the wider scatter around the earlier ones, though there is actually no real difference between them.

INTERCORRELATION AND GROSS AND NET REGRESSION

Whenever there is any correlation between two independent variables[4] — intercorrelation, it is called — the average slopes of the light lines connecting pairs of years in each of which the value of the next variable are equal will be flatter or steeper than the slope of the group of dots as a whole. Where this happens, the demand curve should be drawn in with reference only to the light lines, not to the group of dots as a whole. For the objective is to ascertain, not gross regression (i. e., simple regression, the regression of X on A[5]) but net regression (i. e., partial regression, the regression of X on A independent of its regression on other variables). The group of dots as a whole shows the gross regression of the dependent variable X upon the first independent variable A; but what we are trying to find is the *net* regression of X upon A after the influence of other independent variables has been taken into account.

A more detailed statement of what gross and net regression are may be helpful here. Regression means, roughly, dependence; we may speak of the dependence of X on A, but it is more direct to

---

[4] This sounds like a contradiction in terms, for one might think that if two variables were correlated, they could not be independent. But that would be a mistake. Two variables may be completely independent, completely free of any causal relationship to each other, and yet show some degree of correlation, either because they are both influenced by a third variable, or merely by chance.

[5] Where X = the dependent variable, and A, B, etc., = the independent variables.

speak of the influence[6] of A upon X. When statisticians speak of
the regression of X upon A, they mean, in everyday language, the
influence of A upon X. Now the gross influence of A upon X is
actually the gross influence of a rather extended phrase, namely
"A and everything else correlated with A by chance or otherwise."
And this phrase is not merely a qualification seldom required; it is
the rule, rather than the exception. In our economic world, so char-
acterized by interdependence, it is only rarely that A is not correlated with other variables that have an influence upon X.

It is indeed impossible, practically speaking, to show *the* net
influence of A upon X. What we speak of as the net influence of
A upon X, with the net influence of B taken into account, is actually
the net influence of "A and everything else correlated with A by
chance or otherwise, *except* B." What we speak of as the net influence of A upon X, with the influence of B and C taken into account,
is actually the net influence of "A and everything else correlated
with A by chance or otherwise, except B and C." And so on for
additional variables.

In a world full of complex interrelationships, therefore, successive
net regressions, as more and more independent variables are taken
into account, should be expected to be different, not only from the
gross regression, but from each other. They may even be different
in sign. One almost hesitates to use concrete illustrations, for so
many other intercorrelations are involved than the one selected for
the illustration. But consider the net influence of hog prices upon
corn prices, before the influence of hog numbers has been taken into
account (and assuming that there are no changes in the general price
level to complicate the picture). Hog prices are negatively correlated with hog numbers. If the net influence of hog numbers is
greater than the net influence of hog prices, then the net influence
of hog prices alone before hog numbers are taken into account would
be more than offset by the effect of hog numbers, and would appear
actually negative. But the addition of hog numbers as an additional
variable would change the influence of hog prices (change the slope
of the hog price regression curve) to its proper sign, positive.

This means that absolute net relationships are unattainable,
because we can only ascertain absolute net influence if we take all
other influences into account—literally hundreds of them. And this

---

[6] The word influence is more accurate than the word effect. An influence
may be more or less offset by another influence; this is frequently the case in
economics. An influence is exerted, but not necessarily registered, whereas an
effect is not an effect until it is registered, i.e. effected.

is a practical impossibility. But from a practical point of view, absolute net influences can be closely approximated. Economic reasoning and published studies in the field of agricultural economics both indicate that serviceably accurate results can be attained in most cases by the use of a relatively small number of variables. Practically all of the published studies use only two or three independent variables. While interdependence is ubiquitous, its quantitative importance diminishes rapidly after the most influential variables have been taken into account; and these most influential variables are usually few in number.

Some of the problems of intercorrelation are not as baffling as they appear at first sight. A concrete case will illustrate this. An analysis of the United States average farm price of corn shows that the elasticity of the demand for corn is about —0.6. The bulk of this corn is No. 3 Yellow. But if the price of No. 2 Yellow corn were used as an additional independent variable, the elasticity of the demand for No. 3 corn would become almost infinitely great; that is, the regression of No. 3 Yellow corn prices on corn production would be practically a horizontal straight line. This results from the fact that the price of No. 2 Yellow corn is so highly intercorrelated with the dependent factor that there is not much left over for the other independent variables to explain.

What does this result mean? What is the real or true elasticity of demand for No. 3 Yellow corn—is it —0.6, or is it practically infinity?

The answer is, both. In both cases, the coefficient of elasticity shows what happens to prices when production changes, "the other independent variables being held constant," as it is often expressed, or more accurately, "independent of the accompanying variation of the other variables." If the price of No. 2 Yellow corn were in actual fact "held constant," it is clear that changes in corn production would have very little effect on the price of No. 3 Yellow corn. Or to use the more accurate phrase above, there is very little fluctuation in the price of No. 3 Yellow corn independent of the fluctuation in the price of No. 2. When the price of No. 2 corn is included as one of the variables, the regression of the price of No. 3 corn should be practically zero, as in fact it is. This is merely an extreme illustration of the fact that the addition of another independent variable changes the so-called "net" regression of the dependent on the independent variables whenever (as usually happens) the additional variable is correlated with any of the other independent variables.

CORRELATION AND CAUSATION

One must clearly keep in mind the difference between correlation and causation. Two series may be highly correlated, and this correlation may be used (wrongly) to demonstrate that the one is the cause of the other. But actually the causation may run the other way; or there may be no causal relationship between the two whatever.

About all that can be deduced from a correlation coefficient is that the higher the coefficient the more likely it is that the relationship between the two variables is not due to chance, but is due to some definite relationship, such as cause and effect, between them. For data that are random in character, the standard statistical tests of significance put this statement in precise numerical form.[7] Since most economic time series are not random, however, these tests of significance have only a restricted validity in economics. This matter is discussed at some length in Chapter 13.

As to the nature of the relation between two variables, a correlation coefficient gives no answer. The relation may be one of cause and effect, as in the case of corn production and corn prices (though the correlation shows nothing as to which is cause and which is effect). Or both variables may respond to a third causal factor, as when the prices of two unrelated agricultural products are both affected by industrial prosperity or depression. Or the relationship may result entirely from chance.

ADVANTAGES AND LIMITATIONS

The graphic method has several advantages over the standard method of mathematical correlation analysis, and several limitations. The advantages will be considered first.

1. The graphic method enables the investigator to see just what he is doing. With the mathematical method, he merely feeds the data into the machine and comes out with some numerical coefficients. He does not know without additional testing whether his multiple correlation coefficient, for example, is 0.8 rather than some higher figure because the relationships are curvilinear, because one or two exceptional years were far out of line, or because additional variables are needed. But with the graphic method, he can see just what the curvilinearity is, just how many and which years are exceptional, and whether additional variables are needed, or not. These are ponderable advantages.

[7] See, for example, George W. Snedecor, *Statistical Methods*, Iowa State Univ. Press, 5th ed., 1956, Table 7.6.1, p. 174.

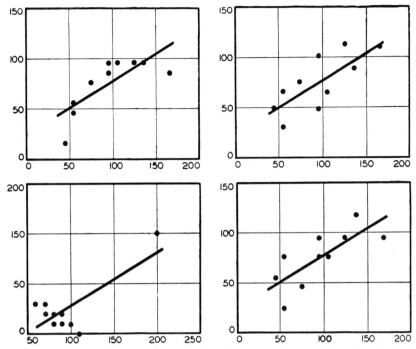

Fig. 9.6 — Linear regression lines fitted to four pairs of variables. Hypothetical data provided by Elmer Working.

These advantages have been arithmetically demonstrated by Elmer Working.[8] He set up four different pairs of variables and plotted each pair in a scatter diagram to show the relation between each pair of items. The four scatter diagrams are shown in Figure 9.6. Two of the relationships shown are curvilinear, one is linear, and one is based upon a very abnormal distribution. Yet the mathematical coefficients—standard deviations and correlation coefficients —are practically identical. This example illustrates how graphic methods would protect the investigator from errors he might not otherwise have discovered (although the fact that the correlations in this example are "significant" but just barely "highly significant" should put him on his guard).

2. In the second place, the graphic method usually saves a good deal of time and energy. In many cases where problems of the same number of observations and variables were treated by both methods, the graphic method proved just as accurate but consumed from one-

---

[8] E. J. Working, "Graphic Methods in Price Analysis," *Journal of Farm Economics,* Vol. 21, No. 1.

fourth to one-third of the time. The greatest saving comes in connection with rather short series, say from 15 to 20 items, such as are common in economic price analysis. The work calls for no more training — in fact, probably for less training — on the part of the worker than is required for the formal mathematical method, and it requires no more complicated computing machinery than a pencil and ruler. In a large research department with plenty of mechanical computing equipment, this consideration is not very important; but in other cases it is.

The saving of time is greatest where the regressions are curvilinear. With the graphic method, it is just as easy to put in a curve freehand as a straight line. But with the mathematical method, the process is complex and laborious. First, the investigator must run the regular straight-line multiple correlation computation. Next, he must test each regression mathematically for curvilinearity. If it exists, he has then to select the mathematical curve most nearly appropriate to the data, add one or more extra terms to his equation, and run the multiple correlation computation again. Finally, he comes out with the coefficients expressing the relationships numerically.

3. Economic data do not usually follow any mathematical formula. They do not arrange themselves, like snowflakes, in geometrical patterns. There is no reason, for example, that the demand curve for wheat should be a straight line, a parabola, a hyperbola, or any other mathematical curve. It is determined by the physiological reactions of consumers, the distribution of income, the effect of different volumes on the intervening charges between producer and consumer, and so forth. The total effect of these things is unlikely to follow any simple mathematical formula.

Accordingly, mathematical curves cannot be expected to fit economic data very accurately. The final result is merely a compromise between the characteristics of the curve chosen by the investigator, and the characteristics of the data. The investigator has to use his judgment in selecting the type of curve to fit, and his choice of curve determines in considerable part the results he gets. The mathematical method, therefore, is not purely objective; it has a large element of subjectivity in it. The results obtained depend to a considerable extent upon the mathematical curve selected.

The graphic method is similarly subjective. The curves are drawn in freehand, and some judgment is required, as for example in deciding how much weight to give one or two extreme items. No two investigators will draw two curves in exactly alike, any more than they will agree on the exact length of a bar they may measure. So exact tests of significance, standard errors, correlation coefficients, betas, etc., cannot be computed. This appears to be a fairly important weakness. Yet tests of significance are so inapplicable to economic time series that it is doubtful whether the weakness is as great as it seems.

With mathematical methods, if two different investigators choose the same mathematical curves, their results will agree out to as many decimal places as they may wish. When the differences resulting from choosing different mathematical curves may run into whole numbers, however, the identicality of results out to several decimal places is more misleading than confirmatory. For mathematical straight lines or curves are unlikely to fit the data any more exactly than two graphic workers fit their data freehand. And the inexactitude of the freehand line is at least clearly shown in the charts, while that of the mathematical method is covered up by figures running with a great profession of accuracy out to several decimal places.

To summarize, then: Practically all of the real issues involved in the use of either method—representativeness of sample, serial correlation, intercorrelation, multiplicative relationship, etc.—are common to both. Any careful user of the mathematical method would use scatter diagrams (i. e., make an informal use of graphic methods) in deciding whether to use straight lines or curves in his formulae; for him, the graphic method is a useful exploratory tool. Conversely, any graphic worker who wished to take the time could well go ahead after he had completed his graphic analysis and express his results in mathematical form. The differences of opinion as to the merits of the two methods then reduce merely to differences in the emphasis to be given to each. The mathematical statistician regards the graphic method as an exploratory tool, useful in preparing the way for mathematical analysis; the economic statistician, on the other hand, is inclined to regard the graphic analysis as the main job, and publish the mathematical coefficients in a footnote.[9]

This difference in emphasis is nothing to provoke serious controversy. It results primarily from the differences in the kind of data with which mathematicians and economists generally work. The graphic method is most useful in problems: (1) Where the number

---

[9] Practical applications of the combined use of the graphic and mathematical methods along with other analytical procedures and concepts developed earlier in this book, are made in two bulletins, "Changes in the Demand for Meat and Dairy Products in the United States Since 1910," Iowa Agr. Exp. Sta. Res. Bul. 368, Nov., 1949, by the present author, and "Economic Analysis of Trends in Beef Cattle and Hog Prices," Iowa Agr. Exp. Sta. Res. Bul. 405, Jan., 1954, by the present author *et al.*

of items is small, not over twenty or thirty for example; with longer series, the labor of plotting may be as great as the labor of computing the coefficients mathematically. (2) Where the number of variables is small, say three or four; with a larger number, the process of working back and forth becomes complicated. (3) Where the correlation is rather high; this reduces the judgment required in drawing in the curves. These conditions are frequently met in economic problems, and this is probably the reason why the graphic method has been used so widely by agricultural economists.

The simultaneous equation method. A more fundamental question is whether to use the elaborate simultaneous equation method of analysis developed chiefly by the Cowles Commission of Yale University,[10] instead of the single equation method described above.

This question is discussed in the next chapter.

---

[10] *Statistical Inference in Dynamic Economic Models,* Tjalling C. Koopmans, editor, by Cowles Commission Research Staff Members and Guests, Wiley, New York, 1950.

10

Simultaneous Equation Techniques[1]

The preceding chapter dealt with multiple correlation analysis.
The results of this kind of analysis can be expressed in graphic form
in a series of charts, one for each independent variable, showing the
net influence of each variable on the dependent variable. Or they
can be shown in the form of a mathematical equation, with the dependent variable represented by a term on the left side of the equality sign, and a constant on the right hand side, followed by a series
of terms, one for each independent variable, showing the net influence of each variable on the dependent variable in numerical form.

As we have seen, agricultural price patterns evolve through
mutual adjustment among a profusion of conditions and economic
impulses. Any single relationship or equation is just one strand
drawn from the whole tissue of economic interaction. When other
closely related processes are assumed to be fixed and frozen, the one
hypothetical relation under study may seriously misrepresent the
joint processes of which it is only one part. This is, unfortunately,
true even if the relationship taken by itself is sensible and verifiable,
and even though the single equation contains many variables.
Furthermore, if there occurs some basic "structural" change in these
closely related processes, the estimates based on past observations
may be grossly in error when applied to the new, changed situation.[2]

---

[1] This chapter owes a great deal to K. A. Fox, *Econometric Analysis and
Public Policy*, Iowa State Univ. Press, 1958, especially Chaps. 1, 2, 3, and 7;
and to M. Ezekial and K. A. Fox, *Methods of Correlation and Regression Analysis*, Wiley, 1959, Chap. 24, which gives a useful summary.

[2] The classic statement of this last point is in J. Marschak, "Economic Measurement for Policy and Prediction," Chap. 1, pp. 1–26 in *Studies in Econometric Method,* W. C. Hood and T. C. Koopmans, editors, Wiley, 1953.

That is to say, the methods worked out in the previous chapters make it possible to estimate relationships between one dependent variable and one or more independent variables. If, however, there are two or more jointly dependent variables to be explained by other independent variables, this "jointness" or simultaneity in the world may need to be expressed by several simultaneous equations, each of which expresses one of the interrelated processes.

This single equation method is appropriate where the line of causation is clear, and one variable (the dependent variable) is unilaterally determined by the others (the independent variables). This condition is met in many agricultural price analyses—for example, in the simple analysis of the effects of corn production and disposable income on the price of corn from December to May. It is clear here that the price of corn is determined by the size of the corn crop harvested in the preceding November, not vice versa; and it is also clear that the price of corn is determined by disposable income, not vice versa. It is obvious which of the variables is dependent and which ones are independent. The single equation approach is appropriate here, although the results of the study need interpretation if changes in demand and supply are correlated, as shown in the preceding chapter.

WHY SIMULTANEOUS EQUATIONS MAY BE NEEDED

In many cases, the line of causation is not unilateral; it does not go only one way. For example, the price considered may be the price of eggs during the production season. In that case, the price may affect the production, as well as the production affect the price. If the production is affected by the price, but not vice versa, a scatter diagram would yield a supply curve. If the price is affected by the production, but not vice versa, this would yield a demand curve. But if the two variables are jointly determined — if the production is affected by the price, and the price is also affected by the production — a scatter diagram yields neither a supply curve nor a demand curve, but a mixture of both.

It is, in fact, impossible to get a demand curve and a supply curve out of a single equation. When two or more variables are jointly determined, it is impossible to get even one curve—supply curve or demand curve — out of a single equation. It is possible, however, to get both curves out of two equations solved simultaneously.

We can see what is involved here if we begin with elementary

SECTION A

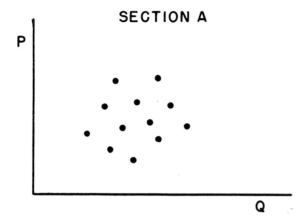

SECTION B

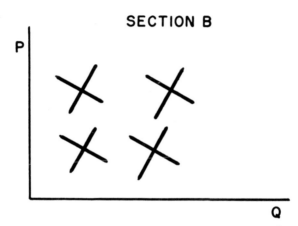

Fig. 10.1 — Hypothetical price and production data plotted in scatter diagrams. Demand and supply both unstable.

concepts and proceed to show when and why simultaneous equation techniques are needed.[3]

Figures 10.1, 10.2, and 10.3 bring together in summary form the elementary concepts developed in the preceding chapter. The raw price and production data for a typical farm product, plotted in a scatter diagram, may look something like Section A of Figure 10.1.

[3] The rest of this section draws on parts of a paper by R. J. Foote, "A Comparison of Single and Simultaneous Equation Techniques," *Journal of Farm Economics*, Vol. 37, No. 5, Dec., 1955, p. 975.

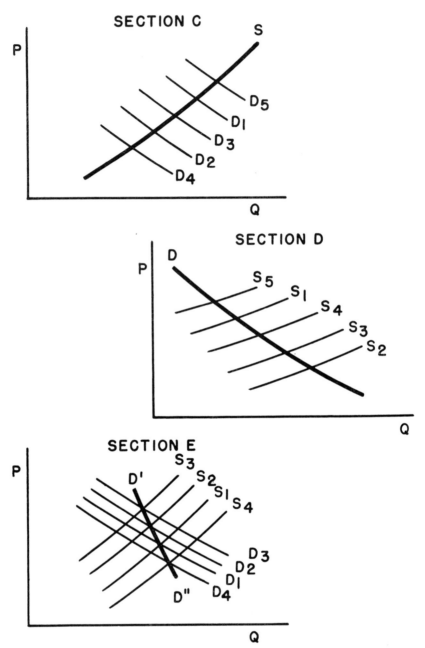

Fig. 10.2 — Hypothetical price and production data plotted in scatter diagrams. Section **C** shows unstable demand and stable supply. Section **D** shows stable demand and unstable supply. Section **E** shows unstable demand and supply, negatively correlated.

Each dot may be thought of as the intersection of a demand and a supply curve, as in Section B; but the elasticities of the curves shown are purely hypothetical, for without further information, neither curve can be determined from the data.

The demand may be unstable, so that the demand curve shifts back and forth over a wide range, while the supply curve remains relatively stable. This is shown in Section C of Figure 10.2. In that case, if the movements of the supply and demand curves are un-correlated, the dots trace out a supply curve. Conversely, if the

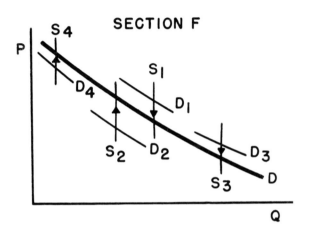

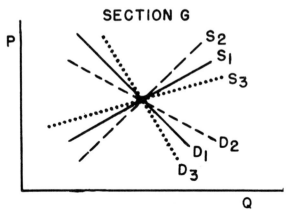

Fig. 10.3 — Hypothetical price and production data plotted in scatter diagrams. Section **F** shows demand and supply both unstable, but demand adjusted to remove instability, and supply completely inelastic. Section **G** shows an intersection point of a demand curve and a supply curve when their elasticities are both unknown.

supply curve is unstable but the demand curve is relatively stable, as in Section D of Figure 10.2, the dots trace out a demand curve.

If the movements of the supply and demand curves are correlated, as in Section E, Figure 10.2, the dots trace out what may look like a demand or supply curve, but the slope will be too flat or too steep.

In many analyses of the demand for agricultural products, the factors that cause the demand curve to shift over time are included as separate variables in a multiple regression equation. In effect, we are then able to derive from our estimating equation an average demand curve. This is indicated in a rough way in Figure 10.3, Section F. In some analyses, we can assume that the quantity supplied is essentially unaffected by current price; in agriculture, a time lag is usually needed before price can affect production. When price is plotted on the vertical scale, the supply curve in such cases is a vertical line, and year-to-year shifts in the supply curve trace out a demand curve, just as they did in Section D of Figure 10.2. Under these circumstances, we may be able to obtain valid estimates of the elasticity of demand by use of a least squares multiple regression analysis for which price is the dependent variable, and supply and some demand shifters are used as independent variables.

For many agricultural products, this set of circumstances permits us to estimate elasticities of demand with respect to price by use of single equation methods. Two points, however, should be kept in mind: (1) price must be used as the dependent variable in order to obtain elasticity estimates that are statistically consistent, since, to use the least squares technique, the supply curve must be a vertical line; and (2) an algebraic transformation must be made after the equation has been fitted to derive the appropriate coefficient of elasticity, since the definition of elasticity is in terms of the percentage change in quantity associated with a given percentage change in price, not the other way around as shown in Section F of Figure 10.3.

What happens if we have a supply curve that is not a vertical line? If we consider any single point, as in Figure 10.3, Section G, we have no way of knowing on which demand and supply curve of a whole family of curves it lies. The basic problem of indeterminateness is similar to that in which correlated shifts in the demand and supply curves take place. What is needed is some hypothesis, adequately tested and proven to be sound, as to the nature of the joint relationships between supply and demand. We should then be able to untangle the two and to obtain a reliable estimate of the slope of each curve. This is essentially what is done by the simultaneous equations approach.

"Simultaneous" refers to the method of algebraically solving or transforming the equations into other equations which can be fitted to the data. It does *not* mean that each equation need not reflect a definite causal relationship; on the contrary, each equation must be "identified," and this usually requires that causal relations be *more* explicitly and boldly stated in simultaneous equations than in multiple regression equations.

Suppose, for example, that X's are dependent variables and Y's are independent variables. The former (single equation) situation may be shown by:

$$X_1 = f\ (Y_1, Y_2, \ldots Y_n \tag{1}$$

and the resulting regression equation might be:

$$X_1 = a + bY_1 + cY_2 + zY_n + u \ldots \tag{2}$$

The latter (simultaneous) situation is shown by:

$$(X_1, X_2 \ldots \ldots X_m) = f\ (Y_1, Y_2, \ldots \ldots Y_n). \tag{3}$$

The resulting simultaneous regression equations might then appear as:

$$X_1 = a + bX_2 + cY_1 + u \tag{4}$$
$$X_2 = a' + b'\ Y_1 + c'\ Y_2 + u'$$
$$X_m = \delta + \beta Y_n + u^2.$$

The most familiar case of this involves price and quantity as the joint outcome of a supply and demand equilibrium. A separate equation stands for each curve, and in equilibrium the P and X values are identical for both equations; this corresponds to solving the equations simultaneously for the values of P and X.

In some respects this method can best be seen as an extension of the methods of the previous chapter, although it does involve some additional algebraic skills and some new terms. More basically, it stresses the need to set forth clear, logical, and theoretically sound relationships to be tested. This is in contrast to the ever-present temptation with multiple correlation to shop around for variables to explain the dependent one, no matter what the result may mean in theoretical terms. Certain disadvantages may accompany this technique, both in computing effort and in possible error, and its usefulness will depend on the nature of the particular case.

There is no distinct consensus yet on (1) exactly which problems need to be formulated in terms of simultaneous equations, or (2) which of several methods of fitting the equations, once they are formulated, should be used. Since each research project has its own aims and requirements, no general verdict would be sensible. Instead the best choice or combination of techniques needs to be worked out for each case. Before summarizing current discussions on these questions, the general method with a simple supply and demand example will be illustrated.

An Illustration

Suppose that we wish to estimate both a supply and a demand curve for a particular commodity using data on its past prices and quantities. These data look like Figure 10.1 when made into a scatter diagram.

Apparently each point shows the equilibrium of supply and demand for one period, and both curves have been shifting randomly, in response to other influences, in about the same degree. If only one curve had been shifting, the other could easily be estimated, but this has not happened. Suppose that shifts in each curve have been independent of shifts in the other.

At each of these equilibrium points, price and quantity are mutually determined; there is no single direction of cause and effect between them which can be logically *identified*, one way or the other. Since P and X are, in fact, jointly dependent variables, which can be jointly "explained" by other variables, a model using simultaneous equations may be best for estimating either the supply or the demand curve, or both together.

A logical form for the supply and demand curves might be:

$$\text{Demand curve:} \quad X = a_1 + b_1P + u \qquad (5)$$

$$\text{Supply curve:} \quad X = a_2 + b_2P + u \qquad (6)$$

That is, the amount demanded depends on the price, in a way described by a straight line (on numerical or log graph paper) which cuts the quantity axis at some level of $X = a_1$ and which has a slope of b_1 (which may be negative). This line (or curve) shifts in the short run about its long-run position in response to numerous random (or "stochastic") disturbances, which are lumped into the term u. Whatever factors u reflects, they are not correlated with levels or changes of P.

The supply equation has an exactly similar meaning, though its slope (b_2) will presumably be positive. These are "structural equations," relating price and quantity in ways which are sensible and defensible in theory. The coefficients a_1 and a_2 and b_1 and b_2

are called *structural parameters;* it is the values of these which we wish to estimate. A single equation, multiple regression approach does not give us estimates of these structural parameters, but it requires less rigid and less hazardous assertions about cause-and-effect than do simultaneous equations.

Though equations (5) and (6) may be logically correct, one can see intuitively that they cannot be fitted to the roundish scatter of $P : X$ dots in a scatter diagram to give a good estimate of either b_1 or b_2 separately. We cannot *identify* whether the supply curve alone determines price and quantity, or if the demand curve does so. To put it in statistical terms, we cannot fit either equation using available data to give unique estimates of the structural parameters b_1 or b_2.[4] But, if two changes are made in the equations, it may be possible to estimate both equations together.

First add to each equation a "predetermined" variable. These correspond to "independent variables" in multiple regression. Such a variable may be either truly exogenous to (or "outside") the model; that is, it may represent any physical, social, or economic factor which unilaterally influences demand or supply, but is not in turn influenced by them — weather, for example, or GNP. Or it may be simply the level of one of the already-present variables (in this case P or X) at an earlier period; that is, a "lagged endogenous variable" such as P_{t-1}, X_{t-2}, etc. A logical choice for the demand equation might be consumer income; although for a corn demand equation, one might use number of beef cattle. For the supply equation some earlier supply measure, such as previous plantings or number of hogs six months previously (i.e., lagged by six months), might be chosen. If such lagged endogenous variables are used, one must be sure that they influence P and X but not the other way around. To be precise, they must be *recursive.*

In selecting the predetermined variables (exogenous or lagged endogenous), we are drawing, out of the grab-bag random u and v terms, the most likely explanatory variables. Just as we add, one

---

[4] If for example price at time one determines quantity at time two, this unilateral causation satisfies identification requirements, and

$$X_2 = a + bP_1 + u$$

can be uniquely estimated for b. This one-way causal relationship between time periods, with no reverse influence from period two on period one, is called a *recursive* relationship. Recursiveness may be required in structural equations as well as in single equation methods; for example, factor Z in equation (8) will probably be recursively related to both X and P. On recursiveness see H. Wold and L. Jureen, *Demand Analysis,* Wiley, 1953, especially pp. 48–71, 202–04. On identification, see T. C. Koopmans, "Identification Problems in Economic Model Construction," Chap. 2 in Hood and Koopmans, *op. cit.;* and Fox, *op. cit.,* pp. 26–29.

by one, only the most reasonable independent variables to multiple regression equations, in this instance too we will select only the most logical variables. Suppose that an income variable Y is chosen for the demand equation and that some factor Z based on weather, or previous plantings, or previous prices, is added to the supply equation. The result of this first step is the two structural equations:

Demand equation: $X = a_1 + b_1P + c_1Y + u'$ (7)

Supply equation: $X = a_2 + b_2P + c_2Z + v'$ (8)

Since the stochastic terms u and v no longer include Y and Z, they are given as u' and v'. The equations are in fact logical hypotheses about demand and supply.

The *second* step uses algebra to transform or solve these equations for P and X, taking P and X as dependent upon the predetermined variables Y and Z and on the shift factors or disturbances u' and v'. This gives the following two equations which are called *reduced-form* equations: [5]

$$P = A_1 + B_1Y + C_1Z + d_1 \qquad (9)$$

$$X = A_2 + B_2Y + C_2Z + d_2. \qquad (10)$$

These equations differ in form from the structural equations, and they sometimes have no inherent logical significance of their own as they stand. But, like the structural equations, they have parameters or coefficients (A, B, C) and these reduced-form parameters can be transformed back algebraically to derive the structural parameters. For instance, in this example d_1 and d_2 include the disturbances u' and v' and the structural parameters b_1 and b_2. And

$$b_1 = C_2/C_1; \quad b_2 = B_2/B_1; \quad C_1 = B_1 [- (b_1 - b_2)];$$
$$C_2 = C_1 (b_1 - b_2).$$

---

[5] Note that the system of structural equations is *complete,* as well as that each separate equation is *identified.* This is because the number of endogenous variables equals the number of equations. This allows us to solve to get these two reduced-form equations in which each endogenous variable is expressed as a function of (i.e., is dependent on) all the predetermined variables in the system. If the system were incomplete — with more endogenous variables than equations — such reduced-form equations could not be derived for each endogenous variable. If, on the other hand, the system of equations included more equations than endogenous variables (this is usually called an overidentified system), the system could not be uniquely estimated. More than one version of some of the reduced forms would be possible, leading to indeterminacy of the estimates of both the reduced forms and the structural parameters. This is the case with equations (5) and (6) above.

Both completeness of the system and identifiability of each single equation are necessary conditions for solving for reduced forms and estimating the structural parameters. For more detailed discussion on this point see Fox, *op. cit.,* Chap. 1. Solution of simultaneous equations above follows customary algebraic methods. A step-by-step solution of these two equations can be found in Ezekial and Fox, *op. cit.,* Chap. 24.

And so on. If we can estimate statistically the reduced-form parameters, then we can work out estimates of the structural parameters, including a_1, a_2, b_1 and b_2. These parameters define the demand and supply curves themselves.

It is possible to fit the reduced-form equations statistically, since each has one "dependent" variable, plus "independent" variables, in the manner of familiar least-squares regression equations. The further statistical requirement that d_1 and d_2, the random residuals of the regression, be independent of Y and Z is also met. If there is any doubt of this, it can be checked after the estimation is done by seeing if the residuals seem to have any systematic pattern. Each equation may now be fitted by itself, using the methods in the previous chapter; that is, by either graphic or, more usually, least-squares estimation, or possibly using the maximum-likelihood methods discussed later in this chapter. Note, however, that a single value estimate of each parameter (A, B, and C) is required, so straight lines only can be fitted; though, of course, logs could be used to provide for some curvilinearity.

If the resulting correlation for each reduced-form equation is satisfactory (in terms of R^2 standard error, and confidence levels; or by a visual check of the scatter) then the algebraic transformation of the reduced-form parameters to the structural parameters will be worth doing. Since this transformation is mathematically precise, it faithfully transmits back into the structural estimates both the accuracy and the errors present in the reduced-form estimates. Similarly the degree of goodness of fit for the structural parameters (in terms of standard errors) can be derived, and the residuals of the structural equations can be analysed for auto-correlation, using ratios of derived values of u^1 and v^1.

Whatever their significance as theoretical propositions, the reduced-form equations may be extremely useful for making predictions or determining policy. This is because they imply a "cause and effect" relation and, when properly fitted, enable one to estimate the degree of change in the dependent variable associated with changes in the independent variables. Since the latter are by definition preknown or preset (possibly under direct policy control) this knowledge may have great practical use.

In partial contrast, structural equations often have a more scholarly role, estimation of their parameters being more generally devoted to hypothesis testing and measuring. Reduced-form estimation might be used in predicting output or prices in the future, and in "predicting" the effects on output or price (in the future or in the past) of given policy changes. To estimate demand or supply elasticities, structural equations are necessary.

This distinction between reduced-form and structural equations is blurred because structural parameters are often crucial for policy, and are, in any event, implicit in the reduced-form parameters. Moreover, the usefulness of the reduced-form parameters for prediction purposes depends on the constancy of the structural parameters which are implied in them. If there are structural changes in the relationships involved — in this case if the demand or supply curves permanently shift (involving a change in an a or a b, or both) — it is clear that the prediction coefficients must be revised. So an understanding of the past and likely future behavior of the structural parameters should underlie any use of the reduced-form equations for prediction.

CHOOSING EQUATIONS AND METHODS

Even after nearly two decades our knowledge about the relative merits of multiple correlation and structural equation techniques, and of alternative methods of estimating them, is at present still in the formative stage. Although certain types of problems have been explored, some of them at great length, there is general agreement that much more testing is needed, and that no general choice between them is either possible or desirable.

The initial elegance and mystique of the simultaneous equations approach has been somewhat dimmed in the face of evidence on several points that it does not solve all problems, nor does it always do the best job even on those for which it is best suited. Despite this, interest in this approach has encouraged a substantial advance in sophistication and care in framing hypotheses and stating questions, and more recently additional practical arguments favoring simultaneous systems have been advanced. Nonetheless, the single equation multiple regression method has turned out to be difficult to defeat, and it may continue to be satisfactory or at least useful for many, if not most, research projects in agricultural price analyses.

Single or Simultaneous Equations?

Karl Fox has concluded on the basis of a number of empirical demand studies that many agricultural situations lend themselves to single equations least-squares estimations as well as or better than to formulation into two or more simultaneous structural equations.[6] For these situations a "uni-equational complete model" gives satisfactory estimates and is economical of computing effort.

Fox cites the recursiveness of many production and marketing processes as one explanation for the fact that in many previous studies both methods have given virtually identical estimates of structural parameters. In these cases, which have included both just-identified and over-identified systems, no departure from the simpler single equation least-squares method seems to be called for. Fox also concluded that structural changes in demand for agricultural products have been more gradual since prewar years than some analysts have thought. Therefore, the need to recognize explicitly the possible changes in these parameters would have been less than has been argued by some.

Fox and others conclude that generally the importance of the bias of least-squares methods, which may stem from their neglect of simultaneity in real world processes, will be less than has been feared. This is partly because simultaneity may not in fact be so prevalent; partly because other problems such as auto-correlation and limited dependent variables may also deserve care; and partly because other feasible methods may not on balance be much superior to the single-equation multiple-regression method.

Methods of Estimation: Least-squares or What?

On a more technical level, there has been extended discussion and some testing of alternative statistical methods of estimating reduced-form and structural parameters, once they have been decided upon; on this there is "no verdict yet."[7] Several alternatives to ordinary least-squares are current, all of them involving simultaneity; namely, "two-stage least-squares;" "limited-information maximum-likelihood;" and "full-information maximum-likelihood" methods. These methods, some aspects of which are still being developed, differ in complexity and ease of use, and an explanation of them would go well beyond this discussion.

There are three ways to evaluate which methods are best for given situations: mathematical theorems, real world studies, and controlled artificial experiments. The first has not been fruitful because it can deal only with infinite samples, and it is precisely for small samples (from say 20 to 60) that comparisons are needed. Real world studies have tended to show similarity among the re-

---

[6] See Fox, *op. cit.*, Part I, pp. 1–150.
[7] "A Symposium on Simultaneous Equations Estimation," *Econometrica*, Vol. 28, No. 4, Oct., 1960, pp. 835–71.

sults given by different methods, with somewhat better results from least-squares than had earlier been expected.

Controlled experiments (so-called Monte Carlo tests) whereby true values are derived for an artificial model programmed in a computer, and then several small-sample estimates are made using alternative techniques, has tended to strengthen confidence in the simultaneous methods, especially for over-identified systems. However, most of the testing models used so far are not of the sort relevant to agricultural price analysis.

Klein has argued recently that even though the alternative statistical methods may give nearly identical estimates of *structural* parameters, these slight differences may be seriously magnified in the transformation to *reduced-form* parameters.[8] For example a .06 difference in estimating the marginal propensity to consume may become a .68 difference in the income multiplier which is related to it. So even if least-squares estimates of structural parameters are only slightly biased from the true values, an estimation or prediction using the reduced-form equations may contain substantial error.

The degree of this magnification depends wholly on the nature of the structural and reduced-form systems; bias may be enhanced, left unchanged, or even diminished by the transformation. In agricultural price analysis instances of increased error in the reduced-forms parameters may be unlikely. Also, if estimation of structural parameters is the main object of the study, then the problem of magnified reduced-form error naturally fades.

The present situation for equations and statistical methods may be summed up briefly, in somewhat more rigorous terms. Single equation least-squares is, in general, likely to give biased estimates, because it ignores possible simultaneity. On the other hand, for small sample estimation it is generally most suitable, since the other methods are known to be unbiased only asymptotically; that is, for very large samples. Simultaneity may also be a mixed blessing, for if some structural equations are incorrectly specified, or if their variables are correct by displaying great variance, simultaneous methods may spread error into estimates for the other equations.

This suggests first that it may not be possible with structural equations simply to set them up on *a priori* grounds and then run the test; some shopping around and exchanging of variables and equation forms may be necessary to get "correct" structural equa-

[8] L. R. Klein, "The Efficiency of Estimation in Econometric Models," Cowles Foundation Paper No. 157; also in *Essays in Economics and Econometrics,* Chapel Hill, 1960, pp. 216–32.

tions. Second, as for statistical techniques, using least-squares is the best safeguard against using an "incorrect" model, but if you are sure of the model, then such methods as limited-information maximum-likelihood may be be somewhat better. The latter will usually have somewhat larger variance; that is, their estimates will be more accurate (centered on the "true" value) but less reliable (more widely spread). If the predetermined variables are correlated among themselves ("multicollinearity") or are auto-correlated (i.e. a variable with regular waves may correlate highly and spuriously with itself), the least-squares results will be liable to error, but less so generally than the other methods. In such situations other precautions will be needed in any case.

For under-identified structural systems, none of the methods satisfactorily estimates the structural parameters, although the reduced forms may be handled best by least-squares. For just-identified systems the methods will be about equally good, both for structural equations and reduced forms, since they are all basically equivalent. For over-identified systems, simultaneous methods are superior though lengthy for estimating structural parameters; from them the reduced forms can be derived without the risk of magnified error which Klein warns against. The advantage of working only with just-identified systems is evident; in this way one in effect fore-stalls the question of methods. Klein also rightly notes that greater access to electronic computers sharply reduces the advantages of single equation least-squares in the way of computational ease.

CRITERIA FOR CHOICE

The decision to use structural equations and the writing of the model, if the decision to use one has been made, depends on an intimate understanding of the real-world processes to be estimated and the variables which may be used. It is important that the equations adopted reflect reasonable, appropriate, and useful hypotheses about the world, as well as that they satisfy certain technical requirements of identifiability, consistency, and ease of fitting.

In addition to these theoretical and statistical standards, the analyst will often need to make special allowance for the eventual uses of the results, for policy and other purposes. This bears on the choice of statistical techniques for fitting simultaneous equations as discussed above. In some cases bias in the estimates would be especially harmful; in other cases possible bias may matter little compared to other possible weaknesses, such as variance. In general, structural equations techniques, like any other approach, may need careful adjustment to the needs and dangers of the particular case.

Several steps or rules are customary in posing and estimating a structural system, such as a supply-demand estimation:

1. All the variables which may be relevant are listed. These may include such "economic" variables as prices, quantity, incomes, costs, acreage and other inputs, imports, and the like; and such others as perhaps rainfall and temperature. The scope of the variables may vary (i.e. state, regional, national, or by sectors); they may include composite index variables or first differences; and lags of various durations may be specified. All of the variables must then be classified as either (a) endogenous or (b) predetermined (exogeneous or lagged endogeneous).

2. The structural equations (i.e. a "model") are worked out, each one representing as accurately as possible some theoretical or factual relationship. Equations may represent (a) hypothesized economic behavior (including most theoretical relationships); (b) institutional rules; (c) technological laws of transformation (such as production functions); or (d) definitions (in the form of identities).

3. Logical and defensible analysis must govern both the classification of variables and the writing of structural equations. Variables should not be reclassified, or equations rewritten, or extra equations added, to make the system identifiable or easier to estimate.

4. One or more equations should contain at least two endogenous (jointly dependent) variables. This of course reflects the assumed simultaneity.

5. The number of structural equations (of all sorts) will equal the number of endogenous variables, to provide completeness of the model. Then any equations containing only one endogenous variable can be fitted straightaway by least-squares. If a logical *and* identifiable system cannot be written, this may simply reflect actual under-identification in the real-world process. In such cases — of which price determination under oligopoly and duopoly conditions may be an example — any estimation would have to be forced, and might yield misleading results.

6. As in any analysis, Occam's razor should be used to keep the model within reasonable bounds, especially if data are unreliable

and the area of research is a new one. Access to an electronic computer will, of course, increase the extent and complexity of systems that may be tried.

7. Solving the structural equations for the endogenous variables provides the reduced-forms, which can then be estimated by least-squares or some other method. In many, if not most cases, least-squares (or even linear graphic analysis) will suffice, but special care should be taken if the reduced-forms are to be used for predictive purposes. Extensive treatment of computational problems is given in Friedman and Foote's 1955 handbook.[9]

The elasticities of demand for various nondurable consumer goods, including foods, have been computed in about 200 different studies by the use of simple equations and simultaneous equations, some over-identified and some just-identified. The results of these studies are brought together in one large 13-page table in "Price Elasticities of Demand for Nondurable Goods, With Emphasis on Food" by Richard J. Foote (USDA, March, 1956). See also G. E. Brandow, "Interrelations among Demands for Farm Products and Implications for Control of Market Supply," Bul. 680, Aug., 1961, Pennsylvania State University, Agr. Exp. Sta., University Park, Pennsylvania.

An excellent discussion and appraisal of simultaneous equations is given in M. J. B. Ezekiel and K. A. Fox, *Methods of Correlation and Regression Analysis*, Wiley, 3rd ed., 1959, Chap. 24. See also R. J. Foote, "Analytical Tools for Studying Demand and Price Structures," Agr. Handbook No. 146, USDA, Aug., 1958.

---

[9] J. Friedman and R. Foote, *"Computational Procedures for Handling Systems of Simultaneous Equations,"* USDA, 1955.

A useful summary of the results of numerous price analyses for the chief farm products in the United States is given in a 131-page mimeographed report by H. E. Buchholz, G. G. Judge, and V. I. West, "A Summary of Selected Estimated Behavior Relationships for Agricultural Products in the United States," USDA Res. Rep't AERR-57, Oct., 1962.

four

SALES, PRICES, COSTS, AND RETURNS

11

The Relation Between Prices and Costs

The relation between the price and the cost of producing a commodity is a perennial problem, and a thorny one, in agriculture.

Basically, this relation is simple. It is the same in agriculture as in other lines. The price must cover the cost of production, or to look at it the other way around, the cost of production must be lower than the price; otherwise the producer sooner or later will run out of money and quit producing.

The direction of causation from the one to the other, however, is a more complicated matter. A good many farmers believe that the line of causation runs from costs to prices in most of the industrial world. They believe that manufacturers, distributors, the service trades, etc. compute their costs, add a margin for profit, and set their prices accordingly. But farmers seem to run under opposite conditions. They are confronted by a price for their products, and they have to cut their costs below the price, or go broke.

Farmers maintain that what is sauce for the goose ought to be sauce for the gander; they ought to operate under the same sort of rules as business. If it costs farmers 60 cents to produce a bushel of corn, surely the price ought to be set high enough to cover those costs, plus a modest profit.

The things farmers buy appear to them to be priced according to their costs, at each step of the way from the manufacturer to the retailer. When the cost of living goes up, labor demands higher wages (higher prices for their labor). When labor asks for higher wages, manufacturers point out that this will increase their costs and that they, the manufacturers, will have to pass these increased costs on in the form of higher prices. The "cost-plus" basis upon which building contractors bid appears to offer another example of the use of cost of production. The local storekeeper provides another. He takes the wholesale price plus transportation as his cost, adds a standard margin to cover his costs and profits, and sets his retail price accordingly. He does not ask the farmer what price he is willing to pay for a can of beans; he tells him what price he will have to pay. Yet when the farmer takes his hogs to market, he cannot compute his costs and name his price as the retailer does. He has to ask the packer what he will pay, and take it or leave it.

Accordingly, it appears to many farmers that they are not getting a square deal. They get it in the neck both coming and going. They seem always to be asking the other fellow—buyer and seller as well—what his price is. They never seem to be able to name their own prices, but the buyer always names his. If, as it appears, others base their prices on their costs of production, or processing, or marketing, it seems to farmers that they ought to be able to do the same.

Are they right, and if so, is their desire attainable?

COST OF PRODUCTION IN INDUSTRY

The appearance that industry simply uses cost of production as the basis for its prices is misleading. There is a more direct relation between costs and prices in industry than in agriculture, but the line of causation runs from prices to costs as well as from costs to prices. This is true of merchandising as well as manufacturing.

Merchandising

"Merchants, engaged in buying and selling finished goods, customarily raise and lower their selling prices in accordance with current changes in wholesale prices, although sometimes with a considerable lag in time. They are able to do this only through changes in the quantity of goods sold. If the retail grocer started out with a definite number of cans of evaporated milk to sell each month, he would have to adjust his price to a point necessary to move this quantity from his shelves, regardless of the cost price. Actually, he first adjusts his retail price to the wholesale cost, then obtains from the wholesaler only as many cans as he is able to sell at that price. Of course, *if farmers could first set a price based on cost and then place on the market only the amount of the commodity that would sell for that price, they, too, could get cost of production.* However, this is impossible because of the peculiarities of farming and farm products.

"It should be noted, however, that the merchant's position is far from being as pleasing as the foregoing might indicate. If his own operating costs, which he adds to the wholesale price in setting his retail selling price, are higher than competition will allow, his volume of sales will be so small that he will be forced out of business. This actually happens, it is estimated, to perhaps 90 per cent of retail store ventures. Thus, the ordinary merchant's ability really is to name a cost price rather than to get it. The farmer, also, could name his cost price, but like many merchants he may be unable to sell at that price.

Manufacturing Industries

Thomsen and Foote[1] state that the greater ability of manufacturers, as compared with farmers, to both name and receive a price covering cost of production is due largely to these conditions:

1. *Manufactured goods are continuously rather than seasonally produced.* Because of this, adjustments in production can be made immediately, whereas with most farm products such adjustments require at least a season, and even then farmers may expect price conditions to change, further prolonging adjustments.

2. *Manufactured goods usually are nonperishable and can be stored in order to take up the 'slack' in the market.* If the supply of goods offered by the manufacturer of a certain commodity will not sell at a price high enough to cover cost, he may store enough so that the remainder will sell for the cost price. At the same time, he is able, because of continuous production, immediately to cut down output so that stocks will not accumulate at too rapid a rate. Here we see the essential difference in farming. We cannot store strawberries. We might store part of the cotton crop for sale in succeeding years; but unless we made a compensating cut in production, this would merely postpone the trouble.

3. *Production of manufactured products can be speeded up or contracted much more easily and quickly than the production of farm products.* In farming, the vagaries of the weather may upset the best laid production plans, so far as any one year is concerned. But there are other and even more important reasons why it is difficult to adjust agricultural production to prices. The proportion of fixed to variable expense is exceptionally large.

---

[1] F. L. Thomsen and R. J. Foote, *Agricultural Prices*, McGraw-Hill, 1952, pp. 91–93.

When the manufacturer reduces output, he also reduces his labor, power, and materials expense, which are relatively large items. The farmer, on the other hand, cannot greatly reduce his costs by reducing output, because the most important items of expense, such as interest, taxes, and family labor, are fixed. If the farm is heavily mortgaged, the farmer may be compelled even to increase his output, in order to keep out of the hands of the sheriff, even though his returns are less than his total fixed and variable costs.

4. *If the price of some manufactured product should fall far below the costs of production of individual manufacturers, the latter would be driven out of business very quickly, thus decreasing supply and tending to raise prices.* It is a difficult matter, however, to drive the farmer out of business, because of his ability to get along over a long period of below-cost prices by gradually using up his capital investment and reducing his standard of living. The difference between farmers and manufacturers in this respect is shown in the accompanying table. Even if the farmer were forced to relinquish his farm, some one else would quickly replace him. Falling prices breed idle factories but not idle farms.

DIFFERENCE IN EFFECT ON FARM AND MANUFACTURING ENTERPRISES OF A 10 PER CENT ANNUAL OPERATING LOSS

	Manufacturing Enterprise	Farm
Capital invested............................	$ 25,000	$25,000
Annual volume of business.................	$200,000	$ 4,000
Annual loss as percentage of volume..........	10	10
Actual operating loss.......................	$ 20,000	$ 400
Number of years required to drive from business	1	20 to 35

DIFFICULTY OF DETERMINING THE COST OF PRODUCTION

The cost-of-production approach is weak in another important respect. Some practical difficulties stand in the way of even determining the cost of producing a farm product, let alone setting a price that will cover it.

Difficulty of Determining Joint Costs of Production

When two products are produced jointly and inseparably, for instance wool and mutton, what is the cost of producing each one?

What Marshall calls the "supply price" for one product may be derived by subtracting the "demand price" for all the other products from the "supply price" of the two or more products that are jointly produced.[2]

This, however, makes the "supply price" (the price at which a given quantity will be produced for market) partly dependent on the "demand price" (the price at which a given quantity will be bought). If the demand price is low, that lowers the supply price. That is the sort of thing that farmers who want cost of production are trying to get away from.

The problem is still more difficult in the case of many farms that produce more than two products. What are the separate costs of producing corn, oats, clover, hogs, and beef cattle on Corn Belt farms? That problem is practically insoluble.

Whose Cost of Production?

Even in the simplest case of a single product (produced on farms that produce no other products), almost insuperable practical difficulties arise.

The cost of producing corn in Palo Alto County, Iowa, for example, was computed separately for 14 producers in a period of relatively low productive costs. The results are shown diagrammatically in Figure 11.1. The cost for the most efficient producer was 28 cents a bushel. The cost for the least efficient producer was $1.18. What was the cost of producing corn in that county?

If the price were to be set at 28 cents, most of the producers in that county would go broke. If it were set at $1.18, that would be such an attractive price for most farmers that they would expand their production beyond the quantity that could be sold at that price.

A compromise solution would be no more satisfactory. If the price were set at the average for all 14 producers, that would have been 49 cents. (This is lower than the average of the extreme low and high costs, because it takes all 14 producers' costs into account, and most of those costs were close to the lower extreme.) At that price about half the producers would have difficulty making ends meet, and the quantity produced might be more, or less, than the quantity that could be sold at that price. And what price should be set in Van Buren County, where the average cost was 77 cents—28 cents higher than the average cost in Palo Alto County?

Similar variations were found in the costs of producing cattle. The lowest cost was $45 per steer. The highest cost was over $200. The same sort of thing was true of hogs. Their costs ranged from

---

[2] Alfred Marshall, *Principles of Economics*, Macmillan, 1922, pp. 388–91.

$8 to $15 per 100 pounds. What was "the" cost of production in these cases?

Another illustration is the cost of production estimates that used to be published annually for three crops — corn, wheat, and oats — by the USDA. These estimates were published separately by groups of states and for the United States as a whole, but were discontinued in 1949.

The estimates usually show a range from low to high such that the cost in the high group of states is more than twice as great as the cost in the low group. The annual data from 1938 to 1946 are shown in Table 11.1. The range in costs shown in this table is much wider than the range of prices that usually exists in the market, by groups of states. If the costs of production for the different groups of states were used as the basis for setting prices for those groups, most of the corn would promptly be drained from the low

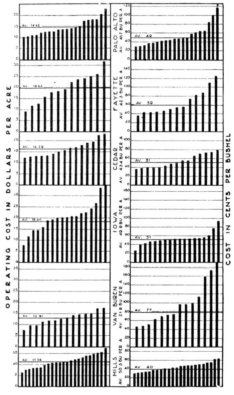

Fig. 11.1 — The variation in costs per acre and per bushel between fields by Iowa counties.

TABLE 11.1

CORN (FOR GRAIN): ESTIMATED COST OF PRODUCTION, BY SELECTED STATES AND GROUPS OF STATES, 1938–46

State or Group	Net Cost Per Bushel, Including Rent								
	1938	1939	1940	1941	1942	1943	1944	1945	1946
Eastern:									
North	$ .77	$ .83	$ .83	$ .86	$1.00	$1.33	$1.52	$1.29	$1.33
South	1.08	1.30	1.21	1.18	1.44	1.70	1.92	1.79	2.02
Ohio, Indiana, Michigan, Wisconsin, and Minnesota	.59	.52	.65	.62	.67	.83	.99	.92	.98
Illinois and Iowa	.47	.43	.47	.48	.53	.63	.77	.84	.72
Missouri and Nebraska	.71	.73	.67	.63	.62	.90	.82	1.03	.98
Kansas, South Dakota, and North Dakota	.73	.76	.74	.66	.62	.93	.76	1.04	1.03
Southwestern	.82	.90	.73	.97	1.18	1.49	1.63	1.51	1.66
Western	.86	.98	.86	.77	.93	1.30	1.29	1.28	1.39
United States	.65	.63	.67	.68	.73	.92	1.01	1.06	1.03

Source: *Agricultural Statistics 1948*, USDA, Table 58, p. 53.

TABLE 11.2
CORN: ESTIMATES OF COST OF PRODUCTION, INCLUDING RENT,
AND MARKET PRICE, 1938–46*
(cents per bushel)

Year	Cost	Price †	Price Minus Cost
1938....................	65	48.6	−16.4
1939....................	63	56.8	− 6.2
1940....................	67	61.8	− 5.2
1941....................	68	75.1	+ 7.1
1942....................	73	91.7	+18.7
1943....................	92	112.0	+20.0
1944....................	101	109.0	+08.0
1945....................	106	127.0	+21.0
1946....................	103	156.0	+53.0

* Source: *Agricultural Statistics*, USDA, *1948*, pp. 43, 53, and *1942*, p. 60.
† Season average price received by farmers.

cost (and price) areas to the high cost and price areas. Feeders and industrial users in the low cost and price areas would not be able to obtain supplies at the local price.

If the cost for the United States were used all over the United States, instead of the separate costs by groups of states, opposite difficulties would arise. Corn then would all stay in the low-cost surplus producing areas, for the price would be the same all over the United States and there would be no price incentive to ship it anywhere.

It is interesting further to compare the annual figures for the United States with the annual prices for corn that existed in the market place. This comparison for the years 1932 to 1946 is shown in Table 11.2. (The USDA ceased publishing cost of production data after 1946.)

The table shows that in the years preceding World War II, the price received was lower than the estimated cost of production. The average price for these years was 9 cents lower than the average cost. The cost and price data for wheat and oats showed similar conditions.

Similar results are shown by studies of other crop costs and prices. The estimated costs of producing butterfat in the Los Angeles County marketing area for eighty-one producers ranged from 46 cents to 67 cents in 1939, and from 87 cents to $1.36 in 1943.[3] The blend price of milk was high enough to cover the cost of less than

[3] G. M. Beal, "Economic Factors Affecting the Production of Fluid Milk in the Los Angeles County Marketing Area," Bureau of Market Enforcement, Calif. State Printing Office, Sacramento, March, 1944, pp. 14–17.

35 per cent of the producers in both years. Yet the area had an abundance of milk during 1939 and 1940, and the quantity produced increased constantly up to 1943.

Farmers are inclined to say "There. That proves it. We told you prices aren't high enough to cover cost of production. Prices ought to be set higher, so we could cover our costs."

But if prices had been set higher, so as to cover the average cost of production, half the producers still would have had higher than average costs; those costs would not have been covered by the price. And the higher price would have reduced consumption and increased production, so that the program sooner or later would have broken down under a flood of surplus production.

For the reasons given above, "the" cost of production has continued to be a fruitful source of controversy, but has not been found adequate or workable as a basis for agricultural prices.

RAISING WAGES AND RAISING PRICES

A final problem remains: Labor unions consistently strive to raise wages and get more money for labor; and except when they go to extremes, their efforts in this direction are approved by most economists. Yet when farm organizations try to do the same thing, and raise the price of farm products so as to get more money for farmers, practically all economists unite in pointing out how bad this is and what serious adverse consequences will follow.

Why is this? Why is sauce for the goose not sauce for the gander? If raising wages is good, why is raising prices bad?

Hourly Rates vs. Piece Rates

The answer to this question involves two things: First, wages are hourly or daily wages to laborers, but prices are *piece-wages* to farmers. Real wages depend fundamentally upon production per worker, and production per man-hour increased about 10 points per year in the 10 years after World War II, as shown in Figure 11.2. Industrial real wages therefore should increase at about the same rate. That is the reason that most economists approve of increases in labor's wages; wages should increase with increasing production.

Figure 11.2 shows that production per worker in agriculture has been increasing also, although at a somewhat slower rate than in industry. Farm "wages" (income) therefore, should have increased at a proportionate rate.

This means that if the real prices of farm products had been maintained at a constant level, that would have increased farmers' gross incomes in line with their increasing production per man.

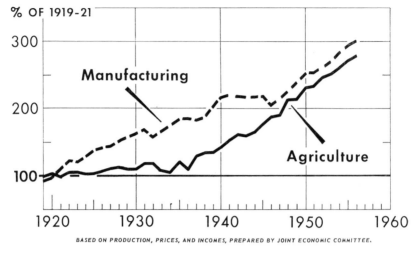

Fig. 11.2 — Comparison of output per man-hour in agriculture and manufacturing, 1920–56.

What would have happened to their net incomes depends upon what
would have happened to their costs.

Relatively Slow-moving and Inelastic Demand

If that were all that was involved, parity prices for farm products
as a group would be a reasonable goal. That goal would insure that
farmers' wages increased in line with their production.

But that is only half the picture. In determining wages, the
demand for the product is as important as the supply. The physical
quantities produced are only one of the factors that determine wages;
the prices at which those quantities will sell are equally important.

Those prices depend upon two things—the relative increase of
supply and demand (relative shifts in the supply and demand
curves) for the product, and the elasticity of the demand.

Discussion in Chapter 1 shows that up to 1920, the demand curve
for farm products in terms of population growth had been shifting
to the right at about the same rate as agricultural supply in
terms of production (Fig. 1.2). The increasing income per person
therefore showed up as an increasing demand for farm products,
and the relative prices of those products rose (Fig. 1.1).

After 1920, however, except for World War II, the demand curve
began moving to the right and upwards at a slower rate than the
supply curve, and relative (real) agricultural prices began de-

clining. And the prospects are that this relative slowing down of the demand curve will continue and become more marked in the future, for reasons given in the text accompanying Figure 1.2.

This relative decline in demand will have pronounced effects on agricultural prices, because of the relative inelasticity of the demand for farm products. The income elasticity for food in terms of quantities of food is low; even in terms of expenditures for food it is only about 0.4. The price elasticities may be greater than these, but are probably well below unity. Thus a relative decline in the demand for farm products of x per cent will depress the prices of farm products more than x per cent, and therefore decrease total returns.

Programs designed to hold the relative prices of farm products up merely by price fixing which does not alter the fundamental conditions which cause the prices of farm products to decline, therefore, are unlikely to be successful. Their progress is limited by the fundamental inelasticity of the human stomach.

This analysis shows, however, how programs to maintain relative agricultural prices can succeed. The solution is to reduce the supply of farmers in line with the relatively slow growth of the demand for farm products, so that the total agricultural income pie will be cut into fewer pieces, and therefore into larger pieces per farmer.

This solution calls for measures which range far from the starting point—direct action to raise prices. It requires recognition of the fundamental fact that birth rates in agriculture are so high that it would result in a continuous increase in the number of farmers if all the farmers born on farms stayed on farms. Farm births exceed farm deaths about 400,000 per year.

The high birth rate on farms can be measured in another way. "Replacement indexes" show the number of young children present in a population group in relation to the number needed to replace the female population of childbearing age. An index of 100 (termed "unity") would signify exact replacement and a population potentially stationary in numbers.[4] In the 1950, the United States replacement index figure for "11 farm-operator households" was 168.[5] (The figure for commercial farms was 171.) That is to say: the number of farm children was 68 per cent higher than the number needed to maintain a stationary farm population.

But we do not need a stationary farm population. The demand for farmers is declining. The farming area in the United States has

---

[4] "Farm Population — Characteristics of Farm-Operator Households by Number of Young Children," USDA, AMS-118, June, 1956, p. 9.

[5] *Ibid.,* p. 25.

remained practically constant at about 350 million acres since 1910, and labor-saving farm practices have reduced the number of farmers needed. Increasing mechanization and the use of larger farm implements has increased the optimum size of farms in the United States. In response to this pressure, the average size of farm in the United States has increased from 175 acres in 1940 to 217 acres in 1950 and to 302 acres in 1959.

The first fundamental requisite for high income per person in agriculture, therefore, is a group of measures that will facilitate the continuous transfer of people out of agriculture and into other lines of work. This calls for equalizing educational opportunities on and off farms; for training some farm boys and girls for urban occupations; for adequate employment services, and so on. These measures will reduce the friction that retards the flow of people out of agriculture. The closer this flow can be made frictionless, the closer will per capita income on farms rise to equality or parity with per capita incomes for equal ability elsewhere in the country.

12

The Theory of Price Stabilization and
Price Discrimination

It was shown in earlier chapters that the effect of production-control programs on the total revenue from the sale of the crop depends upon the elasticity of the demand for that crop. It will be shown in the present chapter that the effect of *price stabilization* programs on the total revenue from the sale of the crop depends primarily upon the curvature of the demand curve for the crop, and secondarily upon its elasticity.

CHARACTERISTICS OF DEMAND CURVES

There appears to be a general belief that in actual life most demand curves are curved lines, concave from above, on arithmetic paper. Practically all of the hypothetical curves found in economic textbooks are thus curved. These concave curves are also common in technical articles in professional journals.

These curves are misleading in two respects. Most of them apparently reflect the belief that the demand curve characteristically is more elastic at the lower end of the curve than at the upper end. This sounds like a reasonable assumption, yet it is incorrect in two respects:

1. Most of the hypothetical curves which are shown as concave on arithmetic paper are actually convex on logarithmic paper, and therefore are less elastic at the lower end than at the higher, as shown in Figure 12.1.

2. Most of the demand curves for agricultural products which have been empirically derived are not concave curves on arithmetic paper; they are approximately straight lines; accordingly, they

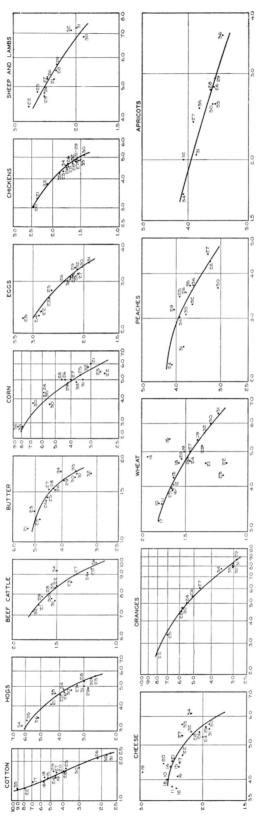

Fig. 12.1 — Empirically derived price-quantity curves for various farm products.
(Source: **Journal of Farm Economics**, Vol. 20, No. 4.)

are strongly convex on logarithmic paper, which means that they are much less elastic at the lower end than at the upper.

This is shown by a study of a considerable number of demand curves empirically derived from market statistics. These curves are shown on logarithmic paper in Figure 12.1. The curves are taken from the published charts, without any comment as to their accuracy other than the closeness (or lack of it) of the scatter of the dots about the curves, which is shown in each case. These analyses are out of date, and several of them would be improved by the use of better indexes of demand than were available when the studies were made, but no new ones are available. Figure 12.1 should be regarded only as tentatively establishing a hypothesis that needs to be investigated more thoroughly and confirmed, amended, or proven erroneous.

All of the curves were published on arithmetic paper in the original analyses. Many of them were straight lines on arithmetic paper. On logarithmic paper, as shown in Figure 12.1, they are all convex, with the exception of the curve for apricots and the upper end of the curve for cotton.

This means that the elasticity is high in the upper part of the curve and low in the lower part. This in turn means that in the simplest case of a straight-line demand curve on arithmetic paper with an average elasticity of unity, both a small crop and a large crop are worth less than an average-sized crop. For the elasticity in the upper half of the curve is higher than unity, so a small crop is worth less than an average crop. Conversely, the elasticity in the lower half of the curve is lower than unity, so a large crop is worth less than an average crop. The crop that is worth the most is the average-sized crop that cuts the whole curve at the middle where the elasticity is unity. This means that stabilization of supplies by storing surpluses from large crop years over to small crop years would not only stabilize prices but would also increase total incomes from the sale of the crop.

This can be shown clearly with the help of a few hypothetical figures. The prices and total revenues for a crop with a straight-line demand curve (on arithmetic paper) with an average elasticity of unity are shown briefly in Table 12.1. The data are all in index form with an average equal to 100.[1]

It is clear from Table 12.1 that a large crop, for instance 130 per cent of average in size, which would sell for an index price of 70, would bring in a total revenue of only 91. A small crop, 70 per cent

---

[1] These relationships were shown in graphic form in Figure 5.1.

TABLE 12.1

PRICES AND TOTAL REVENUES FOR VARIOUS QUANTITIES: STRAIGHT-LINE DEMAND
CURVE WITH AN AVERAGE ELASTICITY OF UNITY

(1) Size of Crop in Percentage of Average	(2) Price per Unit in Percentage of Average	(3) Total Revenue in Percentage of Average [(1) x (2) omitting 00]
60...................	140	84
70...................	130	91
80...................	120	96
90...................	110	99
100...................	100	100
110...................	90	99
120...................	80	96
130...................	70	91
140...................	60	84

of average in size, would sell at 130 and also bring in a total revenue
of 91. These two crops, then (a large crop and a small crop), would
bring in total revenues averaging only 91 per cent of normal. If the
surplus (the excess over 100) were withheld from the large crop
and added to the small crop, that would convert them both into
average-sized crops. They would bring in an average total revenue
over the two years of 100 per cent of normal. Stabilizing supplies in
this case would not only stabilize prices, but would also increase total
revenues from the sale of the crops.

What is the effect of a stabilization program in cases where the
demand curve is not a straight line on arithmetic paper, but has
some sort of curvature?

If the demand curve is so shaped that it has a constant elasticity
of unity throughout its length, then no matter what the size of the
crop—large, average, or small—it brings in the same total revenue.
In fact, a curve with constant unit elasticity is the same thing as a
constant revenue (or constant total value) curve. In that case, of
course, stabilization operations have no effect on total revenue, since
the total revenue is unaffected by the size of the crop. But if a
demand curve with an average elasticity of unity is more concave
than a constant total revenue curve, then a large crop and a small
crop are both worth more than an average crop, and stabilizing
supplies would decrease total revenues.

The section can be summarized in these terms: the way to maximize total revenue is to produce the amount that will cut the demand
curve as close as possible to the point where the elasticity is unity

(where the marginal revenue is zero and the total revenue is the greatest). Where the demand curve is inelastic, reducing the size of the crop (cutting the demand curve at a higher point) will increase total revenue; where the demand curve is elastic, increasing the size of the crop will increase total revenue. In the case of straight-line demand curves with an average elasticity of unity, the elasticity of the demand curve is less than unity in the lower part of the curve and greater than unity in the upper part, and the way to maximize total revenue is to move toward the center from both directions, that is, to convert both large crops and small crops to average-sized crops by storing the excess over average from the large crops and adding it to the small crops. The more convex the demand curve is, the more will stabilizing supplies add to total revenue, and the more concave it is, the less it will add, until the point is reached where the curve is more concave than a constant-total-revenue curve; beyond that point stabilizing supplies will decrease total revenue.

Demand Curves With Constant but not Unit Elasticity

If the demand curve has a constant elasticity that is greater or less than unity, the situation is more complicated. The total revenue curves then are not straight lines, as they are when the demand curve has a constant elasticity of unity. If the elasticity of the demand curve is constant, but less than unity, the total revenue curve associated with it has a concave curvature. It has the same shape as a constant total returns curve; that is, it is a symmetrical hyperbola approaching the x and y axes as asymptotes. In Figure 5.2, a demand curve with a constant elasticity of -0.5 is shown both on logarithmic and arithmetic paper, in the upper part of the chart, and the total revenue curve associated with it is shown in the lower part of the chart. (The elasticity figure, -0.5, written beside the curve in the lower part of the chart shows the elasticity of the original demand curve for purposes of identification, not the elasticity of the total revenue curve; that is -1.0.)

In that case, a large crop, represented by six quantity units along the scale at the bottom of the chart, is shown to bring a total revenue of about 1.5. A small crop, represented by two quantity units, brings a total revenue of 5. The sum of these two total revenues is 6.5. But if the excess of the large crop over average were removed from the large crop and added to the short crop, that would convert them into two average-sized crops (four quantity units) each of which would bring in a total revenue of about 2.5; the sum of these two total revenues would therefore be 5, and this is less than the sum of the large and small crop, 6.5, computed above. A stabilization program in this case would therefore reduce total revenues.

The opposite is true of demand curves with a constant elasticity greater than unity. A curve of this sort, with a constant elasticity of —2.0, is also shown in the upper part of Figure 5.2, with the total revenue curve associated with it in the lower part. The total revenue curve in this case is convex from above; it is a parabola with apex at the origin of the X and Y axes. Stabilizing supplies in this case would increase total revenues.

"Standard" Demand Curves With Straight-line Total Revenue Curves

It was shown earlier that a demand curve with a constant elasticity of unity makes a convenient standard for determining whether stabilization of supplies would increase or decrease total returns. If the demand curve for the particular crop considered has an average elasticity of unity but is less concave than this standard curve (if, for example, it is a straighter line, or a convex line) then stabilization would increase total revenues; if it is *more* concave than this standard curve, stabilization would decrease total revenues.

It was shown above that this standard applies only to demand curves with an average elasticity of unity. Is there another convenient standard or set of standards that can be used for crops whose demand curves have other elasticities than unity?

There is. The criterion for such a set of standard curves is that the total revenue curves associated with them must be straight lines. In that case stabilization will have no effect on total revenues over a period of large and small crops. Figure 5.2 shows that demand curves of constant elasticity (other than unity) cannot be used as standards because their total revenue curves are not straight lines. They may have a positive slope (as where the demand curve is elastic) or a negative slope (as where the demand curve is inelastic) but they must be straight.

Adolf Kozlik has worked out mathematically the sort of demand curves required here, and shown graphically that they are merely curves of constant unit elasticity shifted up or down by constant absolute amounts all along the curve.[2] The validity of this standard

---

[2] A short mathematical proof of this runs as follows:
The total revenue curve $R(Q)$ of a demand curve with the equation $F(Q) = a/Q + b$ is $R(Q) = Q.F(Q) = a + bQ$. This is a straight line, because R increases proportionally with Q. The demand curve whose total revenue curve is a straight line is a demand curve of constant unit elasticity $F(Q) = a/Q$ shifted up and down by the amount b. The total revenue curves of demand curves which are more concave than these demand curves are concave, and the total revenue curves of demand curves which are more convex than these are convex.

set of curves can be understood in everyday language thus: The total revenue curve associated with a constant-unit-elasticity demand curve is a horizontal straight line. If now the demand curve is shifted up one price unit all along its length, the resulting total revenue curve will start in, at the first quantity unit, one value unit higher than the original total revenue curve $(1 \times 1 = 1)$; at the second quantity unit it will be two value units higher $(2 \times 1 = 2)$; at the third, three units higher, and so on. This total revenue curve therefore will be a straight line, with a positive slope. Similar calculations apply to demand curves lower by constant amounts than a curve with a constant elasticity of unity.

If the demand curve for the particular crop concerned, therefore, has an average elasticity other than unity, stabilization would increase or decrease total revenues accordingly as the demand curve is less or more curved than the appropriate standard curve for that elasticity. Since these standard curves are ordinary constant-unit-elasticity curves shifted up (for elastic demand curves) or down (for inelastic demand curves) the comparison of the standard demand curve with the demand curve for the particular crop can be made by sliding a transparent chart with a family of constant-unit-elasticity curves up and down on it (but keeping the Y axes on the two charts superimposed) until a section of one of the standard curves is found which has the same average elasticity as the demand curve for the crop in question. If the demand curve for the crop is less concave from above (that is, if it is straighter than the standard curve, or actually convex), then stabilization of that crop would increase total revenues. If, on the other hand, the demand curve is more concave (more curved) than the standard curve, stabilization would decrease total revenues.

Does Stabilization Benefit Consumers?

It could be argued that consumers are harmed by stabilization to the same extent that farmers are benefited by the increased total value of their crops, for the increased total value of crops to farmers emerges as an increase in the cost of food to consumers. If stabilization increases the total value of a series of crops 6 per cent, for example, it must increase the cost of consumers' purchases by the same amount.

The harm or benefit to consumers cannot be measured, however, merely by the increase or decrease in the amount of money they pay for corn. If a monopolist restricted the production of his product, and the demand for that product were inelastic, consumers would pay more for the small quantity than they did before. They would clearly be harmed, but the harm would not be measured by the extra amount of money they had to pay. For if the demand were elastic instead of inelastic, consumers would pay less for the small quantity than before. No one could claim that they would be benefited because their total outlay for the product had been reduced; least of all could anyone claim that they would be benefited by the amount of the reduction in their total outlay for the product.

The question can be approached from a different direction. Any one consumer gets more satisfaction from a fairly even consumption of a particular food than he does from a scarcity at one time and a glut at another. In technical terms, the total-utility curve is convex from above. A stable supply is therefore worth more to him than a fluctuating supply. The extra worth of the stable supply may be greater or less than the extra money he has to pay for it—there is no way of telling which—so the consumer may benefit by more or less than the extra money he pays. The important point is merely that he does benefit to some extent; the extra money he pays is not all loss, and may even be less than the benefit he receives.

But fluctuations in the production of different foods have a differential effect on different classes of consumers. When supplies and prices fluctuate, consumers with low incomes can make those incomes go farther by buying most heavily of those foods that are cheapest at the time, and buying least heavily—or perhaps not at all—of those foods that are temporarily scarce and high priced. At first thought, therefore, it would appear that stabilizing supplies would work some hardship on the low-income groups; they would be obliged to pay more for their food.

F. V. Waugh has made a further point. He shows that consumers are harmed if the price of any product is stabilized at the simple arithmetic mean of the fluctuating prices. This point is independent of the points made above. It is based upon the concept of consumers' surplus, and depends only upon the fact that the elasticity of the demand curve is negative.[3]

Waugh shows that with any negatively-sloping demand curve (sloping downward to the right) the loss in consumers' surplus from averaging two prices is always greater than the gain. For example, when egg prices vary from 40 cents to 60 cents a dozen, consumers' surplus is greater than it would be if the price were stabilized at 50 cents a dozen. He then confirms this conclusion by an analysis based on indifference curves.

Waugh's theorem is illustrated in Figure 12.2. This figure shows

[3] F. V. Waugh, "Does the Consumer Benefit From Price Instability?" *The Quarterly Journal of Economics*, August, 1944, pp. 602–14.

that the gain to consumers when prices are below average is always greater than the loss when prices are above average. That is, the area in Figure 12.2 marked G (for gain) is always necessarily larger (because of the negative slope of the demand curve) than the area marked L (for loss). Thus consumers are harmed by price stabilization. This is true not only of consumers as a group, but of each consumer separately.

This theorem appears to run counter to common sense, but so far it has stood up pretty well under criticism. Two critics, L. D. Howell and Gertrude Lovasy, made the point that the theorem is true only if prices are stabilized at or above the arithmetic mean of the variable prices. They point out that if prices are stabilized at or below the *weighted* average of the prices (weighted by the consumption at each price), consumers would be *benefited*, not harmed, by the stabilization. This reduces the status of Waugh's theorem from a general rule to a special case.

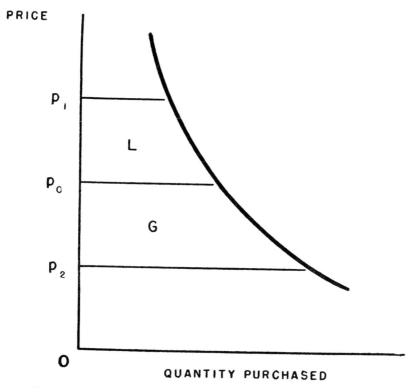

Fig. 12.2 — Comparison of loss and gain from fluctuating prices, showing that the gain is greater than the loss.

The argument then arises as to which is the more reasonable level for prices to be stabilized—at or above the arithmetic mean, or at or below the weighted average? Lovasy points out that the weighted average is the more reasonable level, since it would maintain producers' incomes at the same average level as before, and benefit them by reducing risks and lowering costs. Waugh replies that producers would not be interested in stabilization at that level; they would want a level at least as high as the arithmetic mean. This argument gets out of the field of statistics and economic theory. But it seems to me that it would be settled by the curvature of the demand curve, not by the desires of producers.

Stabilizing prices by storage has to mean stabilizing supplies at the arithmetic means of the varying supplies (unless some of the supplies are to be destroyed or otherwise removed from the market). This means that the point where prices will be stabilized will be determined by the curvature of the demand curve. If the demand curve is a straight line, stabilizing the supplies at their arithmetic means will stabilize prices at *their* arithmetic means. But if the demand curve is curved, concave from above, stabilizing supplies at their arithmetic means will stabilize prices below their arithmetic means. If the demand curve is curved strongly enough, the area L in Figure 12.2 will be so much broader (up and down) than area G, that is will exceed it in area, so that consumers will be benefited, not harmed, by stabilization.

An additional point has been made by D. Gale Johnson, who shows that stabilizing *supplies* at the arithmetic mean of the fluctuating supplies always benefits society as a whole (at least, if carrying costs are neglected). In some cases this would reduce consumers' surplus, but in all such cases this loss would be more than offset by a gain in producers' income.[4] In all such cases the producers could afford to pay consumers compensation for their losses, and would still have a net profit from stabilizing supplies.

THE THEORY OF PRICE DISCRIMINATION

The theory of price stabilization outlined above is in essence the theory of equalizing prices in different time-markets—that is, in markets separated by intervals of time. It is comparatively simple; it is based directly on the relations between point elasticity and marginal, average, and total revenue laid down in earlier chapters. The theory of price *discrimination* is in essence the theory of

---

[4] D. Gale Johnson, *Forward Prices for Agriculture*, Univ. of Chicago Press, 1947.

unequalizing prices. The basic theory of price discrimination is the same as the basic theory of price stabilization. Its exposition is more complicated, however, because it involves two or more different demand curves. The theory of price stabilization involves two or more curves also, one for each year, but they are not different curves; they are identical curves, and are therefore treated as one.

The theory of price discrimination and of price stabilization both call for maximizing total revenue by cutting the demand curve (or curves) as close as possible to the point (or points) of unit elasticity. But whereas the theory of price stabilization deals with a succession of identical demand curves in markets separated by intervals of *time,* the theory of price discrimination deals with two or more different demand curves in contemporaneous markets separated in *space,* in *form,* or in some other basic characteristic. Export-dumping plans are examples of price discrimination between two or more markets separated in *space.* Milk price plans are examples of price discrimination between two or more markets separated in *form* (the original product is sold in two or more different forms, fluid milk, and butter, cheese, ice cream or some other manufactured product). The food stamp plan is an example of price discrimination between two *income-group* markets.

The same principles of price discrimination underlie all three of the plans just mentioned. They can be illustrated comparatively simply by an analysis of export-dumping plans.

PRINCIPLES OF EXPORT DUMPING

Export-dumping plans all have several important features in common: (1) separation of the domestic and foreign markets with respect to price determination; (2) establishment of a higher effective price in the domestic market, possibly based on some standard such as "parity," "cost of production," or "world price plus the tariff"; (3) limitation of the quantity made available for domestic consumption to that amount which will be consumed at the price established for the domestic market; (4) disposition of the remainder of the total output at whatever price it will bring in world markets.

The general principles of export dumping are these:

The effects of export dumping depend upon the relative elasticities of the domestic and foreign demands. If the foreign demand is more elastic than the domestic demand, dumping goods at lower prices abroad increases the total returns from the sale of the goods in the two markets.[5]

Conversely, if the foreign demand is less elastic than the domestic demand, dumping goods at lower prices abroad decreases total returns.

And finally, if the foreign demand has the same elasticity as the domestic demand, dumping goods at lower prices abroad has no effect on total return.

These principles of export dumping are illustrated graphically in Figure 12.3.[6]

In the absence of any dumping operations, the price for the goods sold on the domestic market is 8, the same as the price of the goods sold on the export market. The amount consumed domestically is 260 units, and the amount exported is 120 units. Total returns from the sale of the commodity are 260 units domestically consumed multiplied by a price of 8.0, or 2,080, plus 120 units exported multiplied by the price of 8.0, or 960, a total return of 3,040 units of value.

The solid lines in Figure 12.3 show what happens under an export-dumping plan when the export demand is more elastic than the domestic demand. The domestic price rises from 8.0 to 11.3. The quantity domestically consumed declines from 260 to 220 units. The quantity remaining for export increases from 120 to 160 units, depressing the export price from 8.0 to 6.4. The total returns then consist of 220 units sold at a price of 11.3 or 2,486, plus 160 units exported at a price of 6.4, or 1,024, a total of 3,510. This is 470 value units more than the total returns without dumping.

The dashed curves DD' and ED' represent a different situation. In this case, the export demand is less elastic than the domestic demand. Returns from the sale of the crop in the domestic market are 220 units sold at a price of 8.7, yielding a total return of 1,914. Exports of 160 units are sold at a price of 3.7, giving a return of 592. The combined receipts from the sale of the domestic and exported portions of the commodity, under these circumstances, are 2,506. This is 534 value units less than the total returns without dumping.

This type of diagram shows clearly just what happens under

---

[5] This is true even if the demand in the foreign market is less elastic than unity, and the dumping therefore reduces the total value of the goods sold on the export market. The increase in the total value of the goods sold on the domestic market is greater than the decrease in the total value of the goods sold on the export market.

[6] Figure 12.3 and the arithmetic in the next few paragraphs are taken from F. L. Thomsen, "Export-Dumping Plans," *Journal of Farm Economics*, Vol. 22, No. 2, May, 1940, pp. 446–47 and 453–54.

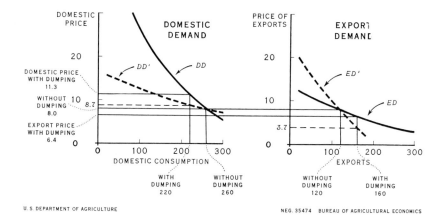

U. S. DEPARTMENT OF AGRICULTURE

NEG. 35474   BUREAU OF AGRICULTURAL ECONOMICS

Fig. 12.3 — Effects of dumping under different conditions of elasticity of demand. (Courtesy, F. L. Thomsen, **op. cit.**)

the conditions given, and how the relative elasticities of the domestic and export demand determine the results. The diagram does
not show directly, however, to what point dumping should be
carried in order to maximize the total returns from the sale of the
crop in the two markets.

That point can be shown by drawing in the marginal revenue
curves based on the average revenue curves (demand curves)
shown in the diagram. That will show the point directly, without
requiring any arithmetical computations. All that is necessary is
to locate the two points, equidistant to the left and right of the
domestic and export quantities that would be sold under open
market conditions, where the marginal revenue in the two markets
would be equal.

It would be easy to draw these marginal revenue curves in
the diagram if the average revenue curves were straight lines,
simply by bisecting the horizontal distances from two points on
each average revenue curve to the Y axis for that curve, and running a line through the bisection points. The average revenue
curves in the diagram, however, happen to be curved, so the job
is geometrically more complicated, requiring that a series of
tangents be drawn in. The diagram is already rather filled up with
lines. The principle of maximizing total revenue by equalizing
marginal returns can most easily be demonstrated by starting from
scratch with a new diagram, similar to the one shown, but with
straight-line average revenue curves. One neat method of doing
this is to superimpose the export part of the diagram on the

domestic part, and add the two amounts together. Another way is to put the two charts back to back.

APPLICATION TO CONDITIONS IN THE UNITED STATES

The analysis presented above shows the principles involved. The application of these principles to the situation in the United States, however, is an additional problem in itself.

The conclusions stated in the analysis are valid only if all the crop (including both the domestic and export portions) is bought and sold by one agency, and the gains and losses are reflected directly back to the growers without the agency itself taking any gain or loss.

Conditions in the United States do not meet this requirement. A crop is bought and sold by domestic mills, etc., and exporters. They all pay the same price (which is above the world market price) but the exporters recoup their losses that result from selling at lower prices abroad from the federal government. Domestic farmers gain; they get higher prices for their grain. Domestic consumers lose; they pay correspondingly higher prices for their grain, flour, bread, etc. The United States government also loses, by the amount of the subsidy it pays on the quantities exported.

GENERAL THEORY OF PRICE STABILIZATION AND PRICE DISCRIMINATION

The general principle underlying price discrimination has not always been adequately stated in the literature of the subject. Various authorities voiced differing principles, none of which was completely adequate. From a mathematical treatment, a principle evolved that can be put in everyday words as follows:

Total revenues are maximized or minimized by the equalization of the marginal revenues in the different markets. In price stabilization, the demand curves in the separate markets (in time) are identical; the equalization of marginal revenues is accomplished by the equalization of the prices in the different markets. This maximizes total revenues if the demand curves are less concave than the "standard" curves defined above (whose associated total revenue curves are straight lines). It minimizes total revenues if the demand curves are more concave than the "standard" curves.

The principle for price discrimination runs in similar but opposite terms. In this case the demand curves in the separate markets may be identical, or they may be different. The principle is the same in either case, but it can be most simply stated for the case where the curves are identical. In that case, the equalization of the marginal revenues may require *unequalizing* prices—charging different prices in the different markets. This maximizes total revenues if the demand curves are more concave than the "standard" curves, and minimizes total revenues if they are less concave. If the demand curves in the different markets are not identical, the principle is the same, but a full exposition of it requires somewhat complicated mathematics. The general idea can be conveyed verbally in terms of the total revenue curves associated with the two demand curves. It is phrased in terms of two different markets here. The principle is the same for more than two markets; only its exposition is more complicated. If the total revenue curves are both concave from above, price discrimination carried to the point where marginal revenues are equal maximizes total revenues; if they are both convex, price discrimination minimizes them. If one of the curves is concave, and the other one is convex, the outcome depends on which curve has the greater curvature. This curvature may be measured by the absolute value of the second derivative of the curve. If the algebraic sum of the two second derivatives is positive, then price discrimination carried to the point where marginal revenues are equal maximizes total revenues; if the sum is negative, it minimizes it.

13

The Significance of the Results of Price Analyses

When price analysts investigate prices, they necessarily investigate prices that have happened. Most price analysts, however, do their work not merely because they want to explain what has happened in the past, but because they believe that their explanation will have some usefulness in meeting current and future problems. For example, a price analyst discovers by study of past statistics that the demand for potatoes had (he cannot, strictly speaking, say "has") an elasticity between −0.3 and −0.4. He does this not because he is a historian, but because he believes that this finding will be useful in the solution of current potato production and marketing problems.

How well founded is this belief? How likely is it that the quantitative relations revealed by the analysis of past statistics of prices, production, income, etc., will be valid guides to action in the present and future?

This is a problem of inference, the basic problem in statistics. Most of our statistics (except those in the Census) are derived from samples of whatever "population" we are talking about, not from the whole population; in many cases, "the whole population" hasn't happened yet. A manufacturer tests a mixture of ingredients and processes once, and it works all right; a second time, and it fails; 10 times, and it fails only twice. What percentage will fail if he goes into production? Does he need a still larger sample? The problem of inference is to determine what we can infer about the whole population from the information we get from a sample, and how confidently we can infer it.

Let us illustrate the problem by an extreme case, and then proceed to more typical cases. Suppose that an investigator were analyzing the price of eggs, and had only two annual price data to work with; eggs were 30 cents a dozen in 1960 and 40 cents in 1961. If he plotted these prices against any other variable that changed in value from one year to the other, he would get a perfect positive or negative correlation. He could thus "explain" the price of eggs in terms of any other variable he chose. In this case the explanation would be so obviously absurd that nobody would consider it, because the number of variables is equal to the number of observations and there are no degrees of freedom left.

But suppose the investigator had data for three years. Some of the innumerable economic series available would still, purely by chance, have a high correlation with the price series. If he had data for four years, fewer series would correlate highly with the prices, and data for five and more years would correlate highly with still fewer series. Statisticians have worked out tables showing, for random data, how high the correlation must be for any given number of variables and of items in each series, in order to be adjudged "significant" or "highly significant" and not merely the result of chance.[1]

Thus, a correlation of plus or minus 1.0 between two series, with only two items in each series (for instance, annual data covering only two years) would not mean a thing as an explanation; it would have no real significance; it would not be statistically significant. Tests of significance show that in the case of two series, each three years long, the correlation would have to be 0.997 or higher before it could be considered significant. If the series were each four years long, the correlation would have to be 0.950 or higher, and so on up.

The precise meaning of the term "significant" here is this: In repeated samples taken at random from a population with a bivariate normal distribution, where the true correlation (for the whole population) is 0, the confidence intervals for the correlation coefficients would include the true correlation of 0 in 5 per cent of such samples, purely because of accidents of sampling (sampling error or variation).

The term "highly significant" has a similar meaning, but applies to the 1 per cent level.

Why do statisticians set the limits of significance at 5 per cent and 1 per cent? Why do they need 100 to 1 or 20 to 1 odds? Why not 60 to 40 or even only 51 to 49?

The importance of a clear answer to this kind of question is shown in a recent specific case. A report of a multiple correlation study of the effect of futures trading was presented, purporting to show "that the variation of prices is reduced by an active futures

---

[1] George Snedecor, *Statistical Methods*, Iowa State Univ. Press, 1956, p. 174.

market." The speaker's conclusions were challenged because most of the coefficients on which the conclusions were based were not statistically significant. This interesting colloquy then took place:[2]

> SPEAKER: ". . . . the tests Mr. Shepherd referred to are tests of statistical significance. 'Significance' is very different in what it means in the ordinary usage of the English language and in tests of statistical significance in which we rule out items on the basis of extraordinarily rigorous standards.
> "Now, I am a short-odds player myself. You don't have to give me 20-to-1 before you get me to bet on a point. And I should say that to take the very arbitrary levels of significance the statistical fraternity uses and say that something is of no value because it doesn't meet those particular standards, impresses me only very negligibly."
> SHEPHERD: "Insignificantly."
> SPEAKER: "Yes."

> > (Laughter)

The speaker's opinions typify a common misunderstanding of the whole concept of statistical significance. Statistics is the science of drawing inferences from data, not the science of betting on horse races, and such. An investigator compares the yields of two varieties of wheat. On those two plots (or more if the trial is replicated) at that station that year, the one variety yields 5 bushels an acre more than the other. Can he release the new variety for general distribution with a statement that it will outyield the other 5 bushels an acre?

Clearly, he would not be justified in doing this. For what he has is only the results of one sample — on the one type of soil at his station, fertilized to the degree he used, with the particular weather he had that year. From that one experiment, he cannot infer that the same results will be obtained in the whole population of various other soils, weather, etc., over the country as a whole in other years. The statistical fraternity has not established "very arbitrary levels of significance;" they have worked out mathematically the validity of inferences concerning the whole population that can be made from a small number of samples. They have established tests of significance to indicate how valid a particular inference based on one sample concerning the parameter of a whole population may be. Determining betting odds is one thing; determining what inferences concerning a whole population can safely (reliably) be drawn from one sample is quite another.

Another real life example illustrates what significance means. A candidate for the Master's Degree recently worked out a thesis in

---

[2] *Futures Trading Seminar, History and Development,* Vol. 1, Mimir Press, 1960, p. 193.

which he ran a multiple correlation analysis of county average data showing net farm income per farm, by counties in Iowa (99 of them). The independent variables he used were county averages of capital inputs, value of land, and man-days of labor, per farm. He got a multiple correlation coefficient of about 0.8. He tested this for significance, and found that it was highly significant (i.e., at the 1 per cent level).

He was asked, during the oral examination, why he tested his coefficient for significance. He was not inferring a parameter of a whole population from a statistic (a characteristic derived from a sample); to begin with he had the whole population. Whatever relations he found, for the whole population, were the relations for that population, and that was that. A test of significance has no significance for a parameter derived from a whole population.

The candidate could have attempted to defend himself by regarding his Iowa data as a sample of farms in the United States as a whole, and drawing inferences concerning relations for United States farms regarded as the population. But if he had, he would have been in hot water on another count — his sample was not a representative random sample of the whole United States. Or he might have regarded his data for one year as a sample of data for all years, and inferred relations for other years (for Iowa) as the population. But the data for the one year would not have been a representative sample of data for all years, or even for a reasonably long period of time, say 100 years; the sample would not have been random, and the population would not have remained constant over those years. Tests of significance, far from being too rigorous when applied to economic data, actually are not rigorous enough. They are likely to overstate the actual significance of the coefficients rather than understate it.

The application of tests of significance to economic data, especially to time series, may give an unwary investigator a confidence in his results which is entirely unwarranted. A series of monthly prices, two years long, would have twenty-four items. A correlation coefficient between it and some other monthly series in excess of 0.404 would be adjudged significant by the application of statistical tests; yet in actual fact the correlation might have no more real significance than the correlation that would result if the monthly data were made into annual data, in which case there would be only two items in each series and the correlation would be perfect.

Other illustrations bring out the point further. Mr. Yule's classic

---

[3] G. Udny Yule, "Why Do We Sometimes Get Nonsense Correlations Between Time Series?" *Journal of the Royal Statistical Society*, Vol. 89, No. 1, 1926, pp. 1–64.

table and chart devised more than thirty years ago[3] showed a high correlation (0.9512) between the annual data showing the proportion of Church of England marriages to all marriages and the standardized mortality per 1,000 persons for the same years, over a period of 45 years. For that number of years, any correlation over 0.290 would be adjudged statistically significant. Yet, as he pointed out, all he had there was in "nontechnical language, a fluke" — a purely chance correlation between two trends, both declining without any causal relation between them. The one series was not in any sense an explanation of the other.

Another illustration is the course of prices during a business cycle. In any five years, prices of butter might show a high correlation with the prices of cranberries, but nobody would claim that the one was an explanation of the other. Both were affected by the same decline and recovery of demand. The correlation coefficient is highly (statistically) significant, but not economically significant.

MOST ECONOMIC DATA ARE NOT RANDOM IN CHARACTER

The development of statistical tests of significance, therefore, has not helped the economic statistician very much. For tests of significance, and established statistical methods generally, are designed for use with data that have several important characteristics. These characteristics are: (1) The population must be homogeneous, (2) the distributions of the values of the variables must be approximately normal, (3) each observation must be independent of the others, and (4) the sample must be selected from the parent universe at random.

If the conditions just given are met, even if only approximately, the standard tests of significance of the results of the analysis of a sample measure how likely it is that the characteristics of the sample are true of the population as a whole. But economic data, especially economic time series, clearly do not meet these conditions: (1) The population from which the sample (the data for a certain period of years) is drawn is not homogeneous. A price analyst, investigating the factors determining the price of barley in the United States before 1918, could not rely on tests of significance of his results, because the advent of prohibition in 1918 changed the population. (2) The condition that the data must be normally distributed may be reasonably closely met, although it is more likely that the logarithms of such economic data as prices have normal distributions, than it is that the original data are normally distributed. (3) Each observation is usually not independent of the others. This is true both of successive items in one price series, and of corresponding observations (in time) in different price series. The price of corn in February is not independent of the price of corn in January and March, for all three of these prices are determined (in a given demand situation) by the size of the same corn crop. Similarly, in a given supply situation, the prices of different goods are related to each other at any one time (they are all high or low) according to the prosperity or depression of the country as a whole. And finally, (4) the sample (the period of years chosen) is usually not selected at random. It generally begins either when the data first became available, or just after World War I or some other sort of bench mark, and runs up to World War II, or in some cases up to the present time.

WHAT CAN BE DONE?

Is there any way to render economic time series more amenable to statistical analysis?

The Durbin-Watson test for serial independence of disturbances[4] is:

$$d = \frac{\Delta^2}{S^2}$$

where

$$\Delta^2 = \sum_{t=2}^{T} (\tilde{u}_t - \tilde{u}_{t-1})^2$$

$$S^2 = \sum_{t=1}^{T} \tilde{u}_t^2$$

$\tilde{u}$ = the residual of the fitted relation for time t.

Thus Yule's original "nonsense correlation" example covered forty-five years, for which by ordinary tests the correlation of 0.95 would be rated highly significant. But application of the procedure described above shows that the size of the sample required to bring the ratio to stability is about fifteen. The forty-five years, therefore, are equivalent only to three independent items; and for series as short as three a correlation coefficient of 0.95 is not significant.

What this means is that a test of significance attributes more significance to relations among nonrandom economic series than

[4] This test was originally presented in *Biometrika*, Vol. 37, p. 409, and Vol. 38, p. 159. An application of this test is discussed in C. Hildreth and F. G. Garrett, *A Statistical Study of Livestock Production and Marketing*, Cowles Commission for Research in Economics, Monograph No. 15, pp. 77–79.

really exists. The actual significance is less than the statistical significance based on random data as shown in significance tables in statistical test books.

There are one or two less technical observations about economic time series that should be made. While change is the order of the day in economics, so that populations (of economic data) are not homogeneous, it is also true that some of these changes are gradual, not sudden; they are evolutionary, not revolutionary. Thus, while tractors and trucks have displaced most of the horses and a fourth of the mules in the country since the time of World War I, the change did not take place all at once, but at the rate of only 1 or 2 per cent per year. Any forecasts which left this important and obvious change out of account would have been only 1 or 2 per cent wrong per year—and forecasts are not usually required to predict changes more than one or two, or at least only a few years ahead. When, as in this case, the direction and extent of a change can be foreseen for several years ahead, its influence can be taken into account. An analysis which includes all the factors that change in the future is really dealing with a homogeneous population. It is changes in factors that are not included in an analysis that change a population and render tests of significance unreliable for that reason. If the number of horses and mules are included as a factor in a price analysis, then (1) future changes in these numbers will not destroy the validity of the analysis, and (2) in this case at least the future changes in this factor can be forecast with some degree of accuracy.

Finally, it must be recognized that there are large random elements in economic data, particularly agricultural economic data. Crop production series meet the requirements for random data rather closely, in those cases where acreage does not change greatly from year to year, since yields fluctuate from year to year chiefly in response to changes in the weather, which are random in character. Fluctuations in *demand* may be cyclic rather than random in character, but that part of a statistical price analysis which deals with the relation between production and price is related to random changes (in yields) and therefore approaches the requirements for random data laid down earlier in this chapter, and is more nearly amenable to statistical analytical methods.[5]

---

[5] For useful observations on this subject, see Mordecai Ezekiel and Karl Fox, *Methods of Correlation Analysis and Regression Analysis: Linear and Curvilinear*, 3rd ed., Wiley, 1959, Chap. 20.

The foregoing considerations mean that the significance of economic analyses depends, not so much upon objective statistical tests, as upon the conformity of the analysis with economic theory on the one hand and with the characteristics of the commodity concerned on the other. It is not sufficient for a price analyst to be familiar with economic theory and statistical methods, although that is indispensable; in addition, he must know a good deal about the particular commodity or service concerned.

five

ANALYSES WITH RESPECT TO PLACE AND FORM

14

Geographical Price Surfaces

Price analysts are interested in three different aspects of prices—differentials in prices over geographical areas, and differentials with respect to different grades of a product, as well as the changes over periods of time. That is, they are interested in prices with respect to space and form as well as time.

Changes in prices over periods of time are important, and have received most of the attention of price analysts, in line with their importance. But changes in prices over areas of space are important, too, particularly in the modern decentralized markets of today which cover large areas of geographical space.

Spatial hog price problems have been well analyzed in several publications.[1] Some more technical difficulties have arisen with respect to several other commodities, especially those that are directly affected by government price-support programs.

When the corn-loan program was being formulated in 1933, there were data available only as far back as 1924, and these were inconclusive. Consequently the structure of the program was revised considerably in the years that followed.

For example, the loan rates for corn during the first few years of the corn-loan program were uniform over the commercial corn area. The corn-loan surface was geographically flat. It was obvious from the first that this did not fit the corn-price surface over the area. Elementary economic theory alone would indicate that, since corn moves in large quantities from the surplus-producing areas of the western and central Corn Belt through to the East,

---

[1] These are summarized in G. S. Shepherd, *Marketing Farm Products — Economic Analysis,* Iowa State Univ. Press, 1962, Chap. 14.

price differentials between the surplus and deficit areas must be at least large enough to cover the costs of transportation.

As additional price data accumulated from the crop-reporting districts (about 10 counties per district), it became apparent that the price surface was even more undulating than had been anticipated earlier. Figure 14.1 shows in some detail the average farm prices of corn during the interwar years, 1924–39, over the commercial corn area. "Iso-price" lines, connecting approximately equal prices, like contour lines on a topographical map, help to bring out the character of the "price surface" over the area.

Figure 14.1 shows that the corn-price surface is not flat like the ocean, nor is it uniformly sloped in any single direction. The rough general tendency is for the price surface to slope downward from the east to the west, and from the south to the north; but the slope is not uniform. Valleys and ridges, plateaus, and even basins, occur in the price surface. In central and eastern Illinois and western and central Indiana during that period there was a basin of 63-cent prices surrounded by a ring of higher prices on all sides. Going west from that area, prices at first do not decline; they rise. It was necessary to surmount a ridge of 64- and 65-cent prices

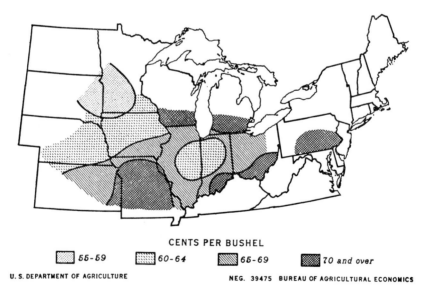

CENTS PER BUSHEL

55-59   60-64   65-69   70 and over

U. S. DEPARTMENT OF AGRICULTURE   NEG. 39475 BUREAU OF AGRICULTURAL ECONOMICS

Fig. 14.1 — The price surface for corn has a general slope upward from west to east, except for a depression in eastern Illinois and western Indiana, where large quantities of corn in excess of local needs are produced. The lowest prices are found in the northwest corner of the Corn Belt. (Average farm price, by crop-reporting districts in the commercial corn area.)

in western Illinois and southeastern Iowa before reaching the low-price valley that ran northwest from central Iowa, deepening as it went.

Actual differences in prices shown in Figure 14.1 were in most cases less than the transportation costs between the different points. It is evident from these price relations, as well as from data regarding corn shipments and destinations, that the corn produced in the surplus-producing areas did not move from the western and central part of the Corn Belt clear over to the eastern states, unless it be in a few exceptional years, and in comparatively small quantities. Corn from western and central Iowa ordinarily goes to eastern Iowa and as far east as Chicago but very little of it seems to go east of Illinois. Less is known about shipments from eastern central Illinois, but it appears from the price charts that corn does not move regularly, year after year, from Illinois to Indiana and Ohio, for prices in Indiana average about the same as in Illinois, and in Ohio they average only 4 or 5 cents higher.

Apparently, what happens is this: The price surface changes greatly from year to year, and in any one year the differentials from certain areas to certain others may be great enough to cover transportation costs between these areas. In another year these price differentials change, perhaps even reverse, and corn flows differently. The average figures show very small average-price differentials, but in any one year the price differentials may be large. Investigation of the years separately is required.

It is difficult to carry several price maps for individual years in the mind's eye at the same time, for comparison; the variability of the price surface from one year to another can be shown more clearly by sacrificing some detail and showing only cross sections rather than entire price surfaces. A cross-section comparison can be made by use of data from a row of crop-reporting districts running from east to west along the middle of the Corn Belt, with the district centers approximately equal distances (about 100 miles) apart. The prices in these districts may be represented by vertical bars, the chart then looking something like a picture of a picket fence with the stakes driven unevenly into the ground.

The Corn Belt widens out toward the west, so that it is advisable not only to show a section along the Corn Belt from east to west, but also a cross section cutting across the western end of the belt from north to south. The districts selected for this north-south section should lie successively adjacent to one another, their centers being closer together than those in the east-west line, because the gradation of prices is steeper and the distances involved are shorter. Each such chart, therefore, consists of two parts, one showing the east-west section and the other showing the north-south section.

Charts of the kind described, one of which has been prepared for each year, are too complicated and numerous to be reproduced here, but they show a story that can be told in a few sentences. They show that the character of the price surface changes greatly from year to year. In most years, it differs widely from the 16-year average surface shown in Figure 14.1. In 1927, 1928, 1929, and 1932, the surface sloped steeply upward from west to east; in 1936, it sloped almost as steeply downward from west to east; in 1925, 1926, 1931, 1934, 1935, and 1937, the general contour was horizontal, but the surface was uneven, in different places in the different years. In the other 5 years, the surface had a general sloping character similar to that of the 16-year average, but it had a different sort of unevenness each year. The price surface of the cross section from north to south was more nearly stable from year to year than that of the cross section from west to east, but in 1931 the normal steep upward slope from north to south was reversed, and in 1932 it was almost flat; and no two years were alike.

VARIATIONS IN CORN PRICE DIFFERENTIALS BETWEEN IOWA, INDIANA, AND OHIO

The price surface varies greatly from month to month, as well as from year to year. The data to show this for all the crop-reporting districts, or even for the cross-section districts, are too numerous to provide any clear mental impression. But the data for a few representative states and districts tell the story more clearly than the mass of data for all of the districts together.

The top line in Figure 14.2 shows the difference between the price of corn in Ohio and the price of corn in Iowa, by years, from 1909 to 1955. The Iowa price is used as the base; it is represented by the horizontal zero line across the chart. The Ohio price is plotted as so much above or below the Iowa price as represented by this horizontal zero line. The chart shows that the Ohio price ranged from 17 cents above to 10 cents below the Iowa price—a total range of 27 cents.

The lower line shows the same sort of comparison of Nebraska and Iowa prices, by years. The price differentials in this case cover a range of 20 cents.

Figure 14.3 shows the same sort of information by months, instead of by years. It shows that the monthly corn price differentials fluctuate rapidly over a wide range, within the season as

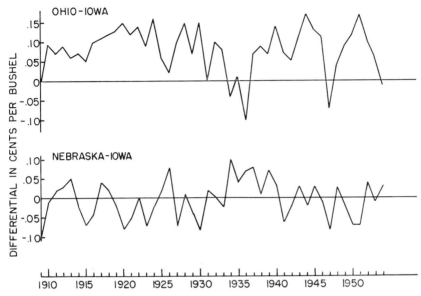

Fig. 14.2 — Annual (December-May average) corn price differentials between Iowa and Ohio, and Iowa and Nebraska, 1909–55.

well as between seasons. The range of the monthly differentials is nearly twice as great as the range of the yearly differentials.

Chief reason for the variations in corn price differentials from year to year among the different states apparently is variations in corn production. Figure 14.4 shows the inverse correlation that exists between relative prices and relative production, for Iowa and three other states during the interwar period 1924–39.

As a result of the study of these and other data, the administrators of the corn-loan program in 1941 replaced the original geographically flat or uniform loan rates by a structure of geographically different rates. The differentials among the loan rates were based upon the average price differentials over the preceding twenty years. It was expected that this structure of loan rates would fit the area with a minimum of disturbance to feeding, shipping, manufacturing, etc., that had been built up under the influence of competitive economic force and had presumably resulted in the most efficient location of these activities.

There was a question whether the differentials in the loan rates should be changed from year to year to conform with the different relative sizes of crops in the different states from year to year. The decision was made not to do this, but to retain a fixed structure of differentials from year to year, conforming with

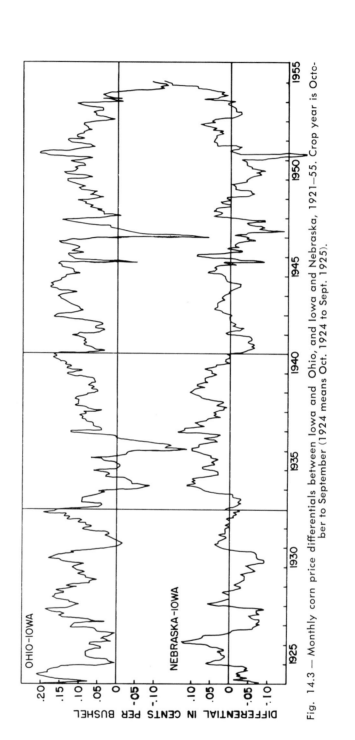

Fig. 14.3 — Monthly corn price differentials between Iowa and Ohio, and Iowa and Nebraska, 1921–55. Crop year is October to September (1924 means Oct. 1924 to Sept. 1925).

average crops and price differentials in the past. This would reduce the amount of shipping out from one state one year and shipping in another year as relative crop sizes changed; it was believed that the costs of moving corn into and out of local storage would be less than the costs of shipping corn into and out of geographical areas.

It was expected that this fixed structure of corn loan rates would reduce the variations in corn price differentials among the states from month to month and from year to year. It is interesting to observe, from Figures 14.2 and 14.3, that this has not happened. The differentials have continued to vary much the same as they did before the corn-loan program started back in 1933.

GEOGRAPHICAL DIFFERENTIALS IN WHOLESALE MEAT PRICES

The discussion cited in Footnote 1 of the present chapter shows that a considerable amount of variability exists among hog prices at different markets. The same thing is true of wholesale meat prices. Figure 14.5 shows how the prices of fresh pork loins at New York, for example, vary in relation to the corresponding prices at Chicago, from 1946 to near the end of 1949.

Effects of the fixed differential price ceilings imposed by the OPA until the middle of 1946 are clearly shown in the chart. So are the unsettling effects of the removal of price ceilings. After things settled down to normal, however, the price relations varied greatly from week to week. "Normal" appears to be represented by considerable variation. The freight rate on fresh pork loins from Chicago to New York was about $1.00 per 100 pounds through most of 1947, rising to $1.43 by September 1, 1949. Price variations before World War II were less in dollars and cents, but greater in percentage terms, than since the war.

If these were daily price data, relative price variations could be explained as the result of relative gluts and scarcities at New York that lasted until smaller and larger shipments could be made from Chicago to wipe them out. It takes a day or two to get pork from Chicago to New York. But these are weekly average price data. It is not easy to explain why packers at Chicago would continue to ship fresh pork loins to New York for a week or two at a time to sell for $2.00 to $3.00 per 100 pounds less than they would bring in Chicago, or why they would let substantial differentials in excess of the freight rate persist for several weeks at a time. The same sort of situation exists for other wholesale cuts of pork, and of beef as well. There must be good reasons for it. A study of the causes and

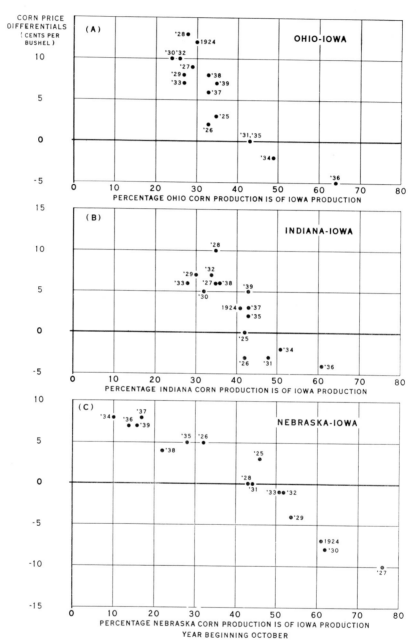

Fig. 14.4 — Relation between corn price differentials and relative corn production for various states; **A.** Corn price differentials between Ohio and Iowa (plotted up the side) and the percentage that Ohio production is of Iowa production (plotted along the bottom); **B.** Same sort of relationship for Indiana and Iowa; **C.** For Nebraska and Iowa.

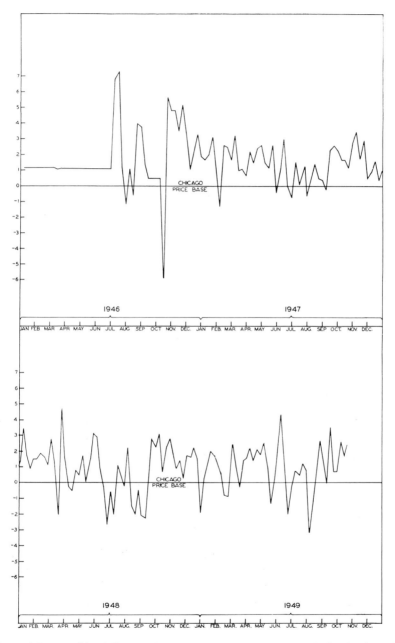

Fig. 14.5 — Weekly differentials in prices, in cents per pound, for fresh pork
loins at New York and Chicago.

[219]

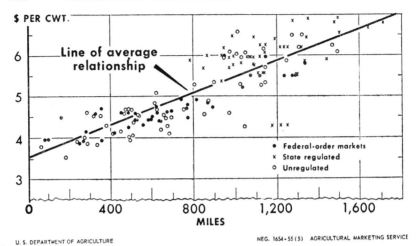

U. S. DEPARTMENT OF AGRICULTURE   NEG. 1654-55 (5)   AGRICULTURAL MARKETING SERVICE

Fig. 14.6 — Fluid milk prices, July 1953–June 1956, plotted against distance from Wisconsin.

effects of this situation would constitute a good marketing research project.

MILK PRICE DIFFERENTIALS [2]

The differentials between the prices of milk in different areas are more stable from month to month and year to year than the differentials for corn. The milk price regulations governing the different milk markets differ from market to market, and it is instructive to study the price differences between the areas at any one time, to see what the effects of the different regulations on prices might be.

Figure 14.6 shows the dealers' buying price for fluid milk at 143 markets located east of the Rocky Mountains, plotted against the distance from Eau Claire, Wisconsin (the heart of the milk surplus area). The chart shows that the price of milk increased an average of 19 cents per 100 pounds per 100 miles increase in distance from Eau Claire. This corresponds roughly with the costs of transportation and other transfer costs.

There is some scatter about the regression line in the chart. Only 75 per cent of the differences in prices was directly associated with distance; the other 25 per cent was the result of other factors. The location of the individual points above or below the line helps to identify the markets which were affected by these other factors.

[2] This section draws on "Regulations Affecting the Movement and Merchandising of Milk," Marketing Res. Rpt. No. 98, AMS, USDA, 1955, pp. 88–93.

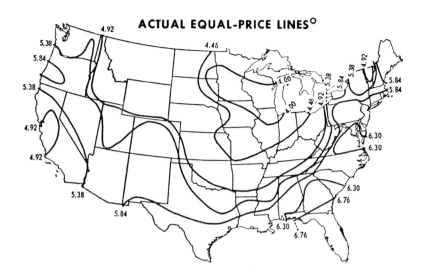

ACTUAL EQUAL-PRICE LINES°

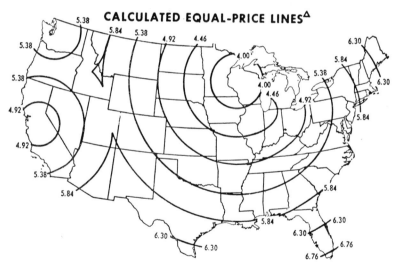

CALCULATED EQUAL-PRICE LINES^

△BASED ON DISTANCE FROM ALTERNATIVE SUPPLY AREAS.　　　°BASED ON PRICES IN 160 MARKETS

U. S. DEPARTMENT OF AGRICULTURE　　　NEG. 1655–55 (5)　AGRICULTURAL MARKETING SERVICE

Fig. 14.7 — Actual equal-price lines (price contours) for milk, July 1953—June 1954, and calculated equal-price lines based on distance from alternative supply areas.

(The names of the individual markets and the number of cents which their prices were above or below the line were given in a table in the original report; it is too long to reproduce here.) This paves the way for investigating in each case what the other factors were.

The relations among the prices of milk at 160 markets all over the United States are shown in a different way, by "iso-price" lines, in the upper part of Figure 14.7. This map includes alternative supply areas from Seattle, Washington, and Fresno, California, as well as from Eau Claire. The lower part of the chart shows prices based on distances from these alternative supply areas. The comparison of two charts shows that actual prices are lower than transportation costs alone would explain, in the intermountain areas of the West, and in the Northeast; they are higher in the East and Southeast.

15

Analysis of the Prices of Futures Contracts

In the markets for grain, cotton, eggs, butter, and other agricultural products that lend themselves to objective grading, a system of trading in futures contracts (contracts calling for the delivery of specified kinds and amounts of the physical commodity at a specified time and place) has grown up along with the marketing system for the physical product.

These futures contracts call for delivery of physical grain at some future date, although in actuality less than 1 per cent of the contracts ever mature and involve delivery of cash grain. More than 99 per cent of the futures contracts are closed out by the exchange of offsetting contracts before the delivery date.

The volume of trading in futures contracts is large relative to the volume of the actual grain. In the case of wheat, it is more than ten times the volume of terminal market trading in the commodity itself. About 90 per cent of all the trading in grain futures in the United States is conducted on the trading floor of the Chicago Board of Trade.

The relations between the prices of these futures contracts and the prices of the physical commodity are matters of great concern to dealers and processors. Large profits and losses hinge upon the correct analysis and interpretation of these futures prices and cash price relationships. They constitute an interesting special case for price analysis.

TWO OBJECTIVES IN FUTURES TRADING

Trading in futures contracts is conducted for two purposes. The one purpose is speculative; the trader's intention is to profit from changes in the price of the futures contract. The other purpose is protective—just the opposite of speculative; the trader's intention in this case is to protect himself against the effects of changes in the price of the physical commodity.

Thus a speculative trader buys futures when he thinks prices are going up, hoping to sell later at a profit, but bears the risk that he will take a loss if the market goes against him. The protective trader, who is a buyer and seller of the physical commodity, enters into opposite sales and purchases of futures, hoping that a possible loss in the one will be offset by a gain in the other, so that he will neither lose nor profit from changes in prices.

It is assumed here that the reader has an introductory knowledge of speculation and hedging on the commodity exchanges. The purpose of this chapter is to explore further some of the more advanced and technical problems involved in these operations.[1]

THE EXTENT OF THE PROTECTION AFFORDED BY HEDGING [2]

The violence of the changes in the prices of the principal grains over a period of ten years is shown by the continuous black lines in Figure 15.1. The price of corn, for example, nearly doubled within a few months from one crop year to the next in 1935. So did the price of oats. Wheat rose 50 per cent. Then within a year, all three prices declined to their previous levels, or lower. These were peace-time fluctuations. The fluctuations during the war and immediate postwar years are not shown, because of the abnormal forces at work then.

During the period 1924–25 to 1940–41, differences between the cash prices of grain in Chicago on Fridays separated by 8-week periods showed declines 47 per cent of the time for wheat prices, 49 per cent for corn, and 45 per cent for oats.

The declines averaged 9.4 cents per bushel for wheat, 7.8 cents for corn, and 4.5 cents for oats. The advances averaged 8.9, 8.2, and 4.3 cents per bushel, respectively.

In the long run, therefore, the declines and advances about offset each other. But in some cases, the declines over 8-week periods amounted to as much as 42 cents per bushel for wheat, 60 cents for corn, and 34 cents for oats. The advances amounted to as much as 45, 50, and 19 cents per bushel, respectively. This indicates that gains and losses from changes in prices over rela-

---

[1] An introductory discussion of hedging and speculation is given in two chapters of my *Marketing Farm Products — Economic Analysis,* Iowa State Univ. Press, Ames, 1962.

[2] This section is based upon L. D. Howell, *Analysis of Hedging and Other Operations in Grain Futures,* USDA Tech. Bul. 971, August, 1948.

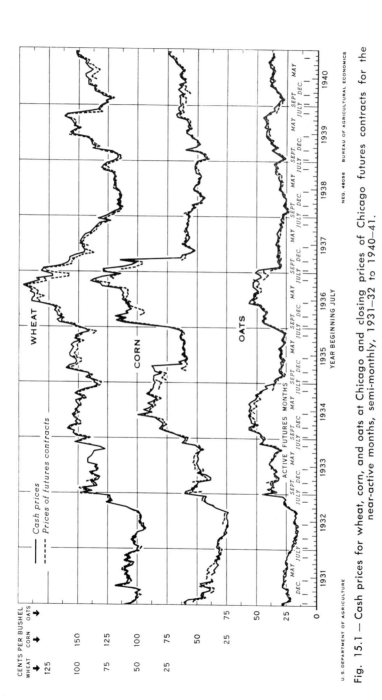

U.S. DEPARTMENT OF AGRICULTURE   NEG. 46036   BUREAU OF AGRICULTURAL ECONOMICS

Fig. 15.1 — Cash prices for wheat, corn, and oats at Chicago and closing prices of Chicago futures contracts for the near-active months, semi-monthly, 1931–32 to 1940–41.

tively short periods may be many times greater than the profits normally expected from merchandising the commodities.

If the prices of the futures contracts for these grains varied correspondingly with the variations in the prices of the physical product, hedging would afford complete protection. The dashed lines in Figure 15.1, representing the prices of the futures contracts for the near active months, show that the futures prices do move similarly to the cash grain prices. But the correspondence is not exact. Figure 15.2 shows that the differences or spreads between the cash and futures prices vary widely from time to time.

In 1937, for example, the prices of Chicago wheat futures for delivery in September changed from 28 cents per bushel below the cash prices at Chicago on February 19, to only 1 cent per bushel below cash prices on July 16. The prices of Chicago corn futures for delivery in September changed from 30 cents per bushel below the cash prices at Chicago on May 7 to 4 cents below cash prices on September 3. And the prices of Chicago oat futures for delivery in September changed from 12 cents per bushel below cash prices at Chicago on June 18 to a figure even with cash prices on August 6. These changes in spread between cash prices and prices of new crop futures usually are greatest toward the end of the old crop year and near the beginning of the new.

Before the early thirties, cash prices usually declined in relation to prices of futures contracts during the harvesting period. Following that period, cash prices usually advanced in relation to prices of futures contracts until near the beginning of the next harvest. These variations in the cash-futures price relationships are largely accounted for by carrying charges.

Within the crop year, with abundant supplies of grain available in the markets, cash prices normally can be expected to advance in relation to prices of futures contracts by an amount approximately equal to the costs (such as storage, insurance, and interest) of carrying the cash commodity. Changes in the immediate and prospective supply and demand situation, however, sometimes cause irregular changes in the spread between cash prices and prices of futures contracts, so that the differences may not even approximate carrying charges.

For example, during the ten years 1931–32 to 1940–41, changes in spread between cash prices and prices of futures contracts from one part of the season to another varied irregularly. This was particularly true after 1933.

Risks from changes in the spread between cash prices and prices of futures contracts (usually referred to as changes in basis)

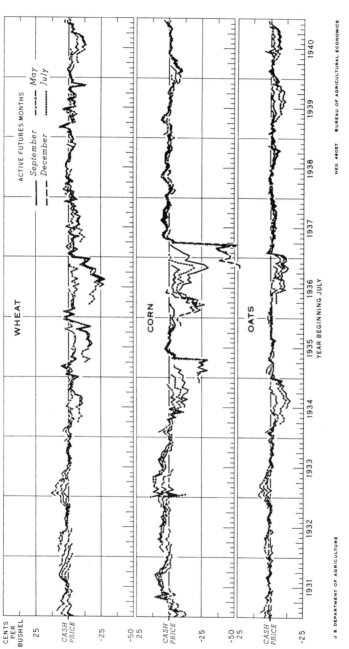

Fig. 15.2 — Variations in closing prices of Chicago futures contracts for wheat, corn, and oats from cash prices of these commodities, semi-monthly, 1931–32 to 1940–41.

are not offset by the normal hedging procedure. They may be responsible for substantial losses on the part of elevators, shippers, exporters, and millers, who may hedge invariably, but who fail to anticipate correctly the changes in basis. In appraising the usefulness of futures contracts as hedges against losses from changes in cash prices, then, it is important to learn how the risks from changes in cash prices compare with the risks from changes in basis.

Price Risks Usually Greater Than Basis Risks

Examination of the data in Table 15.1 shows that the changes in cash prices of grain usually exceeded the corresponding changes in basis. This means that hedging usually would have reduced the gains and losses from changes in cash prices.

Data for 1924–25 to 1940–41 show that changes in basis for grain at Chicago, over 8-week periods, calculated from near-month Chicago futures contracts, averaged about 36 per cent of the corresponding changes in cash prices for wheat, 56 per cent for corn, and 51 per cent for oats.

The proportions by years ranged from less than 16 per cent in 1939 to almost 90 per cent in 1926 for wheat, from 39 per cent in 1930 to 97 per cent in 1931 for corn, and from 25 per cent in 1936 to 133 per cent in 1929 for oats. Although these proportions varied widely from year to year, the variations were not closely related to changes in price level and no very distinct trends were indicated. Figure 15.3 shows that declines and advances in cash prices over 8-week periods usually were substantially greater than the losses and gains on long-basis positions.

Gains and Losses From Changes in Basis

Data on changes in basis at Chicago over 8-week periods, calculated from near-month Chicago futures contracts for the period 1924–25 to 1940–41, show gains on long-basis positions about 55 per cent of the time for wheat, 55 per cent for corn, and 53 per cent for oats, and losses about 34, 36, and 29 per cent, respectively, of the time. The gains averaged 3.0 cents per bushel for wheat, 3.5 cents for corn, and 2.1 cents for oats. The losses averaged 4.5 cents, 5.8 cents, and 3.1 cents per bushel, respectively. The proportion of the time during which changes in basis represented gains and losses and the average amounts of these gains and losses, vary noticeably from one year to another.

The average gains and losses on long-basis positions vary with the length of the interval and the futures contracts used in calcu-

TABLE 15.1

Distribution of Changes in Cash Prices of Wheat at Chicago and the Corresponding Changes in Basis Calculated From Near-Month Chicago Futures Contracts, Over 8-Week Periods, Years 1924–25 to 1940–41

Changes in Cash Prices (cents per bushel)	Changes in Basis (cents per bushel)											Total
	−5	−4	−3	−2	−1	0	1	2	3	4	5	
	(No.)	(No.)	(No.)	(No.)	(No.)	(No.)	(No.)	(No.)	(No.)	(No.)	(No.)	(No.)
−15 and under	25	5	5	6	8	5	9	10	8	1	8	90
−14	2	1	2	1		1	1	1			2	11
−13			2				1		1		2	6
−12	4	1	1	1	1	4	2	1	1	3	3	22
−11	2	1			3	1	1	2	3	1	2	15
−10	2				3		2	4	1		2	16
−9	1		1	4	2	2	2	3	1			24
−8	2	1		2	3	1	3	2	2	4	1	16
−7	1		2	2	4	1	2	3	5	2	3	24
−6	3	1	1	1	4	3	2	4	1	1	4	26
−5	7		2	5	2	6	3	3	4	7	1	31
−4	1	1	2			3	4	5	6	2	9	32
−3	4		1	3	2	7	5	2	4	7	5	31
−2	3	1		2	5	1	7	3	3	4	4	43
−1	4	3		2	7	5	4	10	4	3	2	32
0				2	4	4	3	7	5	3	4	41
1	3	2		2	4	7	5	6	7	3	5	38
2	2	2		6	5	5	5	6	5	2	1	47
3	2	1	2	1	5	6	4	6	4	8	7	33
4	3	1		3	4	3	9	1	2	2	1	47
5	2		2		3	1	5	2	3	4	3	26
6	1		3			4	4		3	1	3	21
7	1	2	2	2	1	1	3	5	1	1	1	21
8	2	1		2	1	3	5	1	3	1		24
9	1		1			3	2	2	3	3		18
10				1	2	1	2	2	3	1		18
11					2		2	2	1			13
12				2		1	2			1	1	10
13	2	1	1	1		3	3				1	13
14	1					2		1				10
15 and over	4	1	8	4	8	16	9	8	9	5	14	86
Total	86	28	41	52	89	101	116	106	96	74	93	882

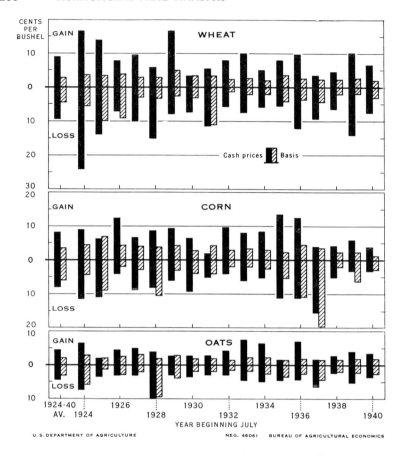

Fig. 15.3 — Average gains and losses from changes in cash prices and in basis for wheat, corn, and oats at Chicago over 8-week periods, by seasons, 1924–25 to 1940–41.

lating the changes. During the ten years 1931–32 to 1940–41, losses on long-basis positions from changes in basis for wheat, corn, and oats, at Chicago, calculated from near-month Chicago futures contracts, averaged about two-thirds as large over 4-week periods and about one and one-half as large over 16-week periods as for 8-week periods. The gains on long-basis positions averaged slightly more than two-thirds as large for 4-week periods and slightly less than one and one-half times as large for 16-week periods as for 8-week periods. These differences vary decidedly from year to year. Gains and losses on long-basis positions calculated from near-month futures contracts usually average somewhat less than those calculated from futures contracts for the more distant months.

Gains and losses on long-basis positions for wheat, corn, and oats at Chicago are fairly typical of those in other markets. During the ten years 1931–32 to 1940–41, gains and losses on long-basis positions over 8-week periods, calculated from near-month Chicago futures contracts for wheat at Chicago, averaged slightly less than at Kansas City, Minneapolis, and St. Louis, and somewhat more than those at Kansas City and Minneapolis, calculated from near-month Kansas City and Minneapolis futures contracts. For corn, the gains and losses from changes in basis at Chicago averaged about the same as at Kansas City and at Minneapolis but somewhat greater than at St. Louis. Similar comparisons for oats show that gains and losses at Chicago averaged slightly less than at Kansas City and St. Louis but slightly larger than at Minneapolis.

Gains and losses on long-basis positions varied considerably from one part of the season to another as well as from year to year. Usually they were greatest toward the end and at the beginning of a crop year. During the years 1931–32 to 1940–41, changes in basis over 8-week periods ended in July and August for wheat and oats and in September, October, and November for corn resulted in losses on long-basis positions that averaged about twice as much as those for periods ended in other months. They resulted in gains on long-basis positions that averaged considerably more than those for periods ended during other months.

The losses on long-basis positions in actual experience would be less than these simple average statistics indicate. From the end of one crop year to the beginning of the next, the cash price descends from its highest seasonal peak (for the old crop) to the lowest seasonal point (for the new crop). The cash price for the old crop usually is substantially higher than the level of the new-crop futures, and rapidly declines as the new crop comes on. Changes in basis then are large, and such as to cause losses on long-basis positions. Grain dealers therefore handle as little grain as they can during those periods. If the basis gains and losses were weighted by the volume of grain transactions at different times of the year, the actual losses would be smaller, and gains probably larger, than the simple averages shown above.

DISCRETIONARY HEDGING [3]

The preceding section shows to what extent hedging reduces price risks. It is based on the generally held assumption that grain

---

[3] This section is based on part of an article by Holbrook Working, "Futures Trading and Hedging," *The American Economic Review*, Vol. 43, No. 3, June, 1953, pp. 320–26.

dealers hedge for the purpose of reducing those risks, so as to avoid speculation. This assumption is substantially valid as regards those who practice hedging uniformly. However, most hedgers are engaged in a business that requires them to keep informed on many aspects of the commodity situation, with the result that many hedgers often form quite definite opinions on price prospects. Except in firms that have a strict rule against taking hedgable risks, it is common for stocks to be carried unhedged at times when the responsible individual expects a price advance, and for stocks of the commodity to be hedged at other times. Some individuals and firms hedge stocks only when they are particularly fearful of price decline.

Such discretionary hedging, involving a firm in the practice of both hedging and speculation, seems to be especially prevalent among dealers and processors who handle commodities such as wool and coffee, that have relatively little public speculation in their futures markets. When hedge selling in such a futures market becomes heavy, the price may readily be depressd to a point where a good many dealers and processors are attracted by the possibilities of profit through speculative holding of the commodity. Even among handlers of commodities which attract broad public participation to their futures markets, such as wheat, discretionary hedging is not uncommon. Consequently the existence of futures trading in a commodity and widespread use of futures for hedging do not in fact mean that the responsibilities of price formation are shifted entirely, or even mainly, to people who deal only in the commodity futures.

A major source of mistaken notions of hedging is the conventional practice of illustrating hedging with a hypothetical example in which the price of the future bought or sold as a hedge is supposed to rise or fall by the same amount that the spot price rises or falls. Let us instead consider hedging realistically in terms of some actual prices. The prices to be used will be those for wheat at Kansas City on the first trading day of each month in which futures matured during the crop year 1951–52.

On the first business day of July, 1951, a merchant or processor considering the purchase of the cheapest quality No. 2 Hard Winter wheat (the quality represented by quotations on Kansas City wheat futures) found such spot wheat selling at 3 cents per bushel under the price of the September future. If he bought spot wheat, hedged it in the September future, and carried the wheat until the first business day of September, the results, in cents per bushel, would have been as shown below:

| Quotation | Date and Price | | Gain or Loss |
	July 2	Sept. 4	
Spot No. 2 Hard (low)...	229¼	232½	. . . . . .
September future........	232¼	233½	. . . . . .
Spot premium.........	−3	−1	+2 (gain)

The profit of 2 cents per bushel is calculated above, in what may seem an awkward way, from the change in spot premium (a negative premium, or discount, on each of these dates). It is awkward, however, only for those to whom it is unfamiliar. The hedger tends to calculate his profits in this way because he would buy the wheat on July 2 primarily for the reason that he could get it at discount of 3 cents per bushel under the price of the September future. In fact, the bargaining which preceded the purchase would normally proceed in terms of discount rather than of price, the price being ascertained by reference to the latest futures price quotation, after sale at a mutually satisfactory discount had been agreed on.

The fact that on September 4, No. 2 Hard Winter wheat sold at a discount under the September future, though it is the grade of wheat currently deliverable on the future, is accounted for by the fact that the spot price applies to wheat "on track," requiring additional expenditure to get it into a warehouse. Wheat was then moving into commercial storage on a large scale because of heavy marketing by producers.

On September 4, our grain merchant or processor would probably not have sold the wheat he bought earlier, but instead would have bought more wheat. If he did that, and held until December 1, the results, in cents per bushel, would have appeared as follows:

| Quotation | Date and Price | | Gain or Loss |
	Sept. 4	Dec. 1	
Spot No. 2 Hard (low) ..	232½	252	. . . . . .
December future.......	238¼	252	. . . . . .
Spot premium.........	−5¾	0	+5¾ (gain)

In this case the spot price of the cheapest deliverable wheat came, on December 1, to exact equality with the price of the December future, and the gross return for storing the wheat was exactly what might have been expected, on September 4, from the fact that such wheat was then selling at a discount of 5¾ cents under the price of the December future.

In these calculations we have left out of account the possibility that a merchant who bought at a discount of 5¾ cents on September 4 might have got wheat of a little better than minimum No. 2 quality — wheat which might have been sold on September 4 at a discount of, say, 5½ cents, rather than 5¾ cents, if the seller had been willing to look farther for a buyer. And we have ignored the possibility that on December 1 the merchant might have sold at a premium of ½ cent over the December future by virtue of the slightly superior quality of the wheat, and by finding a buyer who did not choose to shop around enough to get the best bargain possible. In other words, we have left out of account sources of normal *merchandising* profits.

On December 1, a merchant or processor may seem to have had no incentive for longer holding of wheat for which he had no immediate need. The spot price then was on a par with the December future, and at a premium of 1 cent over the price of the May future. But let us suppose that he continued to hold, with a hedge in the May future, and see what would have happened if he held until May 1. Though we imagine that the wheat is already in storage, we may make the next calculation as though it concerned a new purchase:

Quotation	Date and Price		Gain or Loss
	Dec. 1	May 1	
Spot No. 2 Hard (low)...	252	247¼	. . . . . .
May future.	251	238¼	. . . . . .
Spot premium.	+1	+9	+8 (gain)

This time a merchant would have gained a gross return of 8 cents per bushel from storage. It would have been in part a windfall profit, since he had no advance *assurance* of obtaining it; but he would have gained it on a quite conservative venture. He was well assured of not losing more than 1 cent per bushel (because the spot wheat that he held would surely sell at as high a price as the May future at some time in May), and he could count with virtual certainty on spot wheat going to a substantial premium over the price of the May future at some time between December and May.

As of May 1, there remained no prospect of profit from continued storage of wheat during that crop year, unless perhaps for a few days more. Before the end of the month, the spot premium, based on the May future, would have to fall from 9 cents to near zero. Moreover, the spot price on May 1 was at a premium of 18 cents over the July future, and that premium should be expected to fall to zero or below by July 1. The outcome, if a merchant in fact held any wheat in storage from May 1 to July 1, was as follows:

Quotation	Date and Price		Gain or Loss
	May 1	July 1	
Spot No. 2 Hard (low)...	247¼	218½	. . . . . .
July future............	229¼	225	. . . . . .
Spot premium.........	+18	−6½	−24½ (loss)

Probably some merchants did store a little wheat from May 1 to July 1, hedged in the July future, and did take the loss per bushel indicated by the above calculation. Grain merchants, like operators of retail stores, must try to keep adequate stocks on their shelves to serve their customers. But a merchant who hedged would have seen clearly on May 1 that any wheat that he might continue to hold until July would involve a loss, as surely, though not so completely, as would Christmas trees held until December 26.

The foregoing examples of hedging tend in one respect to be a little misleading; spot premiums do not always follow so obviously logical a pattern through the course of a crop year as they did in 1951–52. If spot wheat in July, were regularly, in all years, at a moderate discount under the September future, and if spot wheat, in September, were always at a large discount under the December future, and spot wheat in May always at a large premium over the July future, merchants and processors would have less need than they do for futures markets. They would then have no need to watch spot-future price relations in order to judge when to accumulate stocks, and when to draw them low. But our purpose at the

moment is merely to see how hedgers use spot-futures price relations as a guide in inventory control, thereby earning a return for
holding stocks that must be stored by someone.

We should now note three facts concerning hedging. First,
contrary to a common impression, hedging of the sort here considered is not properly comparable with insurance. It is a sort of
arbitrage. Most hedging is done in the expectation of a change in
spot-future price relations, the change that is reasonably to be expected being often indicated quite clearly by the current spot-
future price relation.

Secondly, hedging does not eliminate risks arising from price
variability. Risk is less than on stocks held unhedged, but it still
exists. When the commodity involved is of quite different quality
from that which is represented by the future, or in a location re-
mote from that to which the futures price relates, the risks assumed by hedgers tend to be much larger than is suggested by
the examples given here.

And thirdly, hedging is not necessarily done for the sake of
reducing risks. The role of risk avoidance in most commercial
hedging has been greatly overemphasized in economic discussions.
Most hedging is done largely, and may be done wholly, because
the information on which the merchant or processor acts leads
logically to hedging. He buys the spot commodity because the
spot price is low *relative to* the futures price and he has reason to
expect the spot premium to advance; therefore he buys spot *and*
sells the future. Or in the case of a flour miller, he sells flour for
forward delivery because he can get a price that is favorable *in
relation to* the price of the appropriate wheat future; therefore he
sells flour *and* buys wheat futures. (Here the arbitrage, it may
be noted, is between two forward prices, that for flour and that for
wheat.)

Incidentally, recognition of the fact that hedging may be done
purely as a logical consequence of the reasoning on which the
hedger acts (reasoning, for example, that the spot price is low relative to the future) rather than from any special desire to mini-
mize risks, helps to explain why many dealers and processors
sometimes hedge and sometimes do not. As we have remarked,
merchants and processors, even though they hedge, have need to
keep informed on conditions that affect the price of the commodity
and they may often have opinions on prospective price changes.

If a merchant is accumulating stocks at a time when spot premiums are low — his most reliable basis for such action — and if at the same time he is fairly confident of an advance in futures prices as well as in spot premiums, why should he not carry the stocks unhedged, if he can afford to take some extra risk?

Perhaps the main reason that hedging, as commonly practiced on futures markets, has been so widely misunderstood and misrepresented is that economists have tried to deal with it in terms of a concept that seemed to cover all sorts of hedging. This would be desirable if it were feasible, but the general concept of hedging as taking offsetting risks wholly, or even primarily, for the sake of reducing net risk, serves so badly as applied to most hedging on futures markets that we need another concept for that most common sort of hedging. To put it briefly, we may say that hedging in commodity futures involves the *purchase or sale of futures in conjunction with another commitment, usually in the expectation of a favorable change in the relation between spot and futures prices.*

EFFECTS OF DIFFERENT CLASSES OF TRADERS

There has been much conjecture as to the effect of different classes of traders on futures markets, and judgments as to these effects have been embodied in numerous proposals designed to encourage or discourage different types of trading. A number of studies have been made, in an effort to determine as accurately as possible the effects on the market, and on the marketing process, of various kinds of trading. For the most part these studies have been concerned with the effects of the operations of large-scale traders, particularly large-scale speculators.

The role of the small speculative trader in the futures market has been the subject of much discussion. On the one hand it has been held that such traders are a disturbing influence in the market, accentuating price swings, and on occasions contributing to wild and disastrous price fluctuations. On the other hand it has been maintained that such traders are a necessary element in the market since their presence makes it possible for the expert trader—who is presumed to exercise a beneficent influence on prices—to find traders to take the opposite side of his trades, and supply through their losses the income which is necessary to support the continued trading activity of the professional.

THE COMMODITY EXCHANGE AUTHORITY[4]

The Commodity Exchange Authority has made an extensive analysis of the trading behavior of small speculators, which throws some light on their place in the futures market. Their study covers the trading of 9,000 speculators over the period from January 1, 1924, to December 31, 1932 (the period of rapid inflation that led to the market crash of 1929 and subsequent depression years). It confirms a number of commonly held opinions as to the results of speculative trading; it tends to disprove others which have also been widely accepted.

The first obvious conclusion from the analysis is that the great majority of small speculators lost money in the grain futures market. There were 6,598 speculators in the sample with net losses, compared with 2,184 with net profits, or three times as many loss traders as profit traders. Net losses of speculators were approximately six times net profits; there were nearly $12,000,000 of losses, compared with about $2,000,000 of profits. Speculative traders in the sample lost money in each of the four grains traded—wheat, corn, oats, and rye.

The small speculator's characteristic hesitation in closing out loss positions was primarily responsible for the high ratio of losses. An often-quoted maxim for speculative trading is "Cut your losses and let your profits run." Contrary to this advice, speculators in the sample showed a clear tendency to cut their profits and let their losses run. Futures positions or cycles resulting in losses were held open for consistently longer durations than profit cycles—average losses were larger than average profits—and long cycles were kept open for a greater number of days than short cycles. In wheat futures, for example, the average duration of profit cycles was only 10.5 days, compared with 16.3 days for loss cycles. The average duration of the profit trader in wheat futures was 114.8 days, compared with 182.5 days for the loss trader.

Speculators who did make profits on individual trades were inclined to cut them short. The tendency on individual cycles was to settle for profits which were much smaller on the average than the average loss on trades closed out unprofitably. With this situation, plus the shorter time duration of profit cycles, it is not surprising that there were actually more individual profit cycles than loss cycles.

In wheat futures, for example, there were 42,668 profit cycles

---

[4] The remainder of this chapter is based closely on the summary at the end of: Blair Stewart, "An Analysis of Speculative Trading in Grain Futures," Commodity Exchange Authority, USDA, Tech. Bul. 1,001, 1949.

compared with 34,373 loss cycles. But the average gain on the profitable cycles was only $212, while the average loss on those unprofitable was $501. Obviously, the outcome was a net loss, not only from the standpoint of the greatest number of traders, but also from the standpoint of aggregate profits and losses of the group as a whole. What happened, of course, was this: When profits on one trade were combined with losses on other trades, the end result was a net loss for the great majority of speculators.

The study confirms the commonly held impression that the amateur speculator is more likely to be long than short in the futures market. About half of the speculators in wheat and corn had positions only on one side of the market, and of this group, those on the long side only greatly exceeded the number with short positions only. However, the one-side-only traders did only a minor proportion of the total trading. The other half of the speculators who had both long and short cycles accounted for most of the trading in wheat and corn. From the standpoint of market activity, the preference for the long side was not as great as is sometimes supposed. In wheat futures approximately 63 per cent of the cycles were long and 37 per cent short, and in corn 58 per cent were long and 42 per cent short. The preference for the long side was more pronounced in oats and rye.

A great majority of speculators in the sample had relatively small profits and losses. The profits of 84 per cent of the profit traders were less than $1,000 each, and the profits of 39 per cent less than $100 each. The losses of 68 per cent of the loss traders were less than $1,000 each, and 16 per cent had losses of less than $100 each. Obviously, a very large percentage of the traders in the sample operated on a small scale, and many of them discontinued trading before realizing large profits or suffering losses.

Short positions of speculators tended to show profits more frequently than long positions. While a majority of the trades of consistent bulls resulted in losses, consistent bears in all gains had more profits cycles than loss cycles. Among traders who operated on both sides of the market, there was also a greater frequency of profits on short cycles than on long cycles. In spite of this, however, the total losses of short sellers exceeded their total profits—just as in the case of consistent longs.

The representation of large-scale traders in the sample was not broad enough to warrant positive conclusions as to the success of large speculators in grain futures, as compared with the profits and losses of small traders. There was no evidence, however, that the largest size classes included a higher proportion of successful traders than the groups with smaller average positions. Generally speaking, the large and small traders alike were unsuccessful in their trading.

Among all the major occupational groups losses from speculative trading in grain futures greatly exceeded profits. Among managers of business concerns, for example, there were 840 profit traders, compared with 2,563 loss traders. The aggregate profits of this occupational group amounted to $1,076,300, against losses of $6,210,200. Persons with occupations "unknown" had the greatest proportion of profit traders—32.3 per cent. Farmers had the lowest proportion of profit traders—21.2 per cent. "Retired" persons made up the only group having a better-than-average proportion of profit traders in each of the four grains covered by the survey.

From the standpoint of aggregate profits and losses for occupational groups, managers in the grain business were somewhat more successful in speculative trading than other groups. But even with this class aggregate profits in dollars were only 28 per cent of aggregate losses. Semiprofessional workers showed the lowest profit ratio in aggregate dollar amounts—11 per cent. The profit ratio for farmers on this basis was 13 per cent. In general, the chances for success in grain futures trading did not differ greatly from one occupation to another. Special knowledge of the commodity traded seemed to have little effect on the outcome of speculative trading during the period studied.

The study clearly shows the tendency of long speculators to buy on days of price declines, and for shorts to sell on price rises. Analysis of 58,000 two-day cycles showed that almost 62 per cent of the two-day long cycles were initiated on days of decline in the price of the dominant future, and that 55 per cent of the two-day short cycles began on days of advancing prices. Futhermore, the greater the price decline on a given day the larger the number of long cycles initiated. Trading against the current movement of prices was the dominant pattern on both sides of the market, but was not nearly so definite for shorts as for longs.

The tendency of longs to buy on price declines and for shorts to sell on price rises indicates that traders in the sample were predominantly price-level traders. Longs tended to buy when prices fell below levels which they considered proper, and shorts sold when prices advanced above levels which they believed justified. The inclination to trade according to predetermined price opinions apparently was not disturbed by the long period of declining prices from 1929 to 1932. However perverse it may seem, this period of declining prices stimulated speculative buying by small speculators, although the activity of short sellers was dampened slightly.

A final comment should be made involving a most important question. As already indicated, the losses of traders in the sample were much greater than their profits. If these results are representative of trading by small speculators generally, there must be other groups—large speculators, scalpers, spreaders, or hedgers—which make very large profits.

There is no known empirical study, however, which reveals other groups of traders with net profits sufficient to balance such large losses as those suffered by small speculators in the sample. Yet the nature of futures trading is such that all losses are balanced by profits. This raises the most important question left unanswered by this study. Was the sample in this respect not typical of small speculative traders? There is no apparent reason for pronounced bias in the direction of losses. If the sample is representative, is there another group of traders who consistently make profits large enough to balance the losses of small speculators? There is no convincing evidence that such large profits are made by any class of traders. These are questions which can be answered only by further studies of the results of futures trading.

16

The Comparative Cost of Price Supports and Direct Payments

Would a direct-payment program cost more, or less, than price supports?

In answering this question, we need to consider:

1. The cost to the government of the payments it makes for price-supporting purposes or for direct payments to farmers. These payments come sooner or later out of taxes.
2. The cost to consumers of the product.
3. What do consumers get for their money?

We will consider these three items in turn.

ANALYSIS OF COST DISTRIBUTION

Cost to Government

With a given size crop (i.e., with the supply fixed) the only way to support the price above open-market levels is to increase the demand for the crop. Something can be done along these lines by advertising, merchandising, etc., but not much. The results are limited by the fundamental inelasticity of the human stomach, plus the inelasticity of the human pocketbook. If we eat more cranberries, we eat less of some other fruit; if we eat more potatoes, we eat less bread and rice, and so on.

Beyond those rather narrow limits, the government can step in and increase the demand by buying up enough of the product to raise the price to the support level. Then the government has to decide how to dispose of its purchases without sending the price down below support levels again. It can give the product away

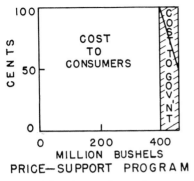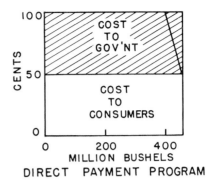

Fig. 16.1 — Costs of a price-support program and of a direct-payment program.

(provided it can figure out how to do this without weakening the demand for the rest of the product on the regular market), or divert it to lower uses, or destroy it.

Our discussion will be most clear cut if we take one or two crops as specific illustrations. Potatoes are one good example. We will use round numbers and the simplest arithmetic, so we can follow it easily.

We will take 400 million bushels as the basic or average potato production, and $1 per bushel as the basic or average farm price. The average crop at the average price, then, would be worth $400 million.

COST OF PRICE SUPPORTS

A price-support program would require the USDA to buy up the excess over average. For a crop 15 per cent over average, the excess would be 60 million bushels. That would cost $60 million of tax money. This is shown in the left-hand section of Figure 16.1.

The USDA can destroy most of its potatoes, or divert most of them to lower uses, as it did when it bought nearly 30 per cent of the big 1948 crop. The costs of diversion were so great that the government lost 87 per cent of the gross cost of the potatoes.[1]

COST OF DIRECT PAYMENTS

Now we can compute the cost of direct payments. The figure needed here is the elasticity of the demand for potatoes — the responsiveness of potato consumption to changes in price. Statistical

---

[1] "Irish Potatoes Price Support and Related Operations," CCC and Section 32 Funds, Jan. 1, 1943 — Dec. 31, 1949, PMS — Fiscal Branch, Financial Analysis Division, USDA, PMA, p. 18.

analysis shows that this elasticity of the demand for potatoes is about 0.3. That is, in percentage terms, the price changes about 3⅓ as much as the production changes. A 15 per cent larger-than-average crop, therefore, would push the price of potatoes down to 50 cents, as shown in the right-hand section of Figure 16.1.

The USDA then would make up the difference—50 cents—by direct payments on the whole crop. That would cost $230 million of taxpayers' money—$170 million more than the $60 million cost of the price-support program.

Cost of Potatoes to Consumers

But this is only the first step. The cost of potatoes to consumers must also be taken into account. What would the cost of potatoes be under the two programs?

We will figure this out the simplest way first, for clarity, leaving out the cost of distribution. Then we will bring in the costs of distribution, for completeness.

With the price-support program, consumers would buy 400 million bushels of potatoes at $1 a bushel — a cost of $400 million. The government would buy 60 million bushels, also at $1 a bushel, which would cost $60 million of taxpayers' money. The total cost therefore would be $400 million plus $60 million, amounting to a total of $460 million. This is shown in the left-hand section of Figure 16.1.

With the direct-payment program, consumers would buy 460 million bushels of potatoes at 50 cents a bushel, that would cost $230 million. The government would make direct payments of 50 cents a bushel. That would cost $230 million. The total cost therefore would be $230 million plus $230 million, amounting to $460 million. This is shown in the right-hand section of Figure 16.1. The whole thing is summarized in Table 16.1.

TABLE 16.1
COSTS OF PRICE SUPPORTS AND DIRECT PAYMENTS*

	Price Supports	Direct Payments
Cost to government.........	60 bu. @ $1 = $ 60	460 bu. @ 50c = $230
Cost to consumers.........	400 bu. @ $1 = 400	460 bu. @ 50c = 230
Total cost..............	$460	$460

* Data are expressed in millions.

The total areas in the two sections of Figure 16.1 are the same. Potato growers get $460 million in either case. They get more of their money from taxpayers, and less from pototo consumers, under the direct-payment program than under the price-support program. But the two plans cost the same. And this is true, as a general rule, whatever the elasticity of the demand.

A further general rule follows: For any crop where the demand is less elastic than 1.0, the tax cost for the direct-payment program is more than for the price-support program. The opposite is true for crops where the demand is more elastic than 1.0. But in all cases the total cost—taxes plus cost of potatoes—is the same under one plan as under the other.

There is, however, some difference in who would foot the bill. Our income taxes are progressive. Wealthy people pay a larger slice of their income as taxes than poor people. We have seen that more of the cost of a direct-payment program comes out of tax money than with a price-support program. Thus, the upper-income group of people would pay a larger share of the $230 million under a direct-payment program than if we had a price-support program.

What Consumers Get for Their Money

This is not the whole of the matter, yet. A third item must be considered—what consumers get for their money.

Under the direct-payment program, consumers would have 60 million bushels of potatoes to eat which they would not have under the price-support program. Now, 60 million bushels of 50-cent potatoes come to $30 million. This would be a net benefit, a clear gain, above what they would get under the price-support program. For the more goods and services we consume, the higher is our standard of living. In terms of the general welfare, then, the country would be $30 million better off under a direct-payment program than under a price-support program.

The producers of other foods than potatoes, however, would be harmed to some extent. As consumers ate 60 million bushels more potatoes, that would reduce their demand for other foods. The prices of those other foods would decline.

This decline in prices would reduce the gross and net incomes of the producers of those foods, because the demand for food is inelastic; the decline in prices would be greater, in percentage terms, than the increase in quantity of food consumed.

TABLE 16.2
Costs of Price Supports and Direct Payments*

	Price Supports	Direct Payments
Cost to government.........	60 bu. @ $1 = $ 60	460 bu. @ $0.50 = $230
Cost to consumers.........	400 bu. @ $2 = 800	460 bu. @ $1.50 = 690
Total cost...............	$860	$920

* Data are expressed in millions.

COSTS OF DISTRIBUTION

When the costs of distribution are brought into account, the results come out the same as above, if we assume that costs of distribution remain unchanged.

On the average, potato producers get only half of the consumer's dollar. The distributor gets the other half.

The consumer, therefore, when the farm price of potatoes was $1 a bushel, would be paying $2 a bushel. That means that under the price-support program, consumers would pay $800 million for the 400 million bushels they could buy.

Under the direct-payment program, consumers would pay $1.50 a bushel (50 cents plus the costs of distribution, which would remain practically constant from year to year at $1 a bushel). The comparative cost of the two programs then would be as shown in Table 16.2.

The direct-payment plan would therefore cost $920 — $860 = $60 million more than the price-support program. This extra $60 million goes to the distributors for handling the 60 million bushels of potatoes.

In effect, consumers get 60 million bushels of potatoes for their $60 million. These 60 million bushels are worth $1.50 a bushel. Their total value is $90 million. But the direct-support program costs $60 million more than the price-support program. The net gain to the country as a whole therefore would be $90 million — $60 million = $30 million.[2] This figure is the same as the one

---

[2] Actually, the costs of distribution vary to some extent with the level of prices, since some of the mosts (the markups, for instance) run in percentage terms. To the extent that the costs of distribution vary, consumers gain somewhat more than they do in the illustration given above. But we don't know just how much more they would gain. Until we do know, for simplicity and definiteness we will stick to our $30 million as the monetary measure of the net gain to consumers from the direct-payment program.

obtained above, before the costs of distribution were taken into account.

RELATIVE SIZE OF GOVERNMENT PAYMENTS

Figure 16.1 shows that a moderately large crop, 15 per cent over average size, is enough to depress prices 50 per cent below average levels. The government payments then would be as great as the market value of the entire crop. This is a big order.

It makes two things clear. First, the "support" level (the level of prices below which payments will be made) should be set no higher than the level that would move an average crop into consumption. If it were set higher than this, the goverment payments would be greater than the market value of the entire crop. In terms of our example, if it were set say at $1.50, the government payments would be twice as great as the market value of the entire crop.

Second, it would be better all around to let the "support" level vary inversely and proportionately with the size of the crop. This would stabilize potato producers' gross returns. It would also reduce the size of the government payments in big crop years. In terms of our example, it would reduce them from 50 cents a bushel to 33.3 cents, a reduction of one-third.

GENERAL PRINCIPLES REVEALED

Several principles, therefore, may now be stated:

1. The cost to the government for purchases to support prices is less than the cost to the government for direct payments to producers, when the demand is less elastic than 1.0. The opposite is true when the demand is more elastic than 1.0.
2. The total cost (the cost of the product to consumers plus the cost of the government purchases or payments) always comes out exactly the same under one plan as under the other, no matter what the elasticity of demand.
3. The price-support program is regressive in two ways, when the demand is less elastic than unity. Less of the total cost is paid out of taxes (chiefly income taxes, which are progressive) and more is paid by consumers, at prices which proportionately (in relation to incomes) are regressive.
4. Under the price-support program, some of the product is diverted to lower uses, or destroyed, in order to keep prices up. Under the direct-payment program, all the crop is consumed. This adds to our standard of living.

DIRECT EFFECT ON TOTAL GROSS FARM INCOME

Under the direct-payment program, consumers get to eat all the potatoes. They eat the 60 million bushels that would be destroyed under the price-support program. What effect would that have on the demand for other food and therefore on total farm incomes?

One might suppose that most consumers in the United States eat about all they can, all the time. If that supposition were correct, the per capita consumption of food would remain constant from year to year; and when consumers ate more potatoes, they would eat correspondingly less of other foods.

But the supposition is not correct. Consumption statistics show that the per capita consumption of food varies considerably from year to year. The index of the per capita consumption of food in the United States (base 1935–39 = 100) varied from 96 in 1945[3] to 104 in 1956 and to 103 in 1962.[4]

This variation in consumption is closely associated with variation in income. Apparently, consumers eat more when they have more money to spend. But this is not a complete statement. Consumers can eat no more food than farmers produce, no matter how much money they have; and farmers sell no less than they produce, except when receipts will not cover even the direct harvesting and shipping costs. These cases are exceptional; otherwise farmers would not incur the overhead costs and costs of planting and cultivating the crop in the first place.

In a direct sense, therefore, income does not determine average per capita consumption: production determines consumption.

A more complete statement requires two or three steps:

1. Income determines how much consumers will pay for food.
2. That payment is one thing that determines how much food farmers will produce.
3. That production determines how much food consumers can eat.

Food production varies in response to weather as well as to consumers' income. With a given national income, when we have good weather and good crops and therefore an abundant supply of food, we eat it all, the same as when we have a higher national income. But we do so at a lower price.

---

[3] "Consumption of Food in The United States, 1909–48," USDA Misc. Publ. 691, June, 1949, p. 91. The variation on a strictly poundage basis (unweighted by prices) is almost as great (p. 104).

[4] "The National Food Situation," ERS, USDA, July, 1962, p. 2.

The price elasticity of the demand for food at retail (based on food prices in relation to nonfood prices) appears to be about —0.3.[5]

The corresponding elasticity of the demand for food at the farm (based on farm prices) must be less than this, because of the relative inflexibility of distributors' margins. If distributors' margins were absolutely inflexible, and the margins took half of the consumers' dollar, the corresponding elasticity of the demand for food at the farm would be just half the elasticity at retail given above, namely —0.15. If distributors' margins were as flexible as retail prices, the elasticity at the farm would be the same as at retail, namely —0.3. Actually, distributors' margins are about half-way between these two degrees of flexibility,[6] so the elasticity of the demand for food at the farm would be about halfway between —0.15 and —0.3, namely about —0.2.

Now we can give an answer to the question we raised at the outset: What effect would the increased consumption of potatoes have on the demand for other foods and therefore on total farm income? It would reduce the demand for other foods. The effect on farm income can be computed as follows:

The per capita consumption of food at retail weights runs about 1,500 pounds a year.[7] The extra 60 million bushels of potatoes that consumers would eat, under the direct-payment plan, would amount to 3,600 million pounds, equal to 20 pounds per capita. If potatoes have about the same food value per pound as the average of other food, this 20 pounds of potatoes would amount to 1.3 per cent of the per capita total consumption of food. This addition of 1.3 per cent to the total supply would reduce prices at the farm

$$\frac{1.3}{0.2} = 6 \text{ per cent} - \text{that is, to 94 per cent of their previous level.}$$

If the previous production and price each are taken as 100, and the total value as $100 \times 100 = 10,000$, then the 101.3 per cent supply at the 94 per cent price would have a total value of 9,522. This is a reduction in total value of 4.8 per cent; for our purposes, this could be rounded off at 5 per cent, in order to keep the arithmetic simple enough so that it can be followed easily.

The total cash agricultural income in the United States in re-

[5] Willard W. Cochrane, "Farm Price Gyrations — An Aggregative Hypothesis," *Journal of Farm Economics*, Vol. 29, No. 2, pp. 383–408.

[6] Richard O. Been, "Price Spreads Between Farmers and Consumers," USDA Agr. Inf. Bul. 4, Nov., 1949, p. 7.

[7] "Supplement for 1960 to Consumption of Food in the United States, 1909–52," ERS, USDA, 1961, p. 452.

cent years has run close to $30 billion. Not all of this, of course, comes from the sale of food. About $2.5 billion comes from the sale of cotton and wool, another $3 billion from the sale of feed crops, $1 billion from tobacco, and about $1.5 billion from that part of the oil-bearing crops not used for food, plus miscellaneous crops. That leaves about $32 billion as income from the sale of food.

A reduction of 5 per cent of this $32 billion would amount to $1.6 billion. The extra consumption of 60 million bushels of potatoes, therefore, would reduce total farm income about $1.6 billion, if potatoes have the same food value per pound as the value of other food.

If potatoes have less value than this, the reduction in farm income would be less. For example, if potatoes had only two-thirds as much food value per pound as other food, the reduction in farm income would be $1.2 billion. Thus, under either of these rough but reasonable assumptions, the reduction would be more than a billion dollars. This reduction results from the inelasticity of the demand for food.

Thus the direct-payments plan for potatoes would increase gross incomes (from sales plus direct payments) for potato producers, but decrease the gross incomes of other producers, because the entire potato crop would be consumed and the total supply of farm products would be included along with other farm products in the total supply of farm products. This would depress the prices of farm products, thus decreasing gross farm income, because the demand for farm products is inelastic.

The point needs to be emphasized, however, that these are the effects of direct payments compared with supporting prices *and destroying the quantities that cannot be sold at the supported prices.* This policy actually was followed with potatoes by the USDA in 1948. But the public revulsion against producing potatoes and then destroying them was so great that the whole program was abandoned, and has not been tried since. It is not likely to be tried again in the future.

If some use is made of the portion of the crop that is withheld in a price-support program, such as storage and return to the market in a later year when the crop is short, then the effects of the program are more nearly similar to the effects of a direct-payment program. The difference then is that market supplies are smoothed out, and the government foots the bill for storage.

ADVANTAGES AND DISADVANTAGES OF DIRECT PAYMENTS

The great *advantage* of direct commodity payments is that they leave prices to seek their own equilibrium level in the market place. This has three effects:

1. It keeps products moving through into consumption. This frees the federal government from the costs involved in trying to support prices by purchase and storage operations.

2. It reduces food costs to consumers.

3. It reduces or eliminates the need for costly subsidies designed to move exports into foreign markets—subsidies which in many cases are offset by countervailing duties imposed by foreign governments, so that our subsidies in effect are simply piped from our treasury into theirs.

In these respects, direct payments make more economic sense than purchase and storage operations.

The great *disadvantage* of direct payments is that they only "cure" the symptoms; they leave the basic disease to run on unchecked, or actually made worse. If the low incomes are caused by an excessive number of farmers dividing up the total income pie, then direct payments to farmers will not reduce the numbers of farmers; they are more likely to increase them. When the basic disease is a maladjustment of productive resources, direct payments tend to perpetuate the disease, not to cure it. In this respect direct payments are no better than price supports.

six

ANALYSIS OF PARITY PRICES

17

Index Numbers

The next few chapters deal with "parity prices." These parity prices are index numbers, and an understanding of parity prices requires first some understanding of how index numbers are constructed. Accordingly, this chapter deals with the theory of index numbers, and applies the theory to computation of parity prices. The following chapters then deal with parity prices directly.

INDEX NUMBERS ARE WEIGHTED AVERAGES

The prices of any single commodity, such as hogs, may be recorded over periods of time and analyzed directly in their original form. But the prices of farm products, as a group, cannot be studied so simply. If we want to know how the prices of farm products, as a group, have changed over the years, we must first add up or average the prices of the different products into a single figure for each year. This single figure is called an index number.

The averaging process needs to take into account the fact that some products are more important than others. A simple averaging process would give equal weight to each item; but a change in the price of beef cattle is more important, and should carry greater weight in the index, than a change in the price of avocados.

Many different formulas and systems of weighting can be used in constructing index numbers, and most of them give different results. Good economic and statistical judgment is required, therefore, in selecting the formula and weights to be used.

DIFFERENT FORMULAS

The two chief kinds of index number formulas are (1) the ratio of aggregates and (2) the average of relatives.

In the formula for the ratio of aggregates, prices of the different products are added up (aggregated) each year. The series of sums then is the series of index numbers. The formula is simply:

$$P = \frac{\Sigma p_1}{\Sigma p_0}$$

where

P is the price index p is the price of a product
$_1$ refers to the given year which is being compared with the base
$_0$ refers to the base period from which changes are measured.

But this simple formula would give all the products equal weighting. In order to give each product its proper weight, commensurate with its importance, its price should be weighted (multiplied) by the quantity sold.

The use of quantity weights neatly compensates for the erratic effect of the choice of the size of the unit used to measure the quantities. If the quantity weights were expressed in pounds, that would give the item 2,000 times as much weight as if it were expressed in tons. But this is exactly compensated for by the fact that the price for a pound would be only one 2,000th as high as the price for a ton.

A question arises whether the price should be weighted by the quantity sold in the base year, or the given year, or some intermediate period. A widely used formula, the Laspeyres formula, uses quantities during the base year. This formula is:

$$P = \frac{\Sigma p_i\ q_0}{\Sigma p_0\ q_0}.$$

Table 17.1 gives a simple illustration of this formula, showing how to compute a price index based on two products, A and B.

The central part of Table 17.1 shows that the sum (aggregate) in the base year was 14. In the given year, the sum was 18. It is easy to see how much prices have risen in the given year if the index in that year is expressed as a percentage of the index in the base year. When this is done here, it shows that prices have risen from an index of 100 in the base year to an index of $(18 \times 100)/14 = 125.7$ in the given year; that is, they have risen 25.7 per cent.

AVERAGE OF RELATIVES

The computation of the index numbers by the use of the other formula, the average of relatives, is shown in the right-hand part of Table 17.1.

The relative change in the price of commodity A is $3/4 = 0.75$. For commodity B, it is $4/2 = 2$.

TABLE 17.1
COMPUTING INDEX NUMBERS BY TWO FORMULAS

	Prices		Ratio of Aggregates			Average of Relatives		
			Quan-tities	Weighted prices		Rela-tives	Value weights	Relatives weighted by values
	Base year p_0	Given year p_1	Base year q_0	Base year $p_0 q_0$	Given year $p_1 q_0$	$\dfrac{p_1}{p_0}$	$p_0 q_0$	
A	4	3	2	8	6	0.75	8	6.0
B	2	4	3	6	12	2.0	6	12.0
Sum.	. . . . . .	. . . . . .	5	14	18	. . . . . .	14	18
Index.	. . . . . .	. . . . . .	. . . . . .	100	125.7	. . . . . .	100	125.7

When weighting these relatives, we need to compensate for the erratic effect of the choice of the size of the quantity units, as in the other formula. For this purpose, quantity will not do, for the number of the quantity units is not offset by the size of the price; the price relative is unaffected by the size of the quantity units. So we weight by base-year values (*prices* × *quantities*) instead of by quantities alone, as shown in the last column of Table 17.1.

The index of prices, the average of relatives, in the given year comes out to be $(18 \times 100)/14 = 125.7$, exactly the same as with the ratio of aggregates formula. The two formulas, in fact, are merely different forms of the same formula, for the average of relatives formula with base-year values is:

$$\frac{\Sigma \dfrac{p_1}{p_0} \ p_0 \ q_0}{\Sigma \ p_0 \ q_0},$$

which by cancellation of the p_0's in the numerator reduces to the Laspeyres ratio of aggregates formula:

$$\frac{\Sigma \ p_1 \ q_0}{\Sigma \ p_0 \ q_0}.$$

The average of relatives weighted by the product of base-year prices and given-year quantities ($p_0 \ q_1$) reduces to the Paasche formula. (The Paasche formula is like the Laspeyres formula but uses given-year weights instead of base-year weights).

The choice between the two formulas depends chiefly upon the desire for relatives showing the movement of different prices or

subgroups of prices separately. If there is no need for these relatives, the ratio of aggregates is the simplest and involves the
least amount of computation. But in many cases the relatives of
different prices or subgroups of prices are useful and worth the
extra computation involved.

WEIGHT-BASE PERIODS

Practical complications arise when the quantities used do not
remain constant over a period of years. Tastes change, and new
products partially replace the old. We now use more tractors and
fewer horses and eat more fruits and vegetables and less bread.

The quantities used in the base year, then, gradually become
inaccurate for the given (current) years. How can this be avoided?

One suggestion is to use given-year weights instead of base-
year weights, using the Paasche formula:

$$\frac{\Sigma\ p_1\ q_1}{\Sigma\ p_0\ q_1}.$$

But this merely means that the quantities used in the current year
are inaccurate for the base and other early years.

Furthermore, both formulas are likely to be not only inaccurate,
but biased. If tastes remain constant, but the relative costs of
producing different goods change, the relative prices of the goods
will change too. Consumers then will buy less of the high priced
items and more of the cheaper ones. The Laspeyres index with
base-year weights would show no change, when actually consumers
would be getting the same amount of satisfaction for less money
than before; the Laspeyres formula then has an upward bias.

The Laspeyres formula has a downward bias if tastes change
but relative costs remain constant. In both cases, the Paasche formula has the opposite bias. These biases may be combined to offset
each other, at least in part. Marshall and Edgeworth suggested
using crossed (that is, average) weights. Their formula is:

$$\frac{\Sigma p_1\ (q_0\ +\ q_1)}{\Sigma p_0\ (q_0\ +\ q_1)}.$$

Irving Fisher made a different suggestion. He recommended
using the geometric mean of the Laspeyres and Paasche formulas

$$\left(\frac{\Sigma p_1\ q_0}{\Sigma p_0\ q_0}\ \cdot\ \frac{\Sigma p_1\ q_1}{\Sigma p_0\ q_1}\right)^{1/2}$$

This is sometimes referred to as Fisher's "Ideal" formula.

Among these formulas, the Fisher formula meets two tests — the time-reversal test and the factor-reversal test. That is, it gives consistent results forward and backward, and with the factors (prices and quantities) interchanged.

But the practical objections to these formulas are formidable. It is difficult to say just what an index number computed by either of these formulas does measure. The fact that the formulas average two opposite biases or inaccuracies does not guarantee that they provide accurate answers. Furthermore, the computations involved in the use of the Fisher formula are more than twice as laborious as those for the Laspeyres or Paasche formulas; and data showing the quantities of the different goods purchased, to be used as current weights, never are actually current but are gathered only at irregular intervals by special surveys, usually several years apart.

Accordingly, the USDA worked out what it considered to be the least unsatisfactory solution.[1] It has adopted a formula for the computation of its indexes of prices received and paid by farmers which uses neither base-year weights nor current-year weights. The USDA recognized that neither base-year weights nor given-year weights, nor any single combination of the two, could be appropriate over a long period; so it used two different sets of weights based on averages for two different periods. It used weights based on averages for the period 1924–29 for its indexes up through March, 1935, and weights based on averages for the period 1937–41 from March, 1935 thereafter, the indexes being linked at March, 1935. In January, 1959, the weight-base period for the index of prices *paid* was moved up to 1955. The weight-base period for the index of prices *received* was moved up to 1953–57.

BRITISH INDEXES OF AGRICULTURAL PRICES

The British indexes of agricultural prices originally were based on 1906–08, and then 1911–13, with 1908 gross value quantity weights. This base became increasingly inaccurate with the passage of time. Accordingly, after 30 years, the British Ministry of Agriculture revised its formula. In 1938, it shifted the price base to 1927–29, and shifted its weight base, not to a more recent *fixed* period, but to a moving average of the five years immediately preceding the current year, each year.

[1] B. Ralph Stauber, Nathan M. Koffsky, and C. Kyle Randall, "The Revised Price Indexes," *Agricultural Economics Research*, BAE, USDA, Vol. 2, No. 2, April, 1950.

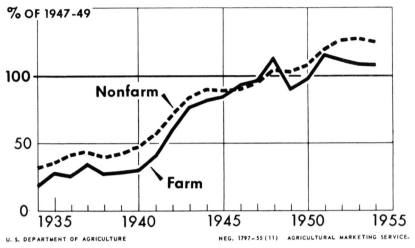

U. S. DEPARTMENT OF AGRICULTURE   NEG. 1797-55 (11)   AGRICULTURAL MARKETING SERVICE.

Fig. 17.1 — Indexes of per capita farm and nonfarm income, computed on a 1947–49 base.

"For example, the index number for 1937 would be obtained by using weights derived from the average annual output of the five years ending 1935–36. Weighting would thus change each year, the latest year's output being added and the earliest year's output being dropped. For the purpose of calculating the index number for each year, the output chosen for that year would be valued at the prices of that year and of the base year; the index number would represent the ratio between the two values. Under such a system, however long the series were continued, it would be possible throughout the series to make accurate comparison between prices in years not very far part, and as satisfactory a comparison as possible, without making separate calculations, between two years separated by a long period, bearing in mind that in agriculture the changes in composition of the total output are gradual."[2]

This formula is a kind of Paasche formula, with current (five-year average) weights. A similar formula is used in New Zealand.

EFFECTS OF USING DIFFERENT BASE PERIODS

The selection of a base period only moves a curve up or down in relation to the base line or to another curve on a chart. But this is a very important movement. We already saw in the first chapter (Fig. 1.1) that using an earlier base would give agricultural prices the appearance of running higher than nonagricultural prices most of the time, instead of lower, as it does in Figure 1.1.

---

[2] C. T. Houghton, "A New Index Number of Agricultural Prices," *Journal of the Royal Statistical Society*, CI (Part II), pp. 294–95, 1938.

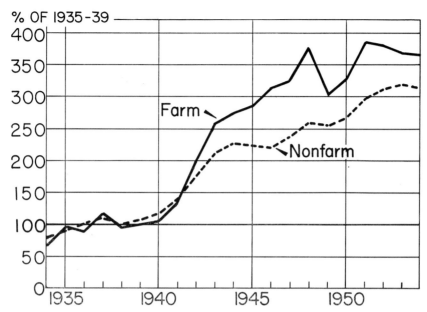

Fig. 17.2 — Indexes of per capita farm and nonfarm income, computed on a 1935–39 base.

Another illustration of the important effects of using different base periods on the story a chart seems to tell is shown in Figure 17.1. In this figure, the data for both lines on the chart are plotted on a 1947–49 base. They appear to show farm income at a disadvantage relative to nonfarm except for a brief period following World War II. The caption for the original USDA chart was "Income per person of farmers lagging behind that of nonfarm people."

The same data are converted to a 1935–39 base in Figure 17.2. This is done simply by dividing each item in the series by the average value for that series in 1935–39. Nothing is changed but the relation, the height of the two lines relative to one another. But the effect on the story the chart seems to tell is striking. It makes farm income look superior to nonfarm income most of the time, and so much superior that the decline, so prominent in Figure 17.1, is hardly discernible in Figure 17.2.

Both charts are equally illusory, though in opposite directions. Figure 17.1 is based on a period when farm incomes were unusually high relative to nonfarm incomes, so that the relation in other years looks unfavorable to agriculture. Conversely, Figure 17.2 is based on a period when farm incomes were unusually low. The reader of any charts of this nature needs to study them carefully before accepting the conclusions they imply.

18

Parity Prices for Farm Products

The agricultural parity concept developed step by step during the late 1920's and early 1930's.[1] ". . .the concept as we now know it did not spring full blown from the brain of some economic Jupiter, but rather grew out of the continuous groping for a concrete measure of justice for the farmer, and was steadily modified by conditions prevailing in the economic life of farmers and the nation. In other words, parity did not develop as the practical application of an economic theory immaculately conceived, free from all taint of original sin in the form of class interest. On the contrary, parity, like Topsy, just growed; and whatever economic justification can be found for it in its present form may be considered largely a rationalization."[2]

OBJECTIVE OF THE PARITY LEGISLATION

The first specific parity formula was incorporated in the Agricultural Adjustment Act of 1933. The objective stated in the act was to "reestablish prices to farmers at a level that will give agricultural commodities a purchasing power, with respect to articles that farmers buy, equivalent to the purchasing power of agricultural commodities in the base period. The base period in the case of all agricultural commodities except tobacco shall be the prewar period,

[1] The development and present status of the present parity price formula is well outlined in "Possible Methods of Improving the Parity Formula," Senate, 85th Cong., 1st sess., S. Doc. 18, 1957, pp. 8–13. See also "An alternative Parity Formula for Agriculture," Res. Bul. 476, Iowa State Univ., Ames, Feb., 1960.

[2] E. W. Grove, "The Concept of Income Parity for Agriculture," Studies in Income and Wealth, Vol. 6, Nat'l. Bur. Econ. Res., New York, 1943.

August, 1909–July, 1914. In the case of tobacco, the base period shall be the postwar period, August, 1919–July, 1929." [3]

Parity prices, then, were to be prices which would give *farm products* the same purchasing power *per unit* (bushel, bale, etc.) for goods and services used in both production and family living as prevailed in the base period.

The legislation was passed, of course, not for the benefit of the farm products concerned as such, but for the benefit of the farmers who produced these products. The objective was to restore the price conditions that existed during the base period, on the assumption that this would restore the economic situation of the producers of the products.

The word parity itself was not used in the AA Act of 1933. It first appeared in agricultural legislation in the AA Act of 1938. The purpose of that act, as stated in the opening paragraph, was to accomplish a number of things "assisting farmers to obtain, insofar as practicable, parity prices for such commodities and parity of income . . . ."

Pursuant to the objective stated in the Agricultural Adjustment Act of 1933, the parity formula was developed to reflect changes in the prices of the "articles that farmers buy." Parity prices then could be computed for agricultural commodities that farmers sell which would give those commodities the same purchasing power that they had in the base period.

CONTENT OF THE PARITY FORMULA

The USDA had been compiling and publishing the price data called for in the AA Act of 1933 for some years previous to 1933. The index of prices *received* by farmers for the products they sell was compiled on a monthly basis beginning with 1909. It was first published in 1921.

The basic data for the index of prices paid for the "articles that farmers buy" were more difficult to obtain. This index was compiled on an annual basis beginning with 1909, on a quarterly basis beginning with 1924, and on a monthly basis beginning with 1937. This index of prices paid by farmers was first published in 1928.[4] At that time, the pre-World War I base, 1910–14, seemed a reasonable base to use for both series — the prices received by farmers,

---

[3] Agricultural Adjustment Act, Public Law 10, *U. S. Statutes at Large,* 73rd Cong., 1st sess., Vol. 48, May 12, 1933, p. 32.

[4] In the Agricultural Acts of 1948 and 1949, the index of prices paid by farmers was legally defined as the parity index.

"What IS parity?"

and the prices paid by farmers. That base was written into the AA Act of 1933.

The parity formula laid down in the AA Act of 1933 was amended and reenacted several times after 1933.[5] The prices of certain services were added to the prices paid by farmers, and "comparable prices" were provided for some products which had not come into general use until after 1929. In addition, the Agricultural Act of 1948 introduced a table of loan rates that varied inversely with the supply of the crop.

Price Bases

The Agricultural Act of 1948 also included provisions which "modernized" the parity formula. It brought the base period for computing the relative parity prices of individual farm products (the parity prices relative to each other) up to a more recent date — the most recent 10-year moving average. The 1910–14 base period was retained, however, for parity prices as a whole. This modernized formula was to become effective in 1950. The Agricultural Act of 1949 modified the formula by the inclusion of farm wage rates in the parity index and the inclusion of direct subsidy payments on dairy products, cattle, and lambs in prices received before it became effective.

To avoid extremely sharp declines in the parity prices of any commodity, transitional parity prices were provided by the 1948 act. They were to be used for those commodities for which the new parity prices were less than 95 per cent of the old parity prices in 1950, 90 per cent in 1951, and so on. In other words, the parity price as calculated under the old method was to be reduced 5 per cent each year until the transitional parity was less than the parity prices as defined by the new act. From then on, the new parity was to be used. These transitional prices were incorporated into the 1949 act. In actual practice, "dual parity" was used for several years with the six basic crops. The parity prices computed by the modernized formula went into effect only if they were higher than prices com-

---

[5] The details concerning these amendments, and the steps involved in the computation of parity prices for different products, are given in B. R. Stauber, et al., "The Revised Price Indexes," *Agricultural Economics Research*, Vol. 2, No. 2, Apr., 1950, pp. 33–62. Some interesting background on the evolution of the term "parity" is given in R. L. Tontz, "Evolution of the Term Parity in Agricultural Usage," *Southwestern Social Science Quarterly*, March, 1955, pp. 345–55.

puted under the old formula. The marketing service of the USDA gives the following explanation: [6]

> For the purpose of illustrating the computation of parity prices the calculation of the effective parity price for corn based on data for January 1960 is given below. The parity price under the new formula of the amended act is computed as follows:
>
> The 120-month, January 1950–December 1959, average of prices received by farmers for corn, adjusted to include an allowance for unredeemed loans, etc., was $1.39 per bushel. The 120-month average of the Index of Prices Received by Farmers, adjusted to include an allowance for unredeemed loans, etc., was 255. Dividing $1.39 by 255 gives $0.545 per bushel, the adjusted base price. Multiplying this adjusted base price by 299, the Parity Index based on data for January 1960, gives the indicated price of $1.63 per bushel as computed using the new formula.
>
> Since the effective parity for corn, a basic commodity, was the transitional parity based on data for December 1959, it was also necessary to compute the transitional parity based on data for January 1960. As noted above the transitional parity for basic commodities during 1960 is 80 per cent of the parity price computed by the old formula. The parity price according to the old formula is calculated by multiplying the average price received by farmers for corn for the 60 months, August 1909–July 1914, which was $0.642 per bushel, by the January 15, 1960, unrevised Index of Prices Paid, including Interest and Taxes, which is 315 per cent. This gives an indicated parity price of $2.02 per bushel under the old formula. Multiplying by 80 per cent gives $1.62 the transitional parity price. Since this is lower than the indicated parity price under the new formula of $1.63 per bushel, the parity price under the new formula is now the effective parity price for corn.
>
> Effective parity prices for most commodities have shifted to the new formula, but for some commodities the transitional parity is still the effective parity price.

Weight Bases

In 1950, the weight base used in computing the index of prices paid was moved up from 1924–29 to 1937–41, and the weights were revised in line with the quantities used in the later period. In January, 1959, the weight-base period was moved up again, to 1955, with weights revised in line with the 1955 Farm Expenditure Survey and the 1955 Food Consumption Survey.[7] The weight base for the index of prices *received* was moved up to 1953–57 (the 5-year period was used so as to average out most of the year-to-year variations in quantities sold which result chiefly from irregular variations in weather).

The indexes of prices received and prices paid from 1910 to 1960 are given in Table 18.1. The ratio between the two indexes (the

---

[6] Agricultural Prices, USDA, AMS, Jan. 29, 1960, p. 44.

[7] B. R. Stauber, R. F. Hale, and B. S. Peterson, "The January 1959 Revision of the Price Indexes," *Agricultural Economics Research*, Vol. 11, Nos. 2 and 3.

TABLE 18.1

INDEXES OF PRICES RECEIVED BY FARMERS FOR COMMODITIES, AND PRICES PAID FOR
COMMODITIES, INTEREST, TAXES, AND WAGE RATES, AND PARITY RATIOS,
UNITED STATES, 1910–60

(Index base, 1910–14 = 100)

Year	Index of Prices Received	Index of Prices Paid*	Parity Ratio	Year	Index of Prices Received	Index of Prices Paid*	Parity Ratio
1910....	104	97	107	1949...	250	251	100
1920....	211	214	99	1950...	258	256	101
1930....	125	151	83	1951...	302	282	107
1940....	100	124	81	1952...	288	287	100
1941....	124	133	93	1953...	255	277	92
1942....	159	152	105	1954...	246	277	89
1943....	193	171	113	1955...	232	276	84
1944....	197	182	108	1956...	230	278	83
1945....	207	190	109	1957...	235	286	82
1946 ...	236	208	113	1958...	250	293	85
1947 ...	276	240	115	1959...	240	298	81
1948 ...	287	260	110	1960...	238	299	80

* Including interest, taxes, and farm wage rates.

parity ratio) is also given. The data since World War II are shown graphically in Figure 18.1.

PERCENTAGES OF PARITY PRICES USED AS BASES FOR CCC LOAN RATES

In October, 1933, the Commodity Credit Corporation was organized for the purpose of stabilizing the supplies and prices of the basic farm products. It operated as a storage agency, making nonrecourse commodity loans to farmers and taking over the commodities for which the loans were not redeemed.

For the first few years, the CCC set the loan rates at appropriate levels for stabilization purposes. The Agricultural Adjustment Act of 1938 took the setting of the loan rates out of the CCC's hands and wrote into law the range of percentages of parity prices within which the loan rates were to be set. The range extended from 52 to 75 per cent of parity. In the case of corn, the loan rate varied within the range, inversely with the size of the crop.

In May, 1941, Congress went further; it directed the CCC to set the loan rates for the "basic" commodities — cotton, corn, wheat, tobacco, and rice — at 85 per cent of parity. This raised loan rates about 50 per cent higher than the 1940 rates on cotton and wheat and 13 per cent higher on corn. The rates for most products were

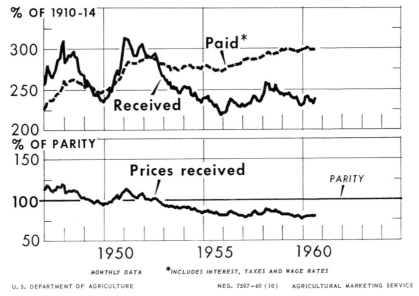

Fig. 18.1 — Prices paid and received by farmers, United States, monthly average, 1947–60.

raised to 90 per cent of parity in 1944, where they remained until they began to be reduced in 1955. The data for corn are given for illustration in Figure 18.2 and Table 18.2.

Effects of Using Percentages of Parity Prices

The effects of this use of percentages of parity prices as the bases for loan rates were spectacular. They distorted the allocative function of prices in the direction of the supported commodities. Agricultural production in the United States was already increasing faster than the demand, under the impact of rapid technological development. The setting of price supports at percentages of parity, above long-run, free-market equilibrium levels, further stimulated overproduction of the supported commodities above market needs, and at the same time reduced the consumption of those products.

As a result, huge stocks of corn, cotton, and wheat, particularly were accumulated by the CCC. Desperate attempts to reduce production by acreage controls and to stimulate consumption by domestic and export consumption subsidies have been only partially successful. The sizes of the stocks in recent years — several times larger than needed for stabilization purposes — are shown in Figures 18.3 and 18.4.

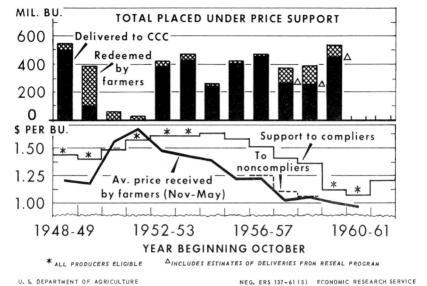

Fig. 18.2 — Corn: Quantities placed under price support, price support levels, and average price received by farmers, annually, 1948–49 to 1960–61.

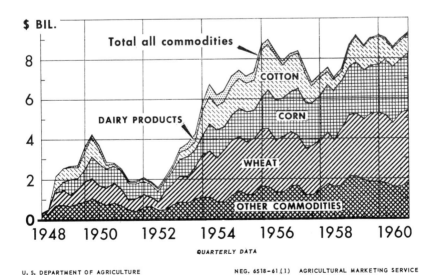

Fig. 18.3 — Price support holdings of cotton, corn, wheat, and other commodities, quarterly, 1948–60.

TABLE 18.2

CORN: U.S. LOAN RATES, U.S. AVERAGE FARM PRICES, AND DIFFERENTIALS BETWEEN THEM, SUPPORT PRICES AND QUANTITY PLACED UNDER SUPPORT, 1933–60*

Year Beginning October	Announced National Average Loan Rate[1] (dollars per bushel)	Average Price Nov.–May[2] (percentage of parity)	Average Price Minus Announced Loan Rate (dollars per bushel)		Placed Under Price Support — Loans[3] (million bushels)	Purchase agreements (million bushels)	Total (million bushels)	Percentage of production	Under Loan or Owned by CCC at End of Crop Year (million bushels)
1933	$0.45	60	$0.45	$0.00	268	.....	268	11.2	82
1934	0.55	68	.83	.28	20	.....	20	1.4	.....
1935	.45	55	.55	.10	31	.....	31	1.3	.....
1936	.55	66	1.06	.51	([4])	.....	([4])	.....	.....
1937	.50	58	.51	.01	61	.....	61	2.3	45
1938	.57	70	.44	–.13	230	.....	230	9.0	258
1939	.57	69	.55	–.02	302	.....	302	11.7	471
1940	.61	75	.58	–.03	103	.....	103	4.2	403
1941	.75	85	.74	–.01	111	.....	111	4.2	197
1942	.83	85	.90	.07	56	.....	56	1.8	8
1943	.90	85	1.12	.22	8	.....	8	.3	6
1944	.98	90	1.07	.09	21	.....	21	.7	9
1945	1.01	90	1.15	.14	3	.....	3	.1	.....
1946	1.15	90	1.38	.23	26	.....	26	.8	.....
1947	1.37	90	2.20	.83	1	.....	1	.....	9
1948	1.44	90	1.20	–.24	377	174[5]	551	15.3	493
1949	1.40	90	1.18	–.22	332	55	387	11.9	650
1950	1.47	90	1.55	–.08	52	2	54	1.8	488
1951	1.57	90	1.66	.09	25	1	26	.9	306
1952	1.60	90	1.47	–.13	309	107	417	12.7	580
1953	1.60	90	1.42	–.18	369	102	471	14.7	736
1954	1.62	90	1.38	–.24	200	59	259	8.5	870
1955	1.58	87	1.21	–.37	356	65	421	13.0	1,060
1956[6]	1.50	84	1.21	–.29	401	76	477	13.8	1,295
1957[6]	1.40	77	1.02	–.38	320	49	369	10.8	1,355
1958[6]	1.36	77	1.05	–.31	343	38	381	10.0	1,400
1959	1.12	66	1.00	–.12	439[8]	38[8]	512[8]	11.7	.....
1960[7]	1.06	65	.....	.....	.....	.....	.....	.....	.....

* Source: USDA, "1956 Agricultural Outlook Charts," Nov., 1955, Table 35, p. 68; USDA, "Grain and Feed Statistics," through 1954; USDA, Stat. Bul. 159, March, 1955, Table 48, p. 46; and USDA, AMS, "The Feed Situation," May, 1959, p. 23.
[1] Applies to commercial area only in years when acreage allotments are in effect.
[2] Average price received by farmers in period when most of the corn is placed under price support. In recent years, loans have been available from time of harvest through May.

ing year during the period 1948 to date.
[4] Included 14 million bushels of 1937 corn placed under loan for first time in 1938 under short-term loan program.
[5] Purchase agreements not available prior to 1947.
[6] Loans were made to noncooperators at $1.25 per bushel in 1956, $1.10 in 1957, $1.06 in 1958.
[7] Minimum support; may be increased at beginning of marketing year if higher support is required.
[8] Preliminary. Compiled from reports of Commodity Stabilization Serv-

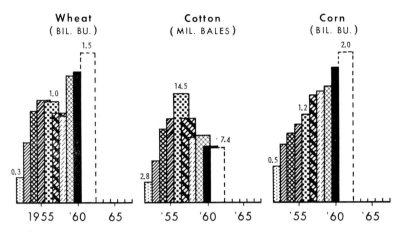

Fig. 18.4 — Carryover of wheat, cotton, and corn, annually, 1952–60.

On May 31, 1962, the total investment of the CCC in price-support programs amounted to $6,959,190,237 — made up of loans outstanding of $2,344,173,988 and the cost value of inventories, $4,615,-016,249. The "realized cost" of "programs primarily for stabilization of farm prices and income" in fiscal 1959 was $2,027,900,000.[8] Only a part of these expenditures went directly to farmers. The rest went to other groups, such as storage agencies for storage fees, and indirectly to construction companies for the building of additional storage space. These other agencies received a substantial part of the income transferred from taxpayers. In fiscal 1958, for example, the "realized cost" of the corn program was $271 million. Of this amount, $110 million — more than a third — went to the grain trade and transportation agencies to cover storage and handling charges. None of this went to farmers.[9] The program thus was a "grain trade program" as well as a farm program.

---

[8] The "realized cost" is large in recent years partly because it includes the cost of acquiring the large inventory built up in those years. If crops were very small in subsequent years, and prices rose enough to pull substantial quantities out of storage for sale on the market, the revenue from those sales would offset a large part of the total costs in those years, and "realized cost" would be relatively small.

[9] Correspondence from CCC.

19

Appraisal of the Parity Price Indexes

The present parity price indexes and ratios may be appraised with reference to the job they were originally set up to do — to measure the prices received by farmers, the prices paid by farmers, and the ratio between the two, for agriculture as a whole and for individual farm products. The parity price indexes and ratios may also be appraised with reference to the uses to which they are now put. These are vastly different from the uses for which the indexes were originally designed. The two appraisals are given separately in order below.

APPRAISAL OF INDEXES WITH REFERENCE TO USES FOR WHICH ORIGINALLY DESIGNED

Type of Formula Used

The parity price indexes are computed by the use of an aggregative Laspeyres type formula, with base-year weights.[1]

This formula meets neither the factor-reversal test nor the time-reversal test. But the use of a formula such as Fisher's Ideal (the geometric average of a Laspeyres formula with base-year weights and a Paasche formula with given-year weights, is impractical. The cost of getting given-year weights for the index of prices paid in time to use for current calculations would be prohibitive. Getting given-month weights would be clearly impracticable.

The Laspeyres type formula is subject to the problem of the increasing obsolescence of the base-period weights with the passage

---

[1] B. Ralph Stauber, Nathan M. Koffsky, and C. Kyle Randall, The Revised Price Indexes, *Agricultural Economics Research,* USDA, Bur. Agr. Econ., April, 1950, p. 53.

of time. The USDA has dealt with this problem by using the same weight base period for a number of years, then using a more recent period and splicing the two indexes at an appropriate point. This has the disadvantage of causing a sudden change in the index of 3.4 per cent, for example, when the last revision was made in January 1959. In principle, this could be avoided or at least reduced to insignificance (actually, spread out in little steps over a period of years) by the use of a recent moving average weight base period. But the cost of obtaining the weights for the index of prices paid would be high and other disadvantages of a more technical nature would be incurred.

Adequacy of Coverage

Another feature of a price index is the adequacy of its coverage of the prices it purports to measure.

The index of prices received by farmers began in 1910 as a weighted average of price relatives for 10 crops; the base period was the average of December 1 prices for 1866–1908. Several years later, livestock prices were added. In 1924, the index included the prices for 30 commodities, and the base period was moved up to August 1909–July 1914. In 1924, prices for 20 more products were added. Some changes in the coverage were made in 1950. The 1959 revision includes the prices for 55 farm products, which are weighted by the quantities marketed in 1953–57, and represent 93 per cent of total farm marketings in 1953–57. The largest single item omitted is farm forest products.[2]

This coverage of 93 per cent is close enough to 100 per cent to be regarded as satisfactory. It probably represents an optimum allocation of limited appropriations to alternative uses.

The index of prices paid by farmers began in 1910 with 142 commodities, expanded to 181 in 1927, to 335 in 1935, and to about 390 in 1959. The production component of the index contains about 230 items; the living, about 200 items (two-thirds as many as the BLS consumer price index) and both production and living, 46 items. These items are weighted by expenditures in 1955. They cover about 84 per cent of farmer expenditures in 1955. The weights are given in Table 19.1.

The most important fields not covered in the family living part of the parity index are medical, dental, and hospital expenses, which

---

[2] B. R. Stauber, *Critical Problems in Index Number Construction,* Agricultural Marketing Service, USDA. Presented to a joint meeting of the American Statistical Association and the American Farm Economic Association, Dec., 1959, pp. 13–14, 21.

TABLE 19.1

PARITY INDEXES: RELATIVE IMPORTANCE OF COMPONENT INDEXES, 1955 AND
JUNE 15, 1961*

| | Relative Importance | | | |
| Commodity Group | Old index | | 1959 revision | |
	1955	June 15, 1961	1955¹	June 15, 1961
	per cent	*per cent*	*per cent*	*per cent*
Living (total)	50.74	48.49	39.50	38.99
Food	17.06	16.08	13.40²	13.46²
Clothing	16.31	16.04	6.34	6.47
Autos and auto supplies	3.94³	3.81³	5.63	5.54
Household operation	4.54	4.26	5.77	5.70
Household furnishings	3.36	3.15	3.99	3.58
Building materials, house	5.53	5.15	4.37	4.24
Production (total)	35.98	34.16	50.90	49.18
Feed	7.13	5.82	12.80	11.04
Livestock	....	....	4.60	4.78
Motor supplies	....	....	8.39	8.25
Motor vehicles	7.00⁴	7.13⁴	4.38⁴	4.68⁴
Earm machinery	4.72	5.39	5.21	5.95
Equipment and supplies	5.31⁵	5.07⁵	3.66	3.42
Fertilizer and lime	1.83	1.66	4.11	3.70
Building and fencing materials	8.13	7.88	5.20	5.26
Seed	1.86	1.21	2.55	2.10
Total Commodities	86.72	82.65	90.40	88.17
Interest	3.46	5.11	.96	1.48
Taxes	9.82	12.24	2.04	2.75
Commodities, Interest, and Taxes	100.00	100.00	93.40	92.40
Cash wage rates	....	....	6.60	7.60
Commodities, Interest, Taxes, and Cash Wage Rates	....	....	100.00	100.00

* Data shown indicate the contribution of each component to the determination of the parity indexes reflecting the relative importance of the product of percentage weights times component price indexes. Source: Crop Reporting Board, SRS, USDA, "Agricultural Prices," Sept., 1961, Suppl. No. 1.

¹ Same as index weights.

² Includes tobacco.

³ Autos only. Auto supplies in Old Index are carried under "Household operation."

⁴ Includes tractors.

⁵ Includes motor supplies.

TABLE 19.2

INDEXES OF PRICES PAID FOR COMMODITIES USED IN PRODUCTION, UNITED STATES, AND TYPES OF FARMING AREA *

[1947–49 = 100]

	1937–41	1947–49	1952	1953	1954	1955	1956
United States†	50	100	117	112	112	112	114
Dairy farms:							
Central Northeast‡	50	100	115	110	109	107	108
Eastern Wisconsin‡	51	100	116	114	114	112	115
Western Wisconsin ‡	51	100	115	114	114	114	116
Hog-dairy farms, Corn Belt‡	54	100	116	114	113	113	114
Hog-beef raising farms, Corn Belt‡	53	100	117	116	114	113	114
Hog-beef fattening farms, Corn Belt	45	100	112	102	105	103	100
Cash grain farms, Corn Belt‡	55	100	119	120	121	123	124
Tobacco-livestock farms, Kentucky Bluegrass‡	45	100	118	118	121	118	120
Tobacco-cotton farms, Coastal Plains, North Carolina‡	§	100	114	116	118	119	123
Tobacco farms (small), Coastal Plains, North Carolina‡	§	100	113	115	117	117	117
Tobacco-cotton farms (large), Coastal Plains, North Carolina‡	§	100	109	110	117	118	123
Cotton farms:							
Southern Piedmont‡	48	100	115	112	108	118	112
Black Prairie, Texas‡	46	100	115	111	111	110	106
Nonirrigated, High Plains, Texas‡	47	100	112	119	104	109	112
Irrigated, High Plains, Texas‡	§	100	108	104	99	101	101
Small, Delta‡	§	100	113	110	109	108	107
Large-scale, Delta‡	§	100	116	107	110	108	107
Wheat-small-grain-livestock farms, Northern Great Plains‡	49	100	115	115	116	116	111
Wheat-corn-livestock farms, Northern Great Plains‡	59	100	117	114	117	117	116
Wheat-roughage-livestock farms, Northern Great Plains‡	51	100	117	115	113	115	112
Winter wheat farms, Southern Plains‡	52	100	118	119	117	120	121
Wheat-pea farms, Washington and Idaho‡	51	100	121	122	120	118	126
Sheep ranches:							
Northern Great Plains livestock area‡	47	100	133	119	117	116	115
Southwest‡	§	100	123	103	97	103	96
Cattle ranches:							
Northern Great Plains livestock area‡	50	100	126	121	119	121	125
Intermountain Region‡	53	100	121	120	115	121	123
Southwest‡	§	100	128	108	110	104	109

* Source: *Policy for Commercial Agriculture*, Joint Committee Print, 1957, p. 516.

† Prices paid for production items, interest, taxes, and wages as published in monthly Agricultural Prices.

‡ Prices paid, including taxes (but not interest), and wages to hired labor as published in *Farm Costs and Returns*, ARS, USDA, Agr. Infor. Bul. No. 158.

§ Not available.

in 1955 amounted to $1,444 million or 7.2 per cent of all farm family living expenditures. Others were personal insurance and recreation which accounted for 2.6 and 2.1 per cent, respectively, of all living expenditures. In production, important omissions are machine hire and custom work, marketing expenses for crops and livestock, cash rent, irrigation, and business insurance, which in 1955 accounted collectively for nearly 9 per cent of all production expenditures.[3]

This coverage appears less adequate than the coverage of the index of prices received.

Separate Parity Indexes for Individual Farm Products

The present legislation provides for the use of the same index for all farm products (except for the use of the "Unrevised Index" for the few commodities still on the transitional basis). The present parity index is a single index for the whole United States. It is based upon the prices of about 389 goods and three services (interest, taxes, and wages). The index shows the prices of goods and services for the average farmer in the United States.

But most actual farmers differ widely from average farmers. Some of them are cotton farmers, using cotton machinery, fertilizer, and labor; some are Corn Belt farmers, using corn planters, pickers, etc.; some are wheat farmers, using "one-way's" and combines; some are truck farmers, ranchers, fruit growers, etc., each with his own list of goods and services purchased, differing in kind and quantity from that of the others. The parity index — an average index for the whole United States — does not accurately fit any of them.

In 1960, prices paid for goods and services on all except the poultry farms were higher than in 1947–49. Lower average prices paid on the poultry farms were due to the reduction in price of feed — the major item of expense on these farms. (This pulled the index of price paid down to 83.) The largest increase in average prices paid was on the cash-grain farms in the Corn Belt — 38 per cent[4] (i.e. to an index of 138).

The prices paid for different items in the parity index have risen at markedly different rates since 1940. Hired labor wages have risen to an index of well over 400 (1935–39 = 100). Machinery prices have more than doubled. But fertilizer prices have risen only 50 per cent. The combination of resources used in the production of different farm products has changed in different ways in different areas. The use of machinery on Southern Piedmont cotton farms

---

[3] *Ibid.*, p. 21.
[4] "Farm Costs and Returns," USDA, Agr. Bul. 230, June, 1961, p. 8.

exactly doubled from 1935 to 1953, but on Central Northeast dairy farms it rose only 36 per cent. The use of labor declined at different rates in the different farm areas. Yet the same weights for all types of farms are used in the parity index. The prices of the different factors of production change at different rates, so the use of the same quantity weights for all farm areas, when in fact the quantity weights change at different rates, means that the single parity index for the United States as a whole is not an accurate index of the prices paid in each of the different farming areas. Parity prices for individual farm products would more accurately reflect the parity purchasing power of those products if the parity index were computed separately for each product.

Separate indexes of prices paid for commodities used in production for 27 types of farms in several major farming areas in the United States, have been computed by the USDA. They are shown in Table 19.2, along with the index for the United States as a whole. Each one of these indexes for important types of farms represents the situation on commercial family-operated farms of a particular type in a particular location. For this reason, the indexes are not necessarily representative of all farms involved in the production of a particular commodity over the nation as a whole. They approximate, however, the differences in price trends for production items that might be expected between farms producing different commodities and also the differences between areas producing the same commodity.

Table 19.2 indicates that all the special prices-paid indexes for the different types of farms shown from 1947–49 to 1955, ranged from a 4 per cent decline for sheep ranches in the Southwest to an increase of 26 per cent for wheat-pea farms in Washington and Idaho. This is a total range of 30 percentage points. The rise in the United States index during the same period was 14 per cent.

There is almost as much variation in some instances in the cost-rates indexes in the production of the same commodity in different areas as there is between different commodities. For example, increases in the specialized price indexes for cattle ranches range from 9 per cent in the Southwest to 25 per cent in the northern Great Plains and Intermountain areas. Similarly, the increases since 1947–49 for cotton farms range from only 1 per cent for irrigated operations in the high plains of Texas to some 12 per cent in the Southern Piedmont.

The USDA study implies that this variety of experience even within a given commodity area constitutes an argument against the use of separate parity indexes. The report says:[5] "A specialized cost rate or prices-paid index reflecting the average wheat farmer under this variety of situations might be considered no more satisfactory to producers in particular areas or particular kinds of operations than the generalized parity index."

This variety of experience seems rather to be a point in favor of using separate parity indexes for separate areas producing the product under different conditions.

A Separate Parity Index for Cotton

We may form some quantitative estimate of the effects of using separate commodity parity indexes by considering the case of cotton. Estimates for cotton are quoted from a USDA report on cotton.[6]

> An index representing the composite average price items used in producing the United States cotton crop was developed for each year 1945 through 1955 and for 1939. Items included were labor, land planting seed, insecticides, fertilizer, irrigation water, power and machinery, and ginning. Items not included were management and general overhead.
>
> The index was computed in the following manner. A weighted aggregate of actual prices of the production items was obtained for each year, using as weights the average quantity of each item used in 1947–49. In the development of the weights, the total quantity of each item actually employed in production was used whether or not it was usually purchased. The 1947–49 period was chosen largely because better data were available for those years than for any others. However, this period is considered representative of the postwar period before reinstitution of acreage allotments and marketing quotas.
>
> The price index for production items was calculated by dividing the weighted aggregates for each year by that for a base year and multiplying the result by 100. To derive a parity price based only on items used in cotton production, the price index for each year was multiplied by the parity price for the same base year, as then calculated.
>
> In addition to being an index for cotton rather than an average index for all farms, this concept differs from the present parity formula in two important respects. Items used in family living are given weights and are included in present parity calculations but not in cotton's own parity calculations.[7] The present parity formula includes and gives weight only to items which are purchased, and weights are assigned on the basis of relative importance in total purchased items. In cotton's own parity full weight is given to each item even though only a part of the item is usually purchased.
>
> Table 19.3 gives results of the calculation of cotton's own parity in index form for selected years and for 2 base years. Two important comparisons can be made from these data. For the period 1945–55, with 1945 taken as a

---

[5] "Possible Methods of Improving the Parity Formulas," Senate, 85th Cong., S. Doc. 18, 1957.

[6] "Report on Various Methods of Supporting the Price of Cotton," 85th Cong., 1st sess., S. Doc. 12, 1957, pp. 13–16.

[7] It might be better to include or exclude items used in family living so as to make the two directly comparable.

TABLE 19.3

INDEXES OF PARITY PRICES OF COTTON

| Year | 1945 = 100 | | 1939 = 100 | |
	Old parity	Cotton's own parity	Old parity	Cotton's own parity
1939........	70	51	100	100
1945........	100	100	143	196
1950........	149	132	214	258
1955........	159	157	238	307

base, the index of cotton's own parity changed in about the same proportion as did the old parity index. If such comparisons are made from the prewar base of 1939, however, it will be noted that the index of cotton's own parity increased about three-fold while the old parity index rose only to about 2¼ times its 1939 level. This difference is due largely to the fact that labor and land account for a substantial part of the total weight in cotton's own parity. Farm wage rates and farmland values have increased at a substantially greater rate since 1939 than have prices of items such as fertilizer and farm machinery.

Representativeness of the Price-Base Period

Another important question concerning the parity price indexes is the representativeness of the base periods.

A recent USDA report on the parity formula stated the requirement for a base period clearly. It said, "The base period should be fairly representative of the kind of agriculture that is likely to prevail for some years ahead. Otherwise, the parity measurement would have little meaning in appraising the agricultural situation as it develops in the future." [8] How do the parity price indexes measure up to this standard?

In the computation of "modernized" parity prices, the adjusted base price for each farm product is computed by dividing the average of the United States average price for that product, over the most recent 10 years, by the average index of prices received by farmers for the same 10 years. This permits the parity prices for individual farm products to reflect recent market forces, but keeps the parity prices for farm products as a group on the original 1910–14 base.

This brings the *relative* parity prices in line with *relative* market prices over the most recent 10-year averages. But it only "modernizes" the relations among the prices. It leaves the parity prices all

[8] "Possible Methods of Improving the Parity Formula," Report of the Secretary of Agriculture pursuant to Section 602 of the Agricultural Act of 1956, 85th Cong., 1st sess., S. Doc. 18, Feb. 1, 1957, p. 18.

high or low relative to the most recent 10-year average relationship, if the 1910–14 base is high or low relative to that most recent 10-year average relationship. It leaves parity prices as a group, and the overall parity ratio, as anciently based as before.

In a world full of pronounced and rapid changes, it is anachronistic to measure relative prices with reference to a 1910–14 base, 50 years and two world wars in the past. Increasingly with the passage of time since 1910–14, therefore, suggestions have been made that the 1910–14 base should be replaced by a more recent base.

Alternative Base Periods

A 1958 USDA report[9] considered several different more recent periods, and computed their effects on the average level of prices. Their figures are shown in Table 19.4. We have added two more recent bases, 1950–59 and 1955–59, to bring their table up to date. The report recommended that the base period be changed from 1910–14 to 1947–56. No legislation to that effect, however, has been passed.

If 1947–56 were a good base for the USDA to recommend in 1957, would 1950–59 be a better base to recommend in 1960?

The answer depends upon what the parity index is used for. If the purpose is still to compare the purchasing power of farm products as a group now with their purchasing in 1910–14, but without the stigma attached to the use of this ancient base, then the use of the 1947–56 base would come within 2 points of doing the job.

If, however, the purpose is to follow the principle laid down in the USDA report, that the base period should be fairly representative of the kind of agriculture that is likely to prevail for some

TABLE 19.4

Indexes of Prices Received and Paid by Farmers and the Parity Ratio, Selected Periods, 1910–59

Period	Index of Prices Received (1910–14 = 100)	Index of Prices Paid (parity index, 1910–14 = 100)	Parity Ratio (1910–14 = 100)	Percentage Change in the Average Level of Parity Prices
1910–14. . . .	100	100	100	0
1925–29. . . .	147	161	91	− 9
1935–39. . . .	107	125	86	−14
1947–51. . . .	275	258	108	+ 8
1947–56. . . .	264	270	98	− 2
1950–59. . . .	254	281	90	−10
1955–59. . . .	237	280	83	−17

[9] *Ibid.*

years ahead, then the 1950–59 base would come closer to doing this job than the 1947–56 base. The use of the 5-year base, 1955–59, would come still closer. Agriculture for some years ahead is likely to be more similar to agriculture over the past 5 or 10 years than to agriculture in 1910–14 or 1949–56.

It is not within the power of the USDA to change the base period on its own initiative. The base period is laid down as 1910–14 in the legislation, amended by later legislation to permit the use of the most recent 10-year average of market prices for individual farm products, but still retaining 1910–14 as the base for farm products as a group. New legislation would be required to permit the use of a more recent base than 1910–14.

APPRAISAL OF PARITY INDEXES WITH REFERENCE TO CHIEF USES TO WHICH THEY ARE NOW BEING PUT

The present parity price indexes were designed originally to measure the prices received by farmers, the prices paid by farmers, and the ratio between the two price indexes. But, with the passage of time, the indexes began to be used also for two other different purposes.

1. The parity ratio — the ratio between the prices received and the prices paid by farmers — is widely used now to measure the economic status of agriculture.[10] This ratio is published on the front page of the monthly USDA publication, *Agricultural Prices,* and is frequently quoted as it comes out by newspapers and farm magazines. When the parity ratio is 79, for example, as it was in July, 1962, that ratio is regarded as indicating that the prices received by farmers are too low; some regard a parity ratio of 79 as indicating that the prices of farm products are 21 per cent too low. Some farm programs are being proposed with the objective of raising the prices of farm products to 100 per cent of parity, presumably in the belief that this would restore agriculture to its fair economic status.

In addition, the ratio between the actual market price for an individual farm product and the parity price of that product is widely used as a measure of the economic status of the producers of that

[10] For example: "The drop in prices . . . caused the parity ratio — index of relative farm prosperity — to fall one point . . ." *(Des Moines Register,* July 28, 1956).

". . . the parity ratio — measure of the farmers' well-being in relation to the whole economy . . ." (News item by Charles Bailey of the *Des Moines Register's* Washington Bureau, *Des Moines Register,* Nov. 30, 1957, p. 11).

"Regardless of the pros or cons of the parity formula in regard to getting price supports, it still is the nation's chief yardstick for measuring the relative position of the farmer and the long-term price trends." John Harms, "Outlook for Ag. Leaders," *County Agent and Vo-Ag Teacher,* Feb., 1959.

product. This ratio for corn, for example, was 65 in July, 1962. These ratios are also published monthly in *Agricultural Prices*. Such a ratio, of course, does not measure the economic status of the producers of the product but merely expresses a purchasing power ratio for the particular commodity.

2. Since the passage of the Agricultural Adjustment Act of 1938, the parity prices for some individual farm products (actually, certain percentages of parity prices) have been used as bases for the price-support operations of the CCC for those products. The operations involve billions of dollars, as shown in the preceding chapter.

Are the indexes well suited to these two purposes?

It is obvious that the parity price indexes are not well suited to these two purposes. Economic status depends upon *income* relationships, not merely upon price relationships. The measurement of income requires that quantities purchased and sold, as well as prices, should be taken in account. Price supports also need to be set with reference to quantities as well as to prices.

An illustration of this is the divergence between movements of the parity ratio from 1951 to 1959 and the income per person on farms over the same period. The parity ratio declined 27 points, from 107 in 1951 to 80 in 1959. But income per person on farms declined only 2 per cent, from $983 to $960. Even income from farming alone declined only about 14 per cent. This point is important, since technological developments in agriculture production have markedly changed the output per unit of input over the past 15 or 20 years. Accordingly, suggestions have been made that these changes in quantities should be included in the present parity price formula.

Here again the USDA is not free to include, on its own initiative, quantities as well as prices in order to measure the purchasing power of the farmer. New legislation would be required for that purpose, also. The USDA, however, has made some estimates of the effects of taking quantities into account, for farm products as a group. These estimates are presented and discussed below.[11]

Illustration of an Efficiency Modifier and Its Effect on Parity Prices.

"The development of a price-support system which permits the adjustment of price supports in line with changes in efficiency involves the calculation of an index of efficiency for a period of years. This index is referred to in this report as the "efficiency modifier."

A preliminary index treating agriculture as a whole has been developed to reflect the trend in the use of productive inputs per unit of farm output

---

[11] The next four paragraphs are quoted from S. Doc. 18, p. 26 (see footnote #8).

since 1940. This index and the separate indexes of the total volume of selected farm inputs and of farm output from which it was derived are shown in Table 19.5 and Figure 19.1.

According to these preliminary calculations, which can only be considered indicative of the general trend, farmers, as a group, used some 23 per cent fewer inputs per unit of farm production in 1955 than in 1940. The chart also indicates that the improvement in efficiency reflected by the reduction in inputs per unit of output was substantially greater in the 5-year war period, 1940 to 1945, than in the ensuing 10 years.

For reasons of lack of data, the index presently cannot be carried back to the 1910–14 base period. Thus, it is impossible to appraise the effects of an adjustment for improved efficiency on parity prices since that period. However, even if only the efficiency increases that have taken place in agriculture since 1940 were given full weight in the parity formula, the level of parity prices for all farm products would have been reduced 23 per cent in 1955. If the adjustment for efficiency were to reflect only the improvement since 1945, the parity prices would be reduced some 10 per cent. In other words, if the base period for parity prices is moved to more recent years, the effect of the efficiency modifier on parity prices would be sharply diminished. Thus, assuming the recent 10-year period as a base, the downward adjustment to the parity level from the efficiency factor would be about 5 per cent.

TABLE 19.5

INDEXES OF SELECTED FARM INPUTS, TOTAL FARM OUTPUT, AND THE
RATIO OF SELECTED INPUTS PER UNIT OF OUTPUT*
[1940 = 100]

Year	Index of Selected Farm Inputs†	Index of Total Farm Outputs‡	Index of Selected Farm Inputs per Unit of Total Farm Outputs§
1940	100	100	100
1941	99	104	95
1942	103	116	89
1943	104	113	92
1944	104	117	89
1945	100	116	86
1946	99	118	84
1947	99	114	87
1948	100	125	80
1949	101	122	83
1950	99	120	82
1951	103	124	83
1952	103	129	80
1953	103	130	79
1954	103	130	79
1955	104	135	77

* Source: S. Doc. 18, p. 27.
† Preliminary. Based on estimated inputs of total farm labor, land, buildings, machinery, fertilizer and lime, combined on basis of average 1947–49 cost rates.
‡ Published regularly on a 1947–49 basis.
§ Preliminary index of selected inputs divided by index of total farm output.

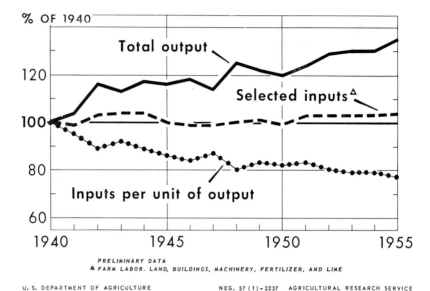

Fig. 19.1 — Farm inputs per unit of output, indexes, annually, 1940–55.

The USDA report then goes on to raise the question whether an efficiency modifier should be used in the parity formula in any case. Its use would imply that the gains from increased production efficiency should be passed on to the consumers in the form of lower prices. The report states that this is not the general practice in the nonfarm economy, and concludes that it should not be adopted in agriculture.

The USDA report also developed an efficiency modifier for a specific farm product, cotton, as follows: [12]

Efficiency Modifier for Cotton

In order to calculate the efficiency modifier, it was necessary to obtain estimates of the quantities of the major items used in producing the United States cotton crop [inputs] during each year of the 1945–55 period and for 1939. . . . The estimates of inputs relate to those actually used in cotton production each year and do not make allowance for resources that might have been unemployed in a given year because of fluctuations in the size of the cotton crop.

Production input data were obtained from several sources. The acreage of cotton planted and harvested, the total quantities of labor, fertilizer, and planting seed used in producing cotton and the cost of ginning were available largely from published information. Estimates of power, machinery, irrigation, and other items were developed from various local area studies and from miscellaneous sources.

---

[12] *Ibid.*, pp. 15, 16.

An index of the quantity of physical inputs required to produce a bale of cotton for the years 1945–55 and for 1939 was computed as follows: A weighted measure of the total quantity of inputs used in production was obtained for each year by applying appropriate average 1947–49 prices as weights to the quantity of each input item used in each year and summing their products. These weighted aggregates were converted to index numbers by dividing the total for each year by the total for a base year and multiplying by 100. An index of the number of bales of cotton produced was also calculated. The index of quantity of inputs was divided by the index of bales produced to derive an index of quantity of inputs per bale of cotton, called the efficiency modifier.

The results of these calculations using the year 1945 as a base are given in Figure 19.2. In general, there has been a sharp decrease in inputs per bale and they were 30 per cent less in 1955 than in 1945. The inclusion or exclusion of land as an input had relatively little effect on the index during the 1945–55 period.

A trend line fitted to the data shown in Figure 19.2 indicates that the quantity of inputs per bale of cotton has decreased at an average rate of about 3 per cent per year from 1945 to 1955. Figure 19.3 shows the parity price for cotton that would result from use of cotton's own parity and the efficiency modifier during the 1945–55 period. As indicated above, the use of cotton's own parity (1945 equals 100) would have resulted in substantially the same parity prices for cotton in most years as those resulting from the use of old parity. In this instance the old parity price for 1945 and cotton's own parity for 1945 were assumed to be the same. The application of the efficiency modifier (1945 equals 100) to the old parity price of cotton and to cotton's own parity would have reduced the parity price of each substantially during the most of the years considered. For example, if in 1955 the efficiency modifier were multiplied by the old parity price and by cotton's own parity, respectively, resulting prices would be about 24.2 and 23.9 cents a pound. Without use of the efficiency modifier, cotton's own parity would have been about 34.6 cents in 1955. Old parity in 1955 was 35.1 cents per pound.

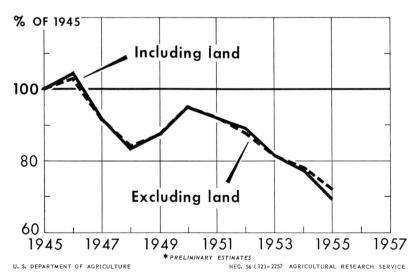

Fig. 19.2 — Production inputs per bale of cotton, indexes, annually, 1945–55.

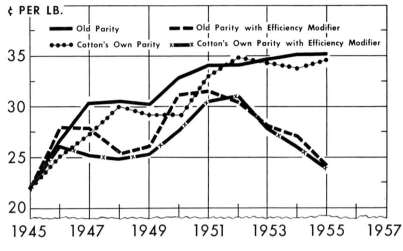

U. S. DEPARTMENT OF AGRICULTURE   NEG. 56 (12)-2258   AGRICULTURAL RESEARCH SERVICE

Fig. 19.3 — Alternative parity prices of cotton, annually, 1945–55.

The use of the efficiency modifier would have had a much larger effect than the use of a separate parity index for cotton; the efficiency modifier would have lowered the parity price of cotton in 1955 by 31 per cent.

PARITY PRICES AS BASIS FOR PRICE SUPPORTS

We may now appraise parity prices in their present widespread use as bases for the price-support and storage operations of the CCC. These are tremendous operations, as shown in the preceding chapter, running into billions of dollars.

It is clear that parity prices are quite unsuited to this purpose. They are subject to the same disabilities as the parity ratio — they are based on the same out-of-date 1910–14 base, unrepresentative of "the kind of agriculture that is likely to prevail for some years ahead." Modernized parity mitigates this shortcoming to some extent, so far as the relations among the prices of farm products are concerned, but leaves the basic situation — that the indexes for farm products as a group remain on the 1910–14 base — unaffected. The use of a more up-to-date base would remove one of the obvious shortcomings of parity prices as bases for loan rates. But a more basic shortcoming would still remain.

Commodity loans and storage operations can be used to stabilize prices against year-to-year variations in supply, if the loan rates are set at or a little below long-run average premarket levels. These levels reflect long-run supply and demand. But parity prices, even on a recent base, are not suited to this job. They reflect only changes in supply (i.e., in the quantities that producers stand ready to bring to market at different prices) and do that very imperfectly, since parity indexes reflect only the *prices* of cost items, not their quantities. In addition, as a group, parity prices ignore changes in demand entirely. They therefore leave out three-quarters of the picture.

The size of the accumulated CCC stocks and the cost of acquiring and maintaining them has amply demonstrated that loan rates cannot for long be set above the long-run market levels determined by demand and supply. Parity prices which reflect demand and supply so imperfectly are obviously not suitable as bases for loan rates. Their use for this purpose has cost billions of dollars, only part of which has gone to farmers, and has brought the farm program into disrepute.

20

Parity Farm Income

The preceding discussion moved step by step from price indexes, which reflect income very imperfectly, to various modifications which bring the price indexes closer and closer to measures of income. This chapter takes the last step and deals with parity income.

PARITY INCOME

It was recognized as parity price indexes were developed that prices were only one of the things that determined income. It was recognized also that what farmers were really interested in was income, not prices. So, along with the development of parity prices went several legislative attempts to define parity income.

During the 1930's the concept of parity income developed as an extension of the parity price concept. It first appeared in legislation in 1936. A declared purpose of the Soil Conservation and Domestic Allotment Act of 1936 was the "reestablishment, at as rapid a rate as the Secretary of Agriculture determines to be practicable and in the general public interest, of the ratio between the purchasing power of the net income per person on farms and the income per person not on farms that prevailed during the 5-year period August 1909–July 1914, inclusive, as determined from statistics available in the United States Department of Agriculture and the maintenance of such ratio."

There was a good deal of criticism of this definition of parity income. In the Agricultural Adjustment Act of 1938, therefore, the definition was changed to read as follows: "Parity, as applied to income, shall be that per capita net income of individuals on farms from farming operations that bears to the per capita net income of individuals not on farms, the same relation as prevailed during the period from August 1909–July 1914."

The 1938 definition of parity income differed from the 1936 definition in four respects. (1) The term "net" was used; it was applied to per capita income of persons not on farms as well as to that of persons on farms. (2) The "purchasing power" provision in the 1936 definition was omitted in the 1938 denfiition. (3) The income of persons on farms included income from farming operations only. (4) The limitation "as determined from statistics available in the USDA" was omitted.

The 1938 definition of net income avoided the difficulty of measuring intangibles — the nonmonetary items of income on the farm and off the farm, such as the independence of the farm operator compared with the dependence of the urban worker on his job, the open air nature of farm work, the generally poorer schools in the country, etc. It did not call for direct comparisons of current net incomes on farms with current net incomes off farms. Thus if current income data showed net farm income to be only half as much as nonfarm income (or twice as much) that would still represent income parity if half (or twice) were the relation that existed in the base period.

The Agricultural Act of 1948 changed the definition of parity farm income again. Title II, Sec. 201 (2), defined parity farm income as follows: " (2) 'Parity,' as applied to income shall be that gross income from agriculture which will provide the farm operator and his family with a standard of living equivalent to those afforded persons dependent upon other gainful occupation." This new definition was incorporated in the Agricultural Act of 1949 and became effective on January 1, 1950.

This definition got away from the problems involved in any formula which includes a base period. It got away, for example, from the problem of what base period to use (one period might have a much higher or lower parity income than another). It also got away from the problem of continuous obsolescence of any base period. But it got into a different problem — the problem of comparing levels of living in different occupations. The new formula involved more than a simple comparison of farm and nonfarm dollar incomes. It required in addition the determination of differences in their purchasing power, as represented by their different levels of living. So far, this new definition, while "effective January 1, 1950," has not been computed and put into actual use.

The Agricultural Act of 1948 also defined parity gross income for individual commodities as follows: " 'Parity' as applied to income from any agricultural commodity for any year, shall be that gross income which bears the same relationship to parity income from agriculture for such year as the average gross income from such commodity for the preceding ten calendar years bears to the average gross income from agriculture for such ten calendar years." This was the first time that a method of apportioning income parity among the individual commodities was prescribed by law. Inasmuch as the over-all level of parity gross income could not be determined, this additional step has not had much significance.

ALTERNATIVE MEASURES OF FARM INCOME

What income data are available which might make it possible to measure the economic status of farmers more accurately than the existing parity prices indexes, and permit parity *income* to be computed?

Measures of gross income (prices received times quantities sold) and of cost (prices paid times quantities purchased) are available, and they can be used to measure net income per farmer. The USDA compiles several measures of this character.

Farm Income Per Capita

The one that is most widely publicized is farm income per capita. It is shown in Table 20.1 and Figure 20.1. These data, in comparison with nonfarm income data, are often used as the basis for the statement that farm income is only about half as high as nonfarm income.

These figures, however, understate the average farm income per person in the usual sense of the word farm, because "farm" in this case is "farm" as defined by the Bureau of Census. This definition includes "farms" all the way down to 10 acres in size if the value of agricultural products sold is $50 or more; it includes places of less than 10 acres if the value of sales or production of agricultural products is $150 or more.

Most of the "farmers" on these small "farms" are not farmers at all in the ordinary sense of the term. Their chief source of income is a nonfarm job, not farming. About 1.3 million of these small farms are classed as noncommercial farms — part-time, residential, or subsistence farms. These are really acreages where city people live, rather than farms. They constitute more than a third of the

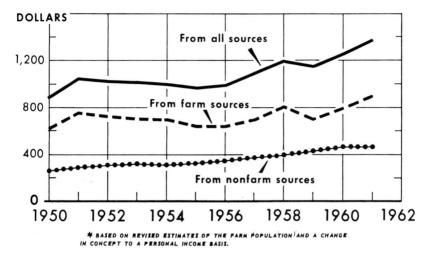

U. S. DEPARTMENT OF AGRICULTURE   NEG. ERS 1238-62 (7)   ECONOMIC RESEARCH SERVICE

Fig. 20.1 — Average farm income per person, farm and nonfarm, United States, annually, 1950–61.

total of 3.7 million farms of all kinds in the United States.[1] This large number of "not really farms" inflates the number of farms and farmers that is divided into the total United States net farm income, and therefore reduces the "average farm income" substantially below the average income for *commercial family* farms, with the part-time, residential, and subsistence farms taken out.[2]

In 1956, these part-time and residential farms, nearly one-third of all farms, made only 2 per cent of all sales of farm products. "Clearly, the welfare of the families on low-production farms is more closely linked with the expanding nonfarm sector of our economy than with agriculture as such." [3]

---

[1] To include them in the farm average is about like computing the average salary of professors by including numerous graduate students receiving part-time stipends, if these stipends were very small and the graduate students lived chiefly on other sources of income.

[2] E. W. Grove and N. M. Koffsky made this point clear in their article, "Measuring the Incomes of Farm People," *Journal of Farm Economics*, Vol. 31, No. 4, Part 2, Nov., 1949, p. 1, 110. So do K. L. Bachman and R. W. Jones, "Sizes of Farms in the United States," USDA Tech. Bul. 1019, July, 1950, p. 7, where they say that this "often gives rise to serious misconceptions," and show that excluding these noncommercial farms raises the average operator's net income 27 per cent.

But Koffsky and Grove, in their later article, "The Current Income Position of Commercial Farmers," Joint Committee Print, Policy for Commercial Agriculture, Nov. 22, 1957, pp. 79–90, overlook the matter, and conclude on the basis of United States average data that "the level of income per person on farms has averaged roughly one-half of the non-farm level." By this they unwittingly give support to the "serious misconception."

[3] *Economic Report of the President*, January, 1959, p. 99.

TABLE 20.1

NATIONAL INCOME: FARM AND NONFARM, 1929–61*

Year	Farm	Nonfarm	Total	Farm as a Percentage of Total
	(*Mil. dol.*)	(*Mil. dol.*)	(*Mil. dol.*)	(*Per cent*)
1929	8,083	79,731	87,814	9.2
1930	6,044	69,685	75,729	8.0
1931	4,727	54,981	59,708	7.9
1932	3,199	39,348	42,547	7.5
1933	3,590	36,569	40,159	8.9
1934	3,603	45,356	48,959	7.4
1935	6,268	50,789	57,057	11.0
1936	5,266	59,645	64,911	8.1
1937	7,029	66,589	73,618	9.5
1938	5,741	61,840	67,581	8.5
1939	5,761	66,992	72,753	7.9
1940	6,073	75,561	81,634	7.4
1941	8,269	96,441	104,710	7.9
1942	12,148	125,546	137,694	8.8
1943	13,864	156,446	170,310	8.1
1944	14,152	168,487	182,639	7.7
1945	14,526	166,722	181,248	8.0
1946	18,235	162,644	180,879	10.1
1947	18,836	179,341	198,177	9.5
1948	21,355	202,132	223,487	9.6
1949	16,332	201,358	217,690	7.5
1950	17,328	224,548	241,876	7.2
1951	19,829	259,484	279,313	7.1
1952	18,807	273,348	292,155	6.4
1953	16,750	288,823	305,573	5.5
1954	16,128	285,666	301,794	5.3
1955	15,234	314,972	330,206	4.6
1956	15,143	335,693	350,836	4.3
1957	15,397	351,546	366,943	4.2
1958	17,369	350,015	367,384	4.7
1959	15,350	385,131	400,481	3.8
1960	16,090	397,140	413,230	3.9
1961	17,274	408,238	425,512	4.1

* Source: "The Farm Income Situation," AMS, USDA, July, 1962, p. 44.
Department of Commerce data, excluding Alaska and Hawaii.

In addition, the estimates of net farm income value the farm products produced on the farm and consumed by the farm household at farm prices. There is some disagreement whether these products should be valued at farm prices or at retail prices. People in town have to buy their food at retail prices, so on the face of it, farm and nonfarm incomes would seem to be more nearly comparable if the food produced on the operator's own farm were valued at retail prices too. Against this it may be well argued that a gallon of peas in the pod just picked from the farm garden by the farm wife, for example, is not at all comparable with the package of frozen peas ready to put in the pot purchased by the city housewife. For another example, however, eggs from the henhouse are just as ready to cook as eggs in the retail store, and usually fresher.

On the average, farmers get less than half the consumer's retail food dollar. The USDA estimates that valuing the food that is included in farm income at retail prices would add a little more than $100 to per capita farm income.[4]

The allowance for the value of housing provided by the farm, including taxes, insurance, interest, maintenance, and depreciation, in recent years has been about $300 per farm. Average nonfarm rental runs about $600. Many farm homes, of course, do not have indoor toilets or baths and other facilities that are usually found in urban homes; but most of them provide more room, quiet, and seclusion than the average urban home. Perhaps the USDA allowance is too conservative.

A part of the difference between the average farm and nonfarm income results from the fact that a large part of the farm population is concentrated in the South where incomes and prices are generally lower than in the North where industrial workers are concentrated. Income comparisons on a state or regional basis reveal about a 25 per cent smaller difference between farm and nonfarm incomes than the straight United States averages quoted above.

The USDA estimates that adjustment to take these food and housing and location matters into account would increase per capita farm income about 30 percent.[5]

Income Per Farm Worker

Another answer concerning relative farm and nonfarm income

---

[4] S. Doc. 18.

[5] "Possible Methods of Improving the Parity Formula," Senate, 85th Cong., S. Doc. 18, 1957, p. 39.

is based on a comparison of income per farm worker[6] with the average annual wage per employed factory worker. These per worker income figures for 1961 were: farm, $2,268; factory, $4,802. Conclusion: Income per farm worker is only about half as high as income per factory worker. Income per farm *operator* was $3,360 in 1961. This is only about 70 per cent as high as income per factory worker.

This situation appears to confirm the conclusion that is usually drawn from the per capita income figures given in the preceding section — that farm income is only about half as great as nonfarm income. But it is also misleading. The farm workers include the family workers, and the farm income includes a good deal of disguised partial unemployment, whereas the factory workers include only *employed* factory workers. The average farm worker's income data, therefore, understate the actual average income much as the per capita income data do, partly for the same reason and partly for different ones.

ALTERNATIVE MEASURES OF PARITY FARM INCOME

The USDA, well aware of the characteristics of the United States average farm income data given above, has discussed their use in parity income computations in the following terms: [7]

> The idea of parity income centers on the relation between incomes of farm people and incomes of nonfarm people. Generally, there are two basic approaches to the problem of determining parity income. One involves the maintenance of a historical income ratio which would provide for farmers' incomes and opportunities for a rising standard of living to grow at the same rate as others. The alternative approach would establish the standard of equal incomes or equal living standards as between farmers and others. Both approaches have appeared in the farm legislation relating to income parity. These alternatives lead to a wide range in results. Historical income ratios as between farm and nonfarm persons on which the two earlier parity income definitions were based indicate that incomes in agriculture in recent years were about at or above parity as compared with 1910–14. On the other hand, direct income comparisons tend to show that farm income falls far short of the nonfarm level, although there are considerable questions as to the meaning of measures of this kind.

Parity Income Based on Historical Income Ratios

Table 20.1 shows the available data on income per person living on farms from all sources, nonfarm as well as farm, and income per person

---

[6] *The Farm Income Situation*, July, 1962, p. 45. This is total United States realized net farm income from farming, including government payments, plus total farm wages, divided by the total average number of persons engaged in agriculture during the year, including farm operators and other family workers (except those doing housework only) as well as hired workers.

[7] S. Doc. 18, p. 39.

not living on farms, from 1910 to 1958, as published regularly by the USDA. It should be noted that estimates of nonfarm income received by farm people, such as wages or salaries from nonfarm occupations, are not available prior to 1934. For purposes of indicating, at least roughly, how income ratios in recent years compared with the 1910–14 period, we have made an assumption that nonfarm income received by farm people in the 1910–14 period totaled $1.5 billion annually. This is shown in Table 20.2. This assumption is based on the probability that poorer transportation in those days restricted nonfarm job opportunities to farm people as compared with recent years.

Figure 20.2 compares income ratios based on the 1910–14 base period, illustrating the definitions involved in the acts of 1936 and 1938 as follows:

(1) Ratios of per capita net income of the farm population from farming to per capita net income of the nonfarm population (1938 legislation). The data for 1956 indicate that the income ratio of farm people to nonfarm people was about the same as in the 1910–14 period, ranging from slightly above the pre-World War I base to slightly below, depending on whether or not income of the nonfarm population is adjusted to exclude nonfarm income received by farm people.

(2) Ratios of per capita net income of the farm population from all sources to per capita net income of the nonfarm population (1936 legislation). Assuming income from nonfarm sources averaged $1.5 billion annually in 1910–14, this series indicates that the 1956 income ratio was 8 per cent higher than in the 1910–14 period. However, a considerable range is actually involved, depending on the assumption made with re-

TABLE 20.2

ILLUSTRATIVE PER CAPITA INCOME PARITY RATIOS OF FARM POPULATION TO NONFARM POPULATION, AS DEFINED IN AGRICULTURAL LEGISLATION OF 1936, 1938, AND 1934–56*

	Ratio of Per Capita Income of Farm Population to Per Capita Income of Nonfarm Population			Ratio of Per Capita Income of Farm Population to Per Capita Income of Nonfarm Population	
Year	Income to farm people from farming only (1938 legislation)	Income to farm people from all sources (1936 legislation)	Year	Income to farm people from farming only (1938 legislation)	Income to farm people from all sources (1936 legislation)
1934	74	85	1946	159	149
1935	115	115	1947	150	144
1936	85	94	1948	162	153
1937	109	112	1949	122	124
1938	91	99	1950	128	128
1939	88	97	1951	139	136
1940	83	93	1952	125	127
1941	98	104	1953	116	121
1942	119	120	1954	116	121
1943	131	129	1955	102	111
1944	129	128	1956†	98	108
1945	138	134			

* Note: Assumes nonfarm income of farm population averaged $1,500,000,000 in the base years 1910–14. No reliable estimate of such income is available for that period. For more recent data, see Table 20.3.

† Tentative estimates; revised Mar. 5, 1957.

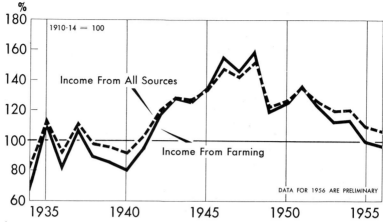

Fig. 20.2 — Ratios of indexes, percapita income: farm persons and persons not on farms, 1934–56.

spect to nonfarm income of farm people in the base period. If the size of that income is assumed to total $2 billion for the 1910–14 average, which would imply approximately the same rate of farmers' participation in nonfarm activities as in recent years, the 1956 income ratio would be 2 per cent lower than in the 1910–14 period. On the other hand, if farmers' participation in nonfarm activities was even less than first assumed, and nonfarm income was only $1 billion for the 1910–14 average, the 1956 income ratio would be 20 per cent higher.

TABLE 20.3

Illustrative Per Capita Income Parity Ratios of Farm Population, as Defined in Agricultural Legislation of 1936, 1938, and 1934–59

	Ratio of Per Capita Income of Farm Population to Per Capita Income of Nonfarm Population	
Year	Income to farm people from farming only (1938 legislation)	Income to farm people from all sources (1936 legislation)
1953.	114	119
1954.	115	120
1955.	99	109
1956.	94	105
1957.	97	108
1958.	117	123
1959.	95	106

Note: Table 20.2 has been revised from 1953 forward, and this table from B. R. Stauber, USDA, presents the later data.

The index or ratio which compares income of farm people from all sources with income of nonfarm people appears to be more appropriate as a measure of farm well-being than the ratio including only the income of farm people from farming. Nonfarm income is becoming increasingly important as a source of income to farm people and as a means of maintaining or increasing living levels.

It should be noted also that comparison of these ratios need not be limited to the 1910–14 base period. If for example, the 10 years (1947–56) were considered as the base period, the ratio involving income per person on farms from farming would be 22 per cent under the base average ratio, and the ratio involving income per person on farms from all sources some 15 per cent lower. The parity price ratio for 1956 was also 15 per cent under the 1947–56 average.

Finally, in considering the appropriateness of historical income ratios, the comparison can involve other series such as earnings in agriculture as compared with earnings in selected other occupations, which are shown in Table 20.4 from 1929 to 1956. For example, the ratio of hourly earnings in agriculture, after allowance for capital investment, to hourly earnings in manufacturing could be used in place of an income ratio.

Direct Comparisons, Farm and Nonfarm

The alternatives relating to direct standard of living or income comparisons between farm and nonfarm people present unusual and difficult problems of measurement and interpretation. For example, the Agricultural Act of 1948 defined parity income, effective January 1, 1950, as 'Parity,' as applied to income, shall be that gross income from agriculture which will provide the farm operator and his family with a standard of living equivalent to those afforded persons dependent upon other gainful occupation. 'Parity,' as applied to income from any agricultural commodity for any year, shall be that gross income which bears the same relationship to parity income from agriculture for such year as the average gross income from such commodity for the preceding 10 calendar years bears to the average gross income from agriculture for such 10 calendar years."

USDA has not been in a position to bring statistical meaning to this definition. The determination of equivalent standards of living involves much more than equivalent dollar incomes. A family's well-being depends not only on income but also on other factors such as the accumulation of assets and consumer goods over the years, the availability of adequate health and educational facilities, and such intangible factors as are involved in evaluating life in the country versus life in the city. It is noteworthy that indexes developed to measure changes in levels of living of farm operator families indicate that there has been persistent improvement each year in farm operator family level of living since 1951 despite declines in farm income during most of that period.

Commercial Family Farm Income, by Areas

The preceding discussion has run in terms of national average incomes, with all the shortcomings of those incomes that have been pointed out. A more appropriate measure of farm income for our purposes is the average income for *commercial family farms.*

The USDA publishes another set of figures which show this income per commercial family farm, by types of farming in different

TABLE 20.4
AVERAGE HOURLY EARNINGS IN AGRICULTURE AND IN SELECTED INDUSTRIES, 1929–59*
[Dollars]

Year	Workers in Agriculture		Production Workers in Industry†					
	Realized return per hour to all farm labor and management‡	Composite hired farm wage rate per hour	Manufacturing	Bituminous coal mining	Building construction	Class I railroads	Telephone	Wholesale trade
1929.....	0.259	0.241	0.566	0.681	....	....	....	....
1930.....	.172	.226	.552	.684	....	....	....	....
1931.....	.093	.172	.515	.647	....	....	....	....
1932.....	.055	.129	.446	.520	....	....	....	....
1933.....	.106	.115	.442	.501	....	....	....	....
1934.....	.172	.129	.532	.673	0.795	....	....	....
1935.....	.203	.142	.550	.745	.815	....	....	0.648
1936.....	.232	.152	.556	.794	.824	....	....	.667
1937.....	.221	.172	.624	.856	.903	....	0.774	.698
1938.....	.187	.166	.627	.878	.908	....	.816	.700
1939.....	.199	.166	.633	.886	.932	0.730	.822	.715
1940.....	.200	.169	.661	.883	.958	.733	.827	.739
1941.....	.315	.206	.729	.993	1.010	.743	.820	.793
1942.....	.450	.268	.853	1.059	1.148	.837	.843	.860
1943.....	.610	.353	.961	1.139	1.252	.852	.870	.933
1944.....	.618	.423	1.019	1.186	1.319	.948	.911	.985
1945.....	.684	.472	1.023	1.240	1.379	.955	.962	1.029
1946.....	.858	.515	1.086	1.401	1.478	1.087	1.124	1.150
1947....	1.010	.547	1.237	1.636	1.681	1.186	1.197	1.268
1948.....	.945	.580	1.350	1.898	1.848	1.301	1.248	1.359
1949.....	.803	.559	1.401	1.941	1.935	1.427	1.345	1.414
1950.....	.826	.561	1.465	2.010	2.031	1.572	1.398	1.483
1951.....	.920	.625	1.59	2.21	2.19	1.73	1.49	1.58
1952.....	.879	.661	1.67	2.29	2.31	1.83	1.59	1.67
1953.....	.874	.672	1.77	2.48	2.48	1.88	1.68	1.77
1954.....	.805	.661	1.81	2.48	2.60	1.93	1.76	1.83
1955.....	.754	.675	1.88	2.56	2.66	1.96	1.82	1.90
1956.....	.839	.705	1.98	2.31	2.80	2.12	1.86	2.01
1957.....	.776	.728	2.07	3.02	2.96	2.26	1.95	2.10
1958....	.970	.757	2.13	3.02	3.10	2.44	2.05	2.17
1959§....	.716	.798	2.22	3.25	3.22	2.54	2.18	2.24

* Data since 1956, and revisions of some data before 1956, from Murray Thompson, USDA.
† *Economic Report of the President*, Jan., 1957, p. 149.
‡ After allowance for capital investment; derived in Table 20.1.
§ Preliminary.

areas. These figures are compiled differently from those given above. They do not show income per farm for the United States as a whole; they show income per commercial family farm for each of the 32 chief types of farming, separately for each of the relatively homogeneous areas shown in Figure 20.3.

The average net income per farm for the past few years is computed separately for each area, and published annually in tabular form.[8] The most recent data are given in Table 20.5. The unweighted average of these incomes was $6,379 in 1960.[9] This on the face of it looks like a pretty good income. It is about 33 per cent higher than the average annual wage per employed factory worker in 1960, $4,802.

But before we conclude from this that average net farm income for commercial family farms really was substantially higher than nonfarm income, we need to recognize that these net farm income figures include what is called the "charge for capital." [10] Deducting this charge for capital from the net income leaves the return to the operator and his family for their labor and management only. This is done for 1961 in the right-hand column of Table 20.5.

---

[8] *Farm Costs and Returns; Commercial Family-Operated Farms by Type and Location,* ARS.

These farm cost and income data are not obtained by a survey of actual farms. They are synthetic figures, calculated by applying estimated changes in prices, yields, inputs, etc., to model type farms. They are estimates of the average costs and returns, not of all commercial family farms in each area, but of the type of farming specified in each area.

[9] This unweighted average is not as accurate an average as if the data were weighted by the numbers of farms in the different types. These numbers are not available at present. I believe that this lack of accuracy is small compared with that of the other averages discussed in the preceding sections. In any case, national averages do not mean much because of the great diversity behind the averages, as shown in Table 20.5. I use them here only because they are used so much in national policy discussion. My chief point is made later with the diverse area data.

[10] "This charge is the current value of land and buildings times the current interest rate on farm mortgages on this kind of property in the area plus estimated current value of working assets (machinery and equipment, livestock, and crops on hand January 1) times the interest rate on intermediate and short-term farm loans," From: ARS, USDA, "Costs and Returns, Commercial Family-Operated Farms by Type and Size, 1930–1951," Stat. Bul. No. 197, Nov., 1956, p. 7.

"There are slight differences in our net farm income as presented in the various statistics on commercial farms and the net farm income released by AMS and given in figure 2, page 5, of AIB No. 176. Our farm series are based on owner-operated farms. Our net farm income therefore is the return to operator and family for their labor and management and for return on all capital or investment regardless of ownership. The net farm income used in figure 2 includes as expenditure interest on farm mortgage debt and net rent to nonfarm landlords," (Letter from Wylie Goodsell, Assistant Chief of Costs, Income, and Efficiency Research Branch, USDA, Dec. 17, 1959).

The charge for land and buildings in the charge for capital was computed differently before 1954, so the returns to operator and family labor before that date are not comparable with the returns for the years after 1954.

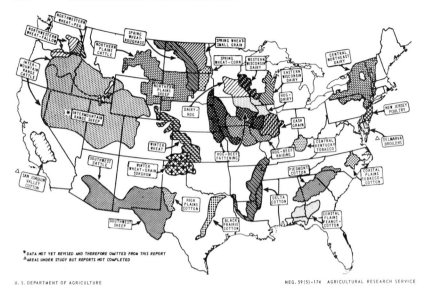

Fig. 20.3 — Locations of types of farms studied for income comparisons.

These labor and management returns are roughly comparable in concept with the United States average farm income data shown above, but they show the average net income for regular commercial family farms in the areas shown in Figure 20.3, separately by types of farming in the different areas, rather than for all "farms" as defined in the census, for the United States as a whole.

The labor and management returns are also more clearly comparable with the earnings of employed factory workers than the net farm income figures given above; they both show the returns to labor, not including a charge for capital in either case.[11]

---

[11] The factory worker ordinarily would not have a "charge for capital" as such, but would have a return on his investments of his savings, comparable in some sense with a farm operator's return on his own savings invested in his farm.

The factory workers' earnings are not perfect for comparison with the labor and management returns to the farm operator. The factory workers' earnings do not include returns to management as the farm returns series does. Also, factory workers are not strictly comparable with farm operators in some other respects. Ordinarily, they do not exercise much management; that is the prerogative of "the management." Furthermore, any income from other members of the family is not included in the factory workers' earnings, whereas they are included in the farm series if the other members of the family worked on the operator's farm, as they do in most cases. But the author does not know of any other authoritative series which is more nearly comparable with farmers' returns for labor and management than the earnings of factory workers.

TABLE 20.5

NET FARM INCOME AND RETURN TO OPERATOR AND FAMILY LABOR, SPECIFIED TYPES OF
COMMERCIAL FARMS, 1960, WITH COMPARISONS*

Type and Location of Farm	1950–59 (average)	1958	1959	1960†	1960 Return to Labor
	(Dollars)	(Dollars)	(Dollars)	(Dollars)	(Dollars)
Dairy farms:					
Central Northeast.............	3,898	4,339	4,236	4,061	1,625
Eastern Wisconsin............	2,745	2,627	3,119	3,090	369
Western Wisconsin............	3,104	3,778	3,414	3,418	1,542
Dairy-hog farms:					
Southeastern Minnesota........	3,886	4,362	3,632	3,858	860
Corn Belt farms:‡					
Hog-dairy...................	5,226	6,919	4,814	4,616	1,242
Hog-beef raising.............	3,611	5,063	3,104	2,967	−43
Hog-beef fattening...........	7,737	9,943	6,591	5,422	256
Cash grain..................	7,923	7,415	5,698	6,780	65
Poultry farms:					
New Jersey (egg-producing)......	2,699	2,484	−1,335	4,462	1,118
Cotton farms:					
Southern Piedmont‡...........	1,992	2,877	2,078	1,847	299
Texas:					
Black Prairie..............	2,461	3,025	2,332	2,225	−114
High Plains (nonirrigated).....	4,646	8,833	6,961	8,072	4,421
High Plains (irrigated)........	12,167	18,188	13,291	14,844	7,714
Mississippi Delta:					
Small......................	1,838	1,372	1,996	1,759	901
Large-scale.................	22,247	16,484	27,151	23,774	10,435
Peanut-cotton farms:					
Southern Coastal Plains........	2,642	3,467	2,428	3,222	2,133
Tobacco farms:					
North Carolina Coastal Plain:					
Tobacco-cotton..............	3,323	3,395	2,624	3,491	1,908
Tobacco-cotton (large)........	4,204	4,427	3,419	4,718	1,992
Tobacco (small).............	2,655	2,668	2,256	3,010	2,218
Kentucky Bluegrass:					
Tobacco-livestock, inner area...	5,708	6,531	5,228	5,494	−544
Tobacco-dairy, intermediate area...................	2,402	2,705	2,535	2,492	1,133
Tobacco-dairy, outer area......	4,033	4,782	4,432	4,582	2,636
Spring wheat farms:					
Northern Plains:					
Wheat-small grain-livestock....	4,818	6,388	2,807	4,389	1,182
Wheat-corn-livestock..........	4,239	7,415	2,343	5,528	2,304
Wheat-roughage-livestock......	3,741	4,971	1,468	5,628	2,700
Winter wheat farms:					
Southern Plains:					
Wheat......................	7,987	13,289	7,777	10,498	4,944
Wheat-grain sorghum.........	4,967	11,247	10,281	12,146	6,759
Pacific Northwest:					
Wheat-pea..................	13,286	10,023	15,940	11,020	199
Wheat-fallow...............	12,518	12,664	12,468	9,643	1,156
Cattle ranches:					
Northern Plains..............	5,018	6,413	5,170	4,988	27
Intermountain region..........	8,884	13,111	12,547	9,573	4,297
Southwest...................	4,368	9,223	8,318	7,102	−2,593
Sheep ranches:					
Northern Plains..............	8,874	13,290	8,180	8,074	2,035
Southwest...................	5,550	11,318	10,805	10,102	−2,410

* Source: ARS, USDA, Agr. Info. Bul. 176, 1961.
† Preliminary.
‡ Revised.

SIGNIFICANCE OF THE RETURN TO OPERATOR AND FAMILY LABOR DATA

The simple United States average of the net farm incomes for commercial family farms in 1960 was $6,379. The United States average "return to operator and family labor" after the charge for capital is deducted from the net farm income, derived from the right-hand column in Table 20.5, was $1,846.

This $1,846 is much lower than the United States average "farm" income from farming of $3,360 for 1960. Neither series is perfect for showing average farm income, but the data given in the table show more nearly what most people have in mind when they talk about farm income.

Two things need to be pointed out here. First, practically all the discussion about farm income is based on the United States average "farm" data which include all census "farms" and provide the average farm income figure for 1960 of $3,360 just quoted. Not one man in a thousand who quotes these figures ever quotes these other more meaningful figures for commercial family farms ($1,846 for 1960), perhaps because in most cases he does not know that they even exist.

It is illuminating to compare average farm income with the incomes of similar small business entrepreneurs in other sectors of the economy. Discussions of farm income policy, which usually means commercial family farm policy, will not be very accurate until they are based on commercial family farm income data.

One such study was made by Kaldor *et al* which compared farm incomes on 16 well-organized Iowa farms in 1954–55 with the adjusted labor incomes of (1) managers of Iowa farm supply companies, (2) managers of Iowa cooperative elevator companies, and (3) production line foremen in two large Iowa manufacturing firms. The authors found that the farm incomes compared favorably with the other incomes, except under assumed market-clearing prices for farm products (at 65 per cent of parity).[12]

The second point is of a different nature. It concerns the dispersion behind the United States average farm income data. Table 20.5 shows that there are wide differences among the average returns to operator and family labor in the different areas. In 1960, the average returns to operator and family labor ranged from —$2,593 in the cattle ranches of the Southwest to $10,435 in the

---

[12] Don Kaldor, Raymond Beneke, and Russell Bryant, "Comparison of Resource Returns of Well-Organized Iowa Farms with Selected Nonfarm Opportunities," Agr. and Home Econ. Exp. Sta., Res. Bul. 491, Iowa State University, Ames, Iowa, March, 1961.

large-scale farms of the Mississippi Delta. The average net farm incomes in 1960 ranged from $1,759 for the small farms in the Mississippi Delta to $23,774 for the large farms in the same area.

Furthermore, most of these differences persist over long periods of time, even in contiguous areas. There is great variation from year to year due to weather and other such causes, but usually the incomes in most of the different areas stay in about the same relation to each other year after year. The high areas remain high and the low areas remain low.

Figure 20.4 shows these two essentials in graphic form. It shows the returns for two types of farming — hog-beef raising and hog-beef fattening — in two contiguous areas. The figure shows the net returns data for the two areas carried back to 1930, along with the earnings of factory workers.

This figure illustrates the essence of the real farm problem in a nutshell. It shows that the problem is twofold.

First, income instability. The urban income series rises fairly steadily over most of the period. But the farm returns series jumps

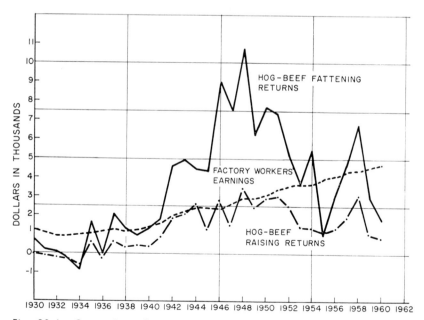

Fig. 20.4 — Comparison, factory workers' earnings with returns for hog-beef raising and fattening, 1930–60.

all over the place — in the case of the hog-beef fattening series, from roughly 3 times as high as the urban series in 1948 to only half as high in 1955. The instability of the farm returns series stands out in marked contrast to the stability of the urban income series.

Second, income level. The chart shows also that the two farm series differ greatly from each other. Year after year, the returns to operator and family labor are about twice as high in hog-beef fattening as they are in hog-beef raising.

This chart illustrates why a price program is an inappropriate way to deal with farm income problems. A price program to help hog-beef raisers just after World War II would have helped hog-beef fatteners too, at a time when their incomes were already several times as great as factory workers' earnings. Or to put it the other way around — hog-beef fatteners did not need a program in 1947 and 1954, for example, but hog-beef raisers did; their returns in those years were less than half as high as factory workers' incomes. What is needed is not price programs, which necessarily raise prices to all producers of the product alike, but income programs, by areas, for those types of farmers who need it.

And by income programs I do not mean direct income payments. Programs of that sort are like price programs in that they treat only the symptoms, and leave the basic disease, the maladjustment, untreated and in some cases aggravated.

In dealing with problems like these we could make much more use of the cost and income data that are already available — the original detailed data on which Table 20.5 is based. These data are published annually by the USDA.[13] They show, area by area, what the details of the costs and incomes for the different types of farming are, item by item. They show which costs have been increasing or decreasing, and give some indication why; which of the different sources of income have been increasing or decreasing; and so forth.

These are the kinds of data that a manufacturer would study if he had plants located in different parts of the country. He would study these data to find out which plants were unprofitable, and why, and what changes would be needed to make them profitable — conversion to other lines of production, expansion or contraction of scale, and so on.

Price policy alone would not solve this kind of problem; it might in fact make the disparity worse.

---

[13] "Farm Costs and Returns: Commercial Family-Operated Farms by Type and Location," ARS, USDA, Agr. Info. Bul. 176.

The inappropriateness of price programs as a solution for farm problems is shown also by a comparison of the returns to two kinds of farms in the Mississippi Delta — small and large-scale. The return for the small farms in 1960 was $901; for the large-scale farms it was $10,435 — more than 11 times greater. Even doubling the price support level for cotton would have brought the returns to the small farms only part way up to the level attained by the large farms.

Furthermore, even production-control programs that succeeded in raising prices by reducing acreage or changing the market structure probably would not increase net farm income in the long run if nothing were done to change the quantity or quality of the human factor, the farmer himself. Much of the gain probably would go to land, as it probably has over the past decade under the impact of new technology and the price-support programs. The average value of farm land and buildings per acre rose 83 per cent from 1947–49 to 1960, but the average per capita income from farming rose only 41 per cent (from $640 to $899) over the same period.[14] There is every reason to expect that the same thing would happen in the future if most of the attention continues to be focussed on programs for farm product prices and very little on programs for farm incomes.

The coal miners under John L. Lewis did not concentrate on programs to raise the price of coal in the hope that this would benefit coal miners; they concentrated on reducing the supply of miners and getting their incomes up. Farmers might well ponder that this has implications for their programs.

The compilation of parity income ratios by areas would show the economic status of farmers, not only for the United States as a whole but area by area. This would facilitate accurate identification of the problem areas within agriculture.

A MEASURE OF PARITY INCOME

The preceding discussion of parity farm income leads to the following comment: The economic status of farmers can be more accurately measured by income per farmer than by prices alone. Several measures of farm income are compiled by the USDA. The one that reports the income of commercial family farms by type of farm in the chief producing areas could be compared with the in-

---

[14] "The Farm Income Situation," AMS, USDA, Feb., 1962, p. 43.

comes for comparable ability in other occupations. The ratios between the two, area by area and for the United States as a whole, could be used as income parity ratios.

Many problems would be involved in a shift from measures of parity prices to measures of parity incomes.[15]

RECOMMENDATIONS

The parity-price ratio, and the parity prices for individual farm products, are evidently inappropriate for the purposes for which they are being used. One reason for this is that they were developed on the basis of what has turned out to be an incorrect diagnosis of the agricultural problem in the first place.

It is incorrect to diagnose the agricultural problem as a price problem, ignoring quantities and costs. In reality, the agricultural problem is an income problem; and it is not a *total gross* agricultural income problem, but a *net per farmer* income problem. This net per farmer income problem requires quite different programs from those that might solve a price problem.

What is needed is to develop and use new and more appropriate measures to deal with the farm problem. Using more recent price bases would, at least, bring the existing price indexes more up to date. Replacing them by per farmer net income indexes or actual dollar figures would be better, although it would take more time to work out the problems involved. Some of these problems are outlined below.

1. Weights Derived From Commerical Farms

The quantity weights used in the existing parity price indexes could be based upon commercial farms (classes I through VI) rather than upon all farms as defined in the census. It would not include the part-time and residential and subsistence farms, which numbered 1,682,000 in 1954, roughly one-third of the total number of all farms, 4,782,000. Even with class VI included, these farms account for only about 3.5 per cent of the value of total farm products sold, but for 35 per cent of the expenditures by farm operators for living. They thus give an unrepresentatively large weight to family living in the parity index which is chiefly relevant to commercial farmers.

---

[15] Some of these problems are discussed in "An Alternative Parity Formula for Agriculture," Iowa State Univ. Res. Bul. 476, Feb., 1960.

2. Separate Parity Indexes

Consideration might well be given to computing separate parity indexes for some of the major farm products, in order to compare them with the single parity index now used for all farm products, measure their differences, and determine how great these differences are in relation to the costs of computing the separate indexes.

3. More Recent Bases

The ancient 1910–14 bases now used in computing the parity price indexes could be replaced by bases that more closely represent "the kind of agriculture that is likely to prevail for some years ahead." New legislation would be required for this purpose.

To this end, the moving average of the most recent 10 years, already being used for the relations among the prices of individual farm products, could be applied to the indexes for all farm products as a group. Alternative bases might be 1950–59 or 1955–59. This base then would apply both to the indexes of prices paid and to the indexes of prices received.

Parity prices on this base would be more useful as well as more representative of current conditions than parity prices on the present 1910–14 base. Most farmers are more interested in a measure of their economic status now, compared with their average status over the past 10 years, than they are their status in the horse-and-buggy 1910–14 period before most of them were born.

In principle, the weight bases could be the same as the price bases. But some features of this possible arrangement need to be considered.

a. If a moving average base, say for the past 10 years, were used both for prices and for weights, the index would not be an unequivocal price index. It would reflect changes in quantities as well as in prices.

Let us take the index of prices received as an illustration. Suppose that a drought or other disaster struck the country one year, and agricultural production declined 3 per cent, as it did in 1947, and prices rose 17 per cent, as they did then (although the drought was not the only reason why prices rose to that extent). The next year, the inclusion of 1947, when crop production was low, in the new 10-year average weights, would change the composition of the weights. The price index for 1948 therefore would reflect the change in the composition of the weights as well as the change in prices. Conceivably, prices from 1947 to 1948 might not change at all, but the price index would change because of the change in the composition of the weights for the different items in the price index.

This effect would be small, because the change in the composition of the weights for the 10-year moving average base would be only one-tenth as large as the change in the one year, 1947. It might be considered preferable to have this small change each year rather than have the large one that takes place when the weight base is moved from one fixed period to the next (such as the 3-point decline that took place in January 1959 when the weight base for the index of prices paid was moved up from 1937–41 to 1955).

b. The weight base for the index of prices paid could not well be a recent moving average, for a very practical reason of cost. The quantities of the different goods and services purchased by farmers are determined by a survey, and surveys are expensive. A period of 18 years elapsed between 1937–41 and 1959, when weight data from the survey in 1955 permitted the most recent revision to be made. The cost of making a fresh survey every year, to include in a moving average base, would be prohibitive. B. R. Stauber of the USDA suggests that regular 5-year intervals between weight-base years would be a reasonable compromise between cost and obsolescence.[16] He further suggests that the revisions of the several major government indexes be based on the same weight-base and price-base periods.[17] We endorse these suggestions,[18] with the proviso that the price-base periods for the agricultural indexes include 5 or 10 years, so as to average out most of the effects of the irregular variations in production and prices which result from irregular year-to-year variations in weather.

4. Measures of Parity Farm Income

The fundamental difficulty with the existing price support programs is that they use indexes of price instead of indexes measuring value received minus cost incurred, which provides net income. Parity-price indexes are inaccurate measures of economic status, because they are only price indexes, not value-received and cost-incurred indexes, showing net income. Neither do they permit a breakdown by type of farming or economic producing areas to show the economic status of farmers in those areas separately.

---

[16] B. R. Stauber, "The 1959 USDA Index Revisions and Some Related Policy Questions," *Journal of Farm Economics, Proceedings,* Vol. 41, No. 5, Dec., 1959, p. 1286.

[17] *Ibid.,* p. 1288.

[18] *Ibid.,* p. 1302, discussion by Geoffrey Shepherd.

One possibility would be to include efficiency modifiers for farm products as a group and for individual farm products in the parity formula. Separate parity indexes for individual farm products could also be included. These have been computed experimentally for cotton, as shown earlier in this report.

This would be a step toward the measurement of income. There is something to be said on psychological grounds for making progress a step at a time. But this step would result in only an approximation, and would involve difficult problems of how the gains from technology should be divided between producer and consumer. It might seem better to go to measures of income directly.

Indexes of gross and net income, by type of farming in different economic areas, would provide relatively accurate and detailed measures of farmers' economic status. The basic data for measures of this sort have been compiled for years by the ARS, USDA; they are published annually in bulletin form, but are not widely used. These measures could be refined and extended and used to replace the existing parity-price indexes. These measures of net farm income, or measures of net returns to farm labor and management, area by area, could then be compared with the wages of industrial workers, or other nonfarm groups, with due allowance for differences in purchasing power and other intangibles, to provide measures of parity income with incomes in other occupations.

5. Moving Average Price Bases for Loan Rates

Many farmers are alarmed at the thought of using more recent bases, because that would reduce parity prices, which have been used as the bases for loan rates. These farmers fear that the loan rates would be lowered along with the parity prices. But experience with storage programs in recent years has demonstrated that parity prices are anachronisms, unsuited as bases for loan rates used with price stabilization programs.

More suitable bases would be recent moving averages of market prices, such as have been adopted for corn. These averages integrate the forces of demand and supply objectively into a single price figure, which is well-suited to use as the basis for loan rates to attain the objective of smoothing out prices about their long-run market equilibrium level, without trying to raise that level.

This smoothing out of prices about their long-run market level is all that storage programs can do over the long run, and recent moving averages of market prices approximate this long-run equilibrium level closely enough to serve well as the bases for loan rates for this purpose.

Setting the loan rates about 10 per cent below the moving average price would provide a high degree of stabilization yet still permit the storage programs to recoup some of their costs from the sale of their stored products at (ideally) 20 per cent above their cost of acquisition, in years of short crops.

The moving average would have one shortcoming, in that it would always be a few years behind the times. This could be overcome by developing an index of demand, projected into the future and used to adjust the moving average price up or down as needed.

If the level of loan rates thus determined would provide incomes too low to be deemed acceptable, the causes of those low incomes would need to be determined and rectified by means appropriate for those causes.

The replacement of percentages of parity prices by moving averages of open market prices as bases for loan rates, would reduce the natural objection which farmers now feel toward the use of recent bases which would reduce the level of parity prices. For that reduction then would not reduce the level of loan rates.

Appendix *A*

Vertical and Horizontal Shifts in Demand and Supply Curves

There is general agreement among economists that the concept of a change in demand refers to a horizontal shift in the position of the demand curve. This concept conforms with the definition of the elasticity of demand, which refers to the responsiveness of consumption to price.

One might say on the face of it that it doesn't make any difference whether the shift takes place horizontally or vertically. But in actual fact it does make a considerable difference.

A multiple correlation analysis made shortly after World War II showed that the per capita demand for meat relative to disposable income, from 1920 to 1941, declined at a rate sufficient to cause prices to decline over the period as a whole (with per capita consumption statistically held constant) at an average rate of 0.23 cents per pound per year. This was equivalent to a decline of 0.64 per cent per year.[1]

Does this mean that the demand declined 0.64 per cent per year?

If a change in demand is regarded as an upward or downward shift in the demand curve, the answer would be yes. If, however, a change in demand is regarded as a horizontal shift to the left or right, the answer would be that the demand declined less than 0.64 per cent per year. Since the elasticity of the demand for meat is about −0.75, a decline of 0.64 per cent per year in price would

---

[1] Geoffrey Shepherd, "Changes in the Demand for Meat and Dairy Products in the United States Since 1910," Agr. Exp. Sta., Iowa State Univ. Res. Bul. 368, p. 388.

represent a decline in demand (a shift to the left in the demand curve) of 0.64×0.75, or 0.48 per cent per year.

This is a sensible working conclusion, in view of the general agreement concerning the definition of a change in demand as a horizontal shift in the position of the demand curve. But it is interesting and worthwhile to explore the matter further, beyond the present area of agreement, into new and unexplored territory.

FURTHER EXPLORATION

The fundamental idea of vertical and horizontal shifts in demand curves is simple. We can deal with it best by starting with the concept of the demand schedule. A typical demand schedule is shown in column A of Table A.1.

The demand curve D based on these figures is shown in Figure A.1. Both the vertical and horizontal scales in the chart are logarithmic. This preserves parallelism in the curves throughout the various shifts in their position that are considered. The reasoning, however, is independent of the kinds of scales used.

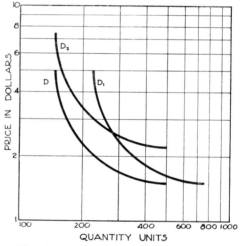

Fig. A.1 — Vertical and horizontal shifts in a concave demand curve.

The use of a curved demand line on a logarithmic scale will help to bring out the point more clearly than the use of a straight line, though the reasoning in both cases is the same. Either a concave or a convex curve may be used. We shall start with the former.

Suppose, now, that twenty years elapse and the population consuming the good in question increases 50 per cent. If no changes have taken place in the demand per consumer, 50 per cent more goods could now be sold at each price than formerly. The new situation is represented in Table A.1, column B, in which each quantity figure is 50 per cent higher than the corresponding figure in column A. The price figures remain unchanged. The new curve D_1, is shown in Figure A.1.

Now let us suppose that, instead of the population increasing 50 per cent, it had remained unchanged, but the purchasing power of each consumer had increased. No other change in demand took place, but, because of their increased purchasing power, consumers were willing to pay, let us say, 50 per cent more for each quantity than formerly. This situation is shown in Table A. 1, column C, where each price figure is 50 per cent higher than the corresponding figure in column A, the quantity figures remaining unchanged. The new curve, D_2, is shown in Figure A.1.

A concrete illustration of this sort of change in demand is a rise or decline of the general price level. This represents a change in the amounts of money which consumers would offer for the same amounts of goods as before. Another illustration is the effect of the increase in distributors' margins that has been taking place in recent years.

The curve D_1 is an illustration of a horizontal shift in the position of the demand curve. The other curve, D_2, is an illustration of an equal vertical shift. The difference between the two curves seems clear.

EFFECT UPON PRICE PAID AND QUANTITY TAKEN

One might think that a vertical upward shift in the demand curve would result in a higher price being paid for the same quantity of goods as before, and that a shift to the right in the demand curve would result in more goods being sold at the same price as formerly.

TABLE A.1
DEMAND SCHEDULES
(Hypothetical Data)

A. Original Demand Schedule		B. Population Increased 50%, Purchasing Power Unchanged		C. Purchasing Power Increased, Population Unchanged	
Price	Quantity Units	Price	Quantity Units	Price	Quantity Units
$5.00	150	$5.00	225	$7.50	150
4.00	155	4.00	232	6.00	155
3.00	170	3.00	255	4.50	170
2.50	190	2.50	285	3.75	190
2.35	200	2.35	300	3.52	200
2.00	235	2.00	352	3.00	235
1.90	250	1.90	375	2.85	250
1.70	300	1.70	450	2.55	300
1.55	400	1.55	600	2.32	400
1.50	500	1.50	750	2.25	500

Conversely, one might reason backwards from the changes in quantity or price, and say that if the price had increased while the quantity taken remained unchanged, the demand curve must have shifted upwards. But this would be wrong. Production and price simply represent the intersection point of a demand and supply schedule. The effect of a horizontal or of a vertical shift in a demand curve depends upon the supply curve as well as upon the demand curve. Whether a shift in the location of a demand curve, either upwards or to the right, will result in an increase in the price or in the quantity taken, or both, depends upon the conditions of supply; that is, upon the slope of the supply curve and changes in its location.

Under conditions of constant costs, for example, a vertical rise in the demand curve would result in an increase, not in the price for the same quantity, but in the quantity taken at the same price. Conversely, with a fixed stock of a good, a horizontal shift to the right in the demand curve would result, not in an increase in quantity taken at the same price, but in an increased price paid for the same quantity. The nature of the supply curve, and shifts that may have taken place in its location, determines the proportion in which an increase in demand, either upward or to the right, is expressed as an increase in the price or in the quantity taken.

This point is illustrated in Figure A.2. In the left-hand section of this figure, a convex demand curve is shown shifting to the right. The supply curve, however, happens to be inelastic (fixed stock). As a result, although the demand curve has moved to the right, the intersection point of the demand and supply curves has necessarily (because of the inelasticity of the supply curve) moved upward. A higher price is paid for the same quantity as before.

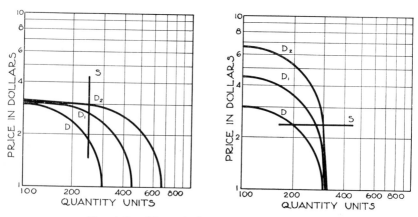

Fig. A.2 — Effect of elasticity of supply curve.

In the right-hand section of Figure A.2, the opposite situation is shown. The demand curve shifts upward, but the supply curve happens to be fully elastic (constant costs). The result of the upward shift in the demand curve is a shift of the intersection point to the right; that is, more goods are taken at the same price as before.

Two things, therefore, are evident. (1) Whenever the demand curve is convex or concave the demand curve as a whole is different in its position after a vertical and after a horizontal shift, and (2) the effect of a shift in demand upon price paid and quantity taken depends, not upon the direction of the shift, but upon the nature of the supply curve.

STRAIGHT-LINE DEMAND CURVES

We come now to the consideration of straight-line demand curves.

Before beginning, we must decide whether we mean straight-line curves on arithmetic paper or on double logarithmic paper. Practically all the statistical price-quantity curves published in recent articles and bulletins are drawn on arithmetic paper. But the concept of changes in demand is fundamentally proportional in character, and changes in demand in actual life are usually[2] proportional. A proportional change in demand shown on arithmetic paper results in a new demand curve that is not parallel with the old. If a proportional change in demand is shown on double logarithmic paper, however, the new demand curve remains parallel with the old. Perhaps the best plan here is to consider separately both arithmetic and logarithmic straight-line demand curves.

Arithmetic Scales

Let us first consider straight-line curves on an arithmetic scale. In this case the difference between the curves resulting from a horizontal and from a vertical shift of 50 per cent is evident, not only when elastic and inelastic curves are used, but also when an intermediate curve with slope of -1 is used. This is shown in Figure A.3. The elasticity of the curves remains unaffected, since the changes in demand are proportional changes, but the slope of the curves is altered.

---

[2] In certain cases a change in demand may be arithmetic. A change in distributors' margins, for example, results in a vertical arithmetic shift.

Logarithmic Scales

If elastic or inelastic straight-line curves on *logarithmic* scales are used, the position of the curve after a 50 per cent upward shift will be different from its position after a 50 per cent shift to the right, and so will the price paid and quantity taken.

It is only in the rare case of a straight-line demand curve on a double logarithmic scale, with a slope of —1 throughout, that the position of the curve would be the same after either shift. In this case the effect of a horizontal shift in demand upon the location of the intersection point, that is, upon production and price, would be identical with that of an equal vertical shift. After population has increased 50 per cent, consumers as a group might either pay higher prices for the same quantity as before, or take larger quantities at the same price as before, or some intermediate combination of the two, according to the nature of the supply curve. If the supply curve were a vertical straight line (fixed stock), the consumers would pay more for the same quantity. If the supply curve were a horizontal line (constant costs), they would take a larger quantity at the same price. If the supply curve had a slope intermediate between vertical and horizontal, the effect on price and quantity would be intermediate—both price and quantity would increase, in proportions determined by the slope of the supply curve.

Reason for Distinction

The reason for distinguishing between vertical and horizontal shifts in demand curves is this: We start with a price series, and find that it fluctuates. What is the reason for the fluctuations? The accepted procedure among economists is to group the possible causes under the two heads: Demand and Supply. Investigating these two groups, we come to the conclusion that the demand changed, or the

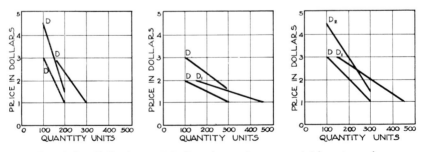

Fig. A.3 — Shifts in straight-line demand curves. Arithmetic scales.

supply changed, or both. If our objective is to reduce price fluctuations in the future, we know then whether we need to concentrate our attention upon changes in demand, or in supply, or in both.

The purpose of the distinction between horizontal and vertical shifts in demand (or supply) curves is to enable us to carry our investigation one step further. We have determined, let us say, that the chief cause of the price fluctuations was the changes that took place in demand. The demand curve shifted, and the question is, which way did it shift—up, down, or sideways, or some combination of these?

This question cannot be answered by observing whether the intersection point *or the range of actual price-experience on the demand curve* (which is merely the range of intersection points) shifted up or sideways. That depends on the nature of the supply curve. The question is answered only by remembering that a demand curve represents demand. Economists define demand as consumers' willingness to buy certain quantities at certain prices; and that willingness exists whether the supply curve has fluctuated enough to reveal it in actual transactions or not. This means that the demand curve extends both ways, beyond the range of past experience in the market—ultimately, until it cuts the vertical and horizontal axes where quantity and price respectively are zero. (The curve will not extend indefinitely; it will cut both axes at some finite points.)[3]

To tell which way the demand curve has shifted, then, is to go behind the original price and quantity data on which the demand curve rests. We are seeking to explain why the data changed. It seems obvious that, if population increased 50 per cent and if no other important change took place, the curve moved to the right, not upwards and to the right. The question can be demonstrated statistically when the demand curve is strongly curved, when, for example, it is a convex curve that cuts both axes at almost right angles, or a sloping straight line that flattens out or gets steeper as either axis is approached; it is equally true, only less obvious, when a straight line is used. We are on logically sounder ground in

---

[3] Usually these points, like those shown in Figure A.3, will represent prices or quantities not greatly (say 100 per cent) in excess of the highest prices or quantities that have been actually experienced in the market, unless the demand is extremely inelastic, as for salt or water, or extremely elastic, as for human foods that can be fed to livestock if produced in excess. Substitution of other products levels off most demand curves as they approach the vertical axis, and rapidly declining marginal utility with increasing quantity causes most demand curves to cut the horizontal axis at a point not very far out to the right.

endeavoring to carry the explanation of price movements down to its ultimate causes if we recognize that a demand curve may shift either horizontally or vertically, or some combination of both, independent of which way (if any) the intersection point or the range of intersection points moved. We need to investigate what happened to the demand curve first, and then turn to a study of what happened to the supply curve; for movements in demand curves and supply curves (except in a roundabout sense, as during inflation or deflation) are independent of one another.

We are not studying movements in the intersection points of demand and supply curves; if so, we would be studying only movements in production and prices. What we are trying to do is to study the movement of demand and supply curves that lie behind and cause these movements in prices and production. Economic theory has provided the research worker with conceptual tools for analyzing movements in prices and production into changes in demand and supply, that is, into movements of demand and supply curves.

The next step is to analyze these movements into their horizontal and/or vertical components. As data concerning population, incomes, pay rolls, wage rate indexes, general price levels, distributive margins, etc. become more detailed and adequate for analytical purposes, economic analysis is carried this one step further to give these questions a quantitative answer.

Appendix *B*

The Graphic Presentation of Seasonal Patterns

The average seasonal pattern of prices from month to month through the year usually is shown by plotting the data in a simple time chart with prices up the side and the twelve months of the year along the bottom. Charts of this nature sometimes include an additional line showing the seasonal pattern of production or receipts of the commodity month by month. The two lines usually show an inverse relationship. A typical chart of this sort, reproduced direct from a marketing bulletin dealing with seasonal movements of prices and production,[1] is shown in Figure B.1.

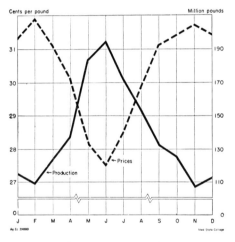

Fig. B.1 — Average seasonal pattern of creamery butter production, and prices of 92-score butter at New York City, 1929–38.

Charts of this kind provide a clear picture of the qualitative relation between prices and production or receipts throughout the year, but they may convey a misleading impression as to the *quantitative* relation between prices and production if the scales are not properly drawn. Figure B.1, for example, would leave most readers with the impression that the average seasonal fluctuation in butter prices is about as great as the average seasonal fluctuation in butter production. Closer inspection of the chart, showing that the scales are both broken at the bottom, would raise a question in some readers' minds as to the accuracy of this impression, but only the technically trained reader would

[1] Eugene Hamilton, "Seasonal Market Variations and Their Importance to Iowa Farmers," Iowa Agr. Exp. Sta. and Iowa Agr. Ext. Serv., Bul. P5 (New Series), 1940, p. 200.

[319]

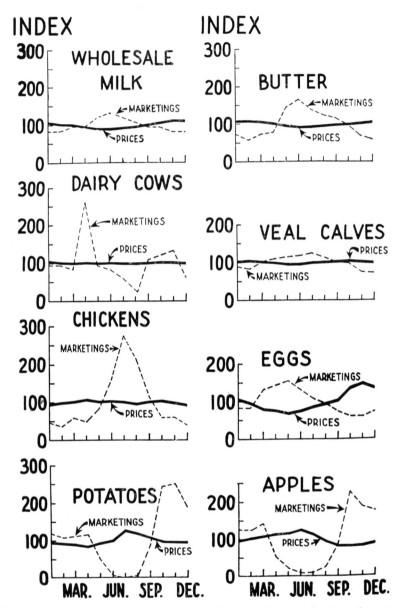

Fig. B.2 — Average seasonal patterns of the marketings and prices of various Pennsylvania farm products, 1933–37. (Courtesy Pa. State Univ.)

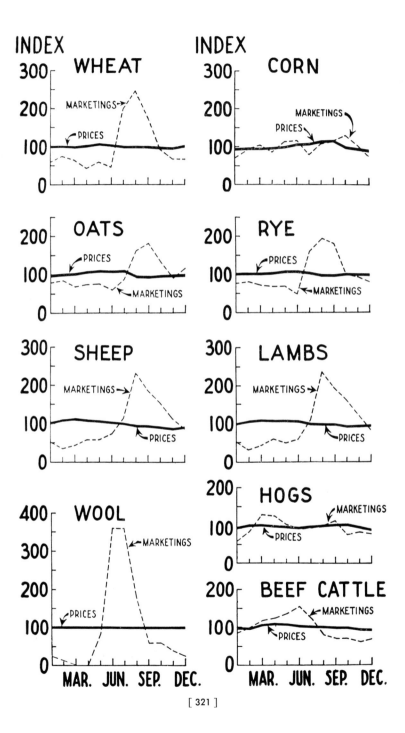

go further and carry through the mental arithmetic involved in comparing the proportions of the parts of the two scales shown.

Yet a little computation shows that the price scale is nearly four
times as great as the production scale. The two scales would not run
down to zero at the same point. Actually, the fluctuation in butter
prices was only about one-fourth as great as the fluctuation in production. Butter prices were much more stable than butter production; they fluctuated only one-fourth as much as production.

There are several ways of avoiding this sort of misrepresentation.
One way is to make both scales run down to zero at the same point
at the bottom of the chart, using no broken scales at all. This is
shown in Figure A.3, reproduced directly from another marketing
publication.[2] A feature of this sort of chart is that it either leaves a
large amount of space blank, below the lines on the chart, or, if the
vertical scales are compressed in order to prevent this, makes the
fluctuations in prices appear small. (The latter alternative was
chosen in Figure B.2.) Perhaps this should be considered an asset
rather than a shortcoming; the statistician would argue that if the
fluctuations actually are small, proportionally, they should be shown
that way. Farmer readers, however, might feel differently about the
matter. They might argue that even a small fluctuation in prices
means a large fluctuation in profits, and profits are what they are
interested in.

Another way of handling the chart is to use large (but still
proportionally equal) price and production scales; that is, make a
very "tall" chart (long from top to bottom) and then cut off the
lower half. This shows up the fluctuations more clearly, but does
not show directly how great the fluctuations are proportionally. And
it does not enable direct comparison of one chart with another, unless the same amount (for example, the lower half) is cut off all the
charts. Still another way is to use logarithmic scales. This is a very
good method in most technical respects, but it has the disadvantage
of being not perfectly clear to the nontechnical reader.

Then what is the best method to use? There is no one method
that best suits all purposes. The thing to do is to use the method
that best conveys the particular message to the particular audience
involved. For a technical audience, perhaps the best method is not
to use a time chart at all, but to use a scatter diagram. This shows
the relation between the two in demand curve form, and enables
observation of any curvilinearity in the relation. This demand curve
is not the consumers' demand curve, but the dealers'.

---

[2] Ellen F. Anderson and F. P. Weaver, "Prices and Pennsylvania Agriculture," Pa. State Univ. Bul. 384, 1939, pp. 17–19.

Index

The letter **n** *indicates footnote material*

[323]